P9-CMF-779

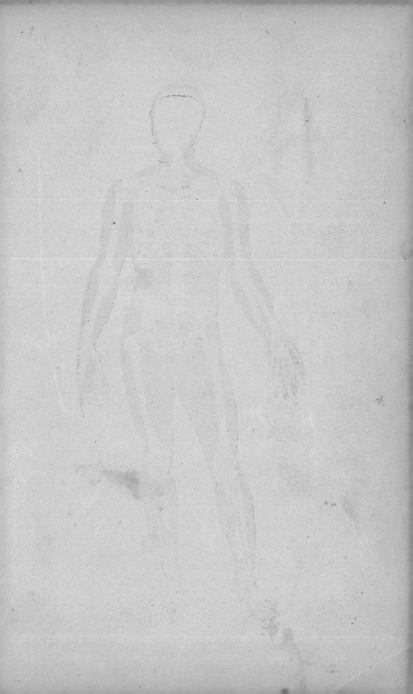

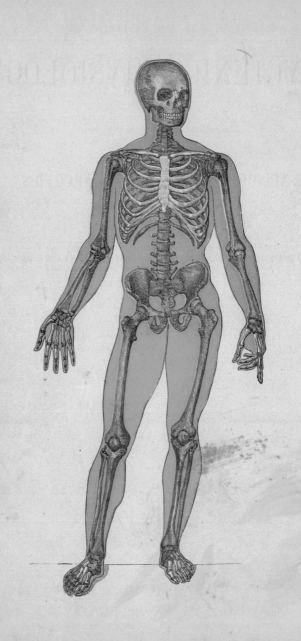

HYGIENIC PHYSIOLOGY

WITH SPECIAL REFERENCE TO THE USE OF

ALCOHOLIC DRINKS AND NARCOTICS

BEING A REVISED EDITION OF THE

FOURTEEN WEEKS IN HUMAN PHYSIOLOGY

BY

JOEL DORMAN STEELE, PH.D.

ENLARGED EDITION WITH SELECTED READINGS

Edited for the use of Schools, in accordance with the recent Legislation upon Temperance Instruction

NEW YORK ·:· CINCINNATI ·:· CHICAGO

AMERICAN BOOK COMPANY

INDORSEMENT.

Boston, *June* 20, 1889.

The Pathfinder Series of Text-Books on Anatomy, Physiology, and Hygiene consists of the following volumes:

I. **Child's Health Primer** (for Primary Grades).

II. **Hygiene for Young People ;** } (for Intermediate Classes)
or, **Young People's Physiology.** }

III. **Hygienic Physiology** (for Advanced Pupils).

The above are the series originally prepared (as their general title indicates) to supply the demand created by the laws for temperance instruction in public schools in the United States. They were written by experts under the supervision of the Scientific Department of the National Woman's Christian Temperance Union, published by the instigation of the same, and have been carefully revised from time to time, under the same supervision, to keep them abreast with the latest teachings of science.

Being both teachable and well adapted to grade, their educational value, as proven by school-room tests, is of the highest order. We therefore cordially indorse and highly recommend the Pathfinder Series for use in schools.

MARY H. HUNT,

National and International Superintendent of the Scientific Dep't of the Woman's Christian Temperance Union ; Life Director of the National Educational Association.

ADVISORY BOARD:

Joseph Cook,	William E. Sheldon,
Albert H. Plume, D.D.	Daniel Dorchester, D.D.

PREFACE

THE term Physiology, or the science of the functions of the body, has come to include Anatomy, or the science of its structure, and Hygiene, or the laws of health; the one being essential to the proper understanding of physiology, and the other being its practical application to life. The three are intimately blended, and in treating of the different subjects the author has drawn no line of distinction where nature has made none. This work is not prepared for the use of medical students, but for the instruction of youth in the principles which underlie the preservation of health and the formation of correct physical habits. All else is made subservient to this practical knowledge. A simple scientific dress is used which, while conducing to clearness, also gratifies that general desire of children to know something of the nomenclature of any study they pursue.

To the description of each organ is appended an account of its most common diseases, accidents, etc., and, when practicable, their mode of treatment. A pupil may thus learn, for example, the cause and cure of "a cold," the management of a wound, or the nature of an inflammation.

The Practical Questions, which have been a prominent feature in other books of the series, will be found, it is hoped, equally useful in this work. Directions for preparing simple microscopic objects, and illustrations of the different organs, are given under each subject.

The Readings, which represent the ideas but not always the exact phraseology of the author quoted, have, in general, been selected with direct reference to Practical Hygiene, a subject which now largely occupies the public mind. The dangers that lurk in foul air and contaminated water, in bad drainage, leaky gas-pipes, and defective plumbing, in reckless appetites, and in careless dissemination of contagious diseases, are here portrayed in such a manner as, it is trusted, will assist the pupil to avoid these treacherous quicksands, and to provide for himself a solid path of health.

Under the heading of Health and Disease will be found Hints about the sick-room, Directions for the use of Disinfectants, Suggestions as to what to do "Till the Doctor comes," and a list of antidotes for Poisons. Questions for Class Use, a full Glossary, and an ample Index complete the book.

Believing in a Divine Architect of the human form, the author can not refrain from occasionally pointing out His inimitable workmanship, and impressing the lesson of a Great Final Cause.

The author has gleaned from every field, at home and abroad, to secure that which would interest and profit his pupils. In general, Flint's great work on the " Physiology of Man," an undisputed authority on both sides of the Atlantic, has been adopted as the standard in digestion, respiration, circulation, and the nervous system. Leidy's "Human Anatomy," and Sappey's "Traité d'Anatomie" have been followed on all anatomical questions, and have furnished many beautiful drawings. Huxley's "Physiology" has afforded exceedingly valuable aid. Foster's "Text-Book of Physiology," Hinton's "Health and its Conditions," Black's "Ten Laws of Health," Williams' practical essay on "Our Eyes and How to Use them," Le Pileur's charming treatise on "The Wonders of the Human Body," and that quaint volume, "Odd Hours of a Physician," have aided the author with facts and fancies. The writings of Draper, Dalton, Carpenter, Valentine, Mapother, Watson, Lankester, Letheby, Hall, Hamilton, Bell, Wilson, Bower, Cutter, Hutchison, Wood, Bigelow, Stille, Holmes, Beigel, and others have been freely consulted.

PUBLISHERS' NOTE.

An **Abridged Edition** of this work is published, to afford a cheaper manual — adapted to Junior Classes and Common Schools. The abridgment contains the essence of this text, nearly all its illustrations, and the whole of the Temperance matter as here presented.

Order **"Hygienic Physiology, Abridged."**

READING REFERENCES.

Foster's "Text-Book of Physiology"; Leidy's "Human Anatomy"; Draper's "Human Physiology"; Dalton's "Physiology and Hygiene"; Cutter's "Physiology"; Johnston and Church's "Chemistry of Common Life"; Letheby's "Food"; Tyndall "On Light," and "On Sound"; Flint's "Physiology of Man"; Rosenthal's "Physiology of the Muscles and Nerves"; Bernstein's "Five Senses of Man"; Huxley and Youmans' "Physiology and Hygiene"; Sappey's "Traite d'Anatomie"; Luys' "Brain and its Functions"; Smith's "Foods"; Bain's "Mind and Body"; Pettigrew's "Animal Locomotion"; Carpenter's "Human Physiology," and "Mental Physiology"; Wilder and Gage's "Anatomy"; Jarvis' "Physiology and Laws of Health."

Hargreaves' "Alcohol and Science"; Richardson's "Ten Lectures on Alcohol," and "Diseases of Modern Life"; Brown's "Alcohol"; Davis' "Intemperance and Crime"; Pitman's "Alcohol and the State"; "Anti-Tobacco"; Howie's "Stimulants and Narcotics"; Hunt's "Alcohol as Food or Medicine"; Schutzenberger's "Fermentation"; Hubbard's "Opium Habit and Alcoholism"; Trouessart's "Microbes, Ferments, and Molds."

CONTENTS

Suggestions To Teachers

SEEING is believing—more than that, it is often knowing and remembering. The mere reading of a statement is of little value compared with the observation of a fact. Every opportunity should therefore be taken of exhibiting to the pupil the phenomena described, and thus making them real. A microscope is so essential to the understanding of many subjects, that it is indispensable to the proper teaching of Physiology. A suitable instrument and carefully prepared specimens, showing the structure of the bones, the skin, and the blood of various animals, the pigment cells of the eye, etc., may be obtained at a small cost from any good optician.

On naming the subject of a paragraph, the pupil should be prepared to tell all he knows about it. No failure should discourage the teacher in establishing this mode of study and recitation. A little practice will produce the most satisfactory results. The unexpected question and the apt reply develop a certain sharpness and readiness which are worthy of cultivation. The questions for review, or any others that the wit of the teacher may suggest, can be effectively used to break the monotony of a topical recitation, thereby securing the benefits of both systems.

The pupil should expect to be questioned each day upon any subject passed over during the term, and thus the entire knowledge gained will be within his grasp for instant use. While some are reciting to the teacher, let others write on slates or on the blackboard. At the close of the recitation, let all criticise the ideas, the spelling, the use of capitals, the pronunciation, the grammar, and the mode of expression. Greater accuracy and much collateral drill may thus be secured at little expense of valuable school-time.

The Introduction is designed merely to furnish suggestive material for the first lesson, preparatory to beginning the study. Other subjects for consideration may be found in the section on Health and Disease, in the Selected Readings, and among the questions given in the Appendix. Where time will allow, the Selected Readings may profitably be used in connection with the topics to which they relate. Questions upon them are so incorporated with those upon the text proper that they may be employed or not, according to the judgment of the teacher.

Note.—Interest in the study of Physiology will be much increased by the use of the microscope and prepared slides. These may be obtained from any good optician.

INTRODUCTION.

PHYSIOLOGICAL STUDY in youth is of inestimable value. Precious lives are frequently lost through ignorance. Thousands squander in early years the strength which should have been kept for the work of real life. Habits are often formed in youth which entail weakness and poverty upon manhood, and are a cause of life-long regret. The use of a strained limb may permanently damage it. Some silly feat of strength may produce an irreparable injury. A thoughtless hour of reading by twilight may impair the sight for life. A terrible accident may happen, and a dear friend perish before our eyes, while we stand by powerless to render the assistance we could so easily give did we "only know what to do." The thousand little hints which may save or lengthen life, may repel or abate disease, and the simple laws which regulate our bodily vigor, should be so familiar that we may be quick to apply them in an emergency. The preservation of health is easier than the cure of disease. Childhood can not afford to wait for the lesson of experience which is learned only when the penalty of violated law has been already incurred, and health irrevocably lost.

Nature's Laws Inviolable. — In infancy, we learn how terribly Nature punishes a violation of certain laws, and how promptly she applies the penalty. We soon find out the peril of fire, falls, edged tools, and the like. We fail, however, to notice the equally sharp and certain punishments which bad habits entail. We are quick to feel the need of food, but not so ready to perceive the danger of an excess. A lack of air drives us at once to secure a supply; foul air is as fatal. but it gives us no warning.

Nature provides a little training for us at the outset of life, but leaves the most for us to learn by bitter experience. So in youth we throw away our strength as if it were a burden of which we desire to be rid. We eat any thing, and at any time; do any thing we please, and sit up any number of nights with little or no sleep. Because we feel only a momentary discomfort from these physical sins, we fondly imagine when that is gone we are all right again. Our drafts upon our constitution are promptly paid, and we expect this will always be the case; but some day they will come back to us, protested; Nature will refuse to meet our demands, and we shall find ourselves physical bankrupts.

We are furnished in the beginning with a certain vital force upon which we may draw. We can be spendthrifts and waste it in youth, or be wise and so husband it till manhood. Our shortcomings are all charged against this stock. Nature's memory never fails; she keeps her account with perfect exactness. Every physical sin subtracts from the sum and strength of our years. We may cure a disease, but it never leaves us as it found us. We may heal a wound, but the scar still shows. We reap as we sow, and we may either gather in the thorns, one by one, to torment and destroy, or we may rejoice in the happy harvest of a hale old age.

I.

THE SKELETON.

"Not in the World of Light alone,
    Where God has built His blazing throne
    Nor yet alone on earth below,
    With belted seas that come and go,
    And endless isles of sunlit green
    Is all thy Maker's glory seen—
    Look in upon thy wondrous frame,
    Eternal wisdom still the same!"

HOLMES.

ANALYSIS OF THE SKELETON.

Note.—The following Table of 206 bones is exclusive of the 8 sesamoid bones which occur in pairs at the roots of the thumb and great toe, making 214 as given by Leidy and Draper. Gray omits the bones of the ear, and names 200 as the total number.

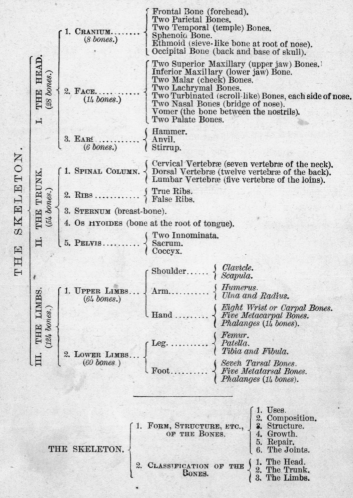

THE SKELETON.

I. THE HEAD. (28 bones.)

1. CRANIUM. (8 bones.)
- Frontal Bone (forehead).
- Two Parietal Bones.
- Two Temporal (temple) Bones.
- Sphenoid Bone.
- Ethmoid (sieve-like bone at root of nose).
- Occipital Bone (back and base of skull).

2. FACE. (14 bones.)
- Two Superior Maxillary (upper jaw) Bones.
- Inferior Maxillary (lower jaw) Bone.
- Two Malar (cheek) Bones.
- Two Lachrymal Bones.
- Two Turbinated (scroll-like) Bones, each side of nose.
- Two Nasal Bones (bridge of nose).
- Vomer (the bone between the nostrils).
- Two Palate Bones.

3. EARS (6 bones.)
- Hammer.
- Anvil.
- Stirrup.

II. THE TRUNK. (54 bones.)

1. SPINAL COLUMN.
- Cervical Vertebræ (seven vertebræ of the neck).
- Dorsal Vertebræ (twelve vertebræ of the back).
- Lumbar Vertebræ (five vertebræ of the loins).

2. RIBS
- True Ribs.
- False Ribs.

3. STERNUM (breast-bone).

4. OS HYOIDES (bone at the root of tongue).

5. PELVIS
- Two Innominata.
- Sacrum.
- Coccyx.

III. THE LIMBS. (124 bones.)

1. UPPER LIMBS (64 bones.)
- Shoulder
  - *Clavicle.*
  - *Scapula.*
- Arm
  - *Humerus.*
  - *Ulna and Radius.*
- Hand
  - *Eight Wrist or Carpal Bones.*
  - *Five Metacarpal Bones.*
  - *Phalanges (14 bones).*

2. LOWER LIMBS (60 bones.)
- Leg
  - *Femur.*
  - *Patella.*
  - *Tibia and Fibula.*
- Foot
  - *Seven Tarsal Bones.*
  - *Five Metatarsal Bones.*
  - *Phalanges (14 bones).*

THE SKELETON.

1. FORM, STRUCTURE, ETC., OF THE BONES.
1. Uses.
2. Composition.
3. Structure.
4. Growth.
5. Repair.
6. The Joints.

2. CLASSIFICATION OF THE BONES.
1. The Head.
2. The Trunk.
3. The Limbs.

THE SKELETON.

I. FORM, STRUCTURE, ETC., OF THE BONES.

(*See page* 269.)

The Skeleton, or frame-work of the "House we live in," is composed of about 200 bones.*

Uses and Forms of the Bones.—They have three principal uses: 1. To protect the delicate organs; †
2. To serve as levers on which the muscles may act to produce motion; and 3. To preserve the shape of the body.

Bones differ in form according to the uses they subserve. For convenience in walking, some are long; for strength and compactness, some are short and thick; for covering a cavity, some are flat; and for special purposes, some are irregular. The general form is such as to combine strength and light-

---

* The precise number varies in different periods of life. Several which are separated in youth become united in old age. Thus five of the "false vertebræ" at the base of the spine early join in one great bone—the sacrum; while four tiny ones below it often run into a bony mass—the coccyx (Fig. 6); in the child, the sternum is composed of eight pieces, while in the adult it consists of only three. While, however, the number of the bones is uncertain, their relative length is so exact that the length of the entire skeleton, and thence the height of the man, can be obtained by measuring a single one of the principal bones. Fossil bones and those found at Pompeii have the same proportion as our own.

† An organ is a portion of the body designed for a particular use, called its *function*. Thus the heart circulates the blood; the liver produces the bile.

ness. For example, all the long bones of the limbs are round and hollow, thus giving with the same weight a greater strength,* and also a larger surface for the attachment of the muscles.

The Composition of the Bones at maturity is about one part animal to two parts mineral matter. The proportion varies with the age. In youth it is nearly half and half, while in old age the mineral is greatly in excess. By soaking a bone in weak muriatic acid, and thus dissolving the mineral matter, its shape will not change, but its stiffness will disappear, leaving a tough, gristly substance † (cartilage) which can be bent like rubber.

If the bone be burned in the fire, thus consuming the animal matter, the shape will still be the same, but it will have lost its tenacity, and the beautiful,

---

* Cut a sheet of foolscap in two pieces. Roll one half into a compact cylinder, and fold the other into a close, flat strip; support the ends of each and hang weights in the middle until they bend. The superior strength of the roll will astonish one unfamiliar with this mechanical principle. In a rod, the particles break in succession, first those on the outside, and later those in the center. In a tube, the particles are all arranged where they resist the first strain. Iron pillars are therefore cast hollow. Stalks of grass and grain are so light as to bend before a breath of wind, yet are stiff enough to sustain their load of seed. Bone has been found by experiment to possess twice the resisting property of solid oak.

† Mix a wine-glass of muriatic acid with a pint of water, and place in it a sheep's rib. In a day or two, the bone will become so soft that it can be tied into a knot. In the same way, an egg may be made so pliable that it can be crowded into a narrow-necked bottle, within which it will expand, and become an object of great curiosity to the uninitiated. By boiling bones at a high temperature, the animal matter separates in the form of gelatine. Dogs and cats extract the animal matter from the bones they eat. Fossil bones deposited in the ground during the Geologic period, were found by Cuvier to contain considerable animal matter. Gelatine was actually extracted from the Cambridge mastodon, and made into glue. A tolerably nutritious food might thus be manufactured from bones older than man himself.

pure-white residue* may be crumbled into powder with the fingers.

We thus see that a bone receives hardness and rigidity from its mineral, and tenacity and elasticity from its animal matter.

The entire bone is at first composed of cartilage, which gradually *ossifies* or turns to bone.† Certain portions near the joints are long delayed in this process, and by their elasticity assist in breaking the shock of a fall.‡ Hence

FIG. 2.

The Thigh-bone, or Femur, sawed lengthwise.

* From bones thus calcined, the phosphorus of the chemist is made. See Steele's "Popular Chemistry," page 114. If the animal matter be not consumed, but only charred, the bone will be black and brittle. In this way, the "bone-black" of commerce is manufactured.

† The ossification of the bones on the sides and upper part of the skull, for example, begins by a rounded spot in the middle of each one. From this spot the ossification extends outward in every direction, thus gradually approaching the edges of the bone. When two adjacent bones meet, there will be a line where their edges are in contact with each other, but have not yet united; but when more than two bones meet in this way, there will be an empty space between them at their point of junction. Thus, if you lay down three coins upon the table with their edges touching one another, there will be a three-sided space in the middle between them; if you lay down four coins in the same manner, the space between them will be four-sided. Now at the back part of the head there is a spot where three bones come together in this way, leaving a small, three-sided opening between them: this is called the "posterior fontanelle." On the top of the head, four bones come together, leaving between them a large, four-sided opening; this is called the "anterior fontanelle." These openings are termed the *fontanelles*, because we can feel the pulsations of the brain through them, like the bubbling of water in a fountain. They gradually diminish in size, owing to the growth of the bony parts around them, and are completely closed at the age of four years after birth.—DALTON.

‡ Frogs and toads, which move by jumping, and consequently receive

the bones of children are tough, are not readily fractured, and when broken easily heal again;* while
those of elderly people are liable to fracture, and do
not quickly unite.

The Structure of the Bones.—When a bone is
sawed lengthwise, it is found to be a compact shell

FIG. 3.

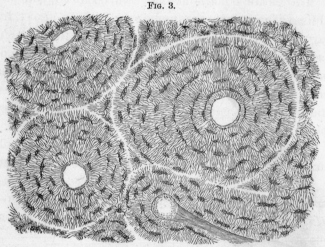

*A thin slice of Bone, highly magnified, showing the lacunæ, the tiny tubes (canali-
culi) radiating from them, and four Haversian canals, three seen crosswise and one
lengthwise.*

filled with a spongy substance. This filling increases
in quantity, and becomes more porous at the ends of
the bone, thus giving greater size to form a strong
joint, while the solid portion increases near the

so many jars, retain these unossified portions (epiphyses) nearly through
life; while alligators and turtles, whose position is sprawling, and whose
motions are measured, do not have them at all.—LEIDY.

* This is only one of the many illustrations of the Infinite care that
watches over helpless infancy, until knowledge and ability are acquired to
meet the perils of life.

middle, where strength alone is needed. Each fiber of this bulky material diminishes the shock of a sudden blow, and also acts as a beam to brace the exterior wall. The recumbent position of the alligator protects him from falls, and therefore his bones contain very little spongy substance.

In the body, bones are not the dry, dead, blanched things they commonly seem to be, but are moist, living, pinkish structures, covered with a tough membrane, called the per-i-os'-te-um* (*peri*, around, and *osteon*, a bone), while the hollow is filled with marrow, rich in fat, and full of blood-vessels. If we examine a thin slice with the microscope, we shall see black spots with lines running in all directions, and looking very like minute insects. These are really little cavities, called *la-cu'-næ*,† from which radiate tiny tubes. The lacunæ are arranged in circles around larger tubes, termed from their discoverer, *Haversian canals*, which serve as passages for the blood-vessels that nourish the bone.

Growth of the Bones.—By means of this system of canals, the blood circulates as freely through the bones as through any part of the body, The whole structure is constantly but slowly changing,‡ old

---

* The relations of the periosteum to the bone are very interesting. Instances are on record where the bone has been removed, leaving the periosteum, from which the entire bone was afterward renewed.

† When the bone is dry, the lacunæ are filled with air, which refracts the light, so that none of it reaches the eye, and hence the cavities appear black.

‡ Bone is sometimes produced with surprising rapidity. The great Irish Elk is calculated by Prof. Owen to have cast off and renewed annually in its antlers eighty pounds of bone.

material being taken out and new put in. A curious illustration is seen in the fact that if madder be mixed with the food of pigs, it will tinge their bones red.

Repair of the Bones.—When a bone is broken, the blood at once oozes out of the fractured ends. This soon gives place to a watery fluid, which in a fortnight thickens to a gristly substance, strong enough to hold them in place. Bone-matter is then slowly deposited, which in five or six weeks will unite the broken parts. Nature, at first, apparently endeavors to remedy the weakness of the material by excess in the quantity, and so the new portion is larger than the old. But the extra matter will be gradually absorbed, sometimes so perfectly as to leave no trace of the injury. (See p. 271.)

A broken limb should always be held in place by splints, to enable this process to go on uninterruptedly, and also lest a sudden jar might rupture the partially-mended break. For a long time, the new portion consists largely of animal matter, and so is tender and pliable. The utmost care is therefore necessary to prevent a malformation.

The Joints are packed with a soft, smooth cartilage, or gristle, which fits so perfectly as to be airtight. Upon convex surfaces, it is thickest at the middle, and upon concave surfaces, it is thickest at the edge, or where the wear is greatest. In addition, the ends of the bones are covered with a thin membrane, the *synovial* (*sun*, with ; *ovum*, an egg), which secretes a viscid fluid, not unlike the white of an egg. This lubricates the joints, and prevents the noise and wear of friction. The body is the only machine that oils itself.

The bones which form the joint are tied with stout ligaments (*ligo*, I bind), or bands, of a smooth, silvery white tissue,* so strong that the bones are sometimes broken without injuring the fastenings.

————•♦•————

II. CLASSIFICATION OF THE BONES.

FOR convenience, the bones of the skeleton are considered in three divisions: the *head*, the *trunk*, and the *limbs*.

1. THE HEAD.

The Bones of the Skull and the Face form a cavity for the protection of the brain and the four organs of sense, viz.: sight, smell, taste, and hearing. All these bones are immovable except the lower jaw, which is hinged† at the back so as to allow for the opening and shutting of the mouth.

The Skull is composed, in general, of two compact plates, with a spongy layer between. These are in several pieces, the outer ones being joined by notched edges, sutures (sūt′yurs), in the way carpenters term dove-tailing. (See Fig. 4.)

---

* The general term *tissue* is applied to the various textures of which the organs are composed. For example, the osseous tissue forms the bones; the fibrous tissue, the skin, tendons, and ligaments.

† A ring of cartilage is inserted in its joints, something after the manner of a washer in machinery. This follows the movements of the jaw, and admits of freer motion, while it guards against dislocation.

The peculiar structure and form of the skull afford a perfect shelter for the brain—an organ so delicate that, if unprotected, an ordinary blow would destroy it. Its oval or egg shape adapts it to resist pressure.

FIG. 4.

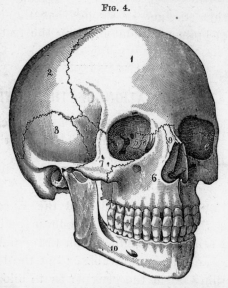

The Skull.—1, *frontal bone;* 2, *parietal bone;* 3, *temporal bone;* 4, *the sphenoid bone;* 5, *ethmoid bone;* 6, *superior maxillary (upper jaw) bone;* 7, *malar bone;* 8, *lachrymal bone;* 9, *nasal bone;* 10, *inferior maxillary (lower jaw) bone.*

The smaller and stronger end is in front, where the danger is greatest. Projections before and behind shield the less protected parts. The hard plates are not easy to penetrate.* The spongy packing deadens

---

* Instances have been known where bullets, striking against the skull, have glanced off, been flattened, or even split into halves. In the Peninsular Campaign, the author saw a man who had been struck in the forehead by a bullet which, instead of penetrating the brain, had followed the skull around to the back of the head, and there passed out.

every blow.* The separate pieces with their curious joinings disperse any jar which one may receive, and also prevent fractures from spreading.

The frequent openings in this strong bone-box afford safe avenues for the passage of numerous nerves and vessels which communicate between the brain and the rest of the body.

2 THE TRUNK.

The Trunk has two important cavities. The upper part, or *chest*, contains the heart and the lungs, and the lower part, or *abdomen*, holds the stomach, liver, kidneys, and other organs (Fig. 31). The principal bones are those of the *spine*, the *ribs*, and the *hips*.

The Spine consists of twenty-four bones, between which are placed pads of cartilage.† A canal is hollowed

Fig. 6.

The Spine; the seven vertebræ of the neck, cervical; the twelve of the back, dorsal; the five of the loins, lumbar; a, the sacrum, and b, the coccyx, comprising the nine "false vertebræ" (p. 3).

Fig. 5.

* An experiment resembling the familiar one of the balls in Natural Philosophy ("Steele's Popular Physics," Fig. 6, p. 26), beautifully illustrates this point. Several balls of ivory are suspended by cords, as in Fig. 5. If A be raised and then let fall, it will transmit the force to B, and that to C, and so on until F is reached, which will fly off with the impulse. If now a ball of spongy bone be substituted for an ivory one anywhere in the line, the force will be checked, and the last ball will not stir.

† These pads vary in thickness from one fourth to one half an inch.

out of the column for the safe passage of the spinal cord. (See Fig. 50.) Projections (processes) at the back and on either side are abundant for the attachment of the muscles. The packing acts as a cushion to prevent any jar from reaching the brain when we jump or run, while the double curve of the spine also tends to disperse the force of a fall. Thus on every side the utmost caution is taken to guard that precious gem in its casket.

The Perfection of the Spine surpasses all human contrivances. Its various uses seem a bundle of contradictions. A chain of twenty-four bones is made so stiff that it will bear a heavy burden, and so flexible that it will bend like rubber; yet, all the while, it transmits no shock, and even hides a delicate nerve within that would thrill with the slightest

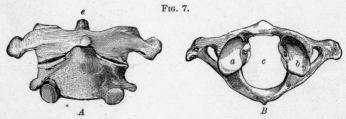

Fig. 7.

B, *the first cervical vertebra, the atlas;* A, *the atlas, and the second cervical vertebra, the axis;* e, *the odontoid process;* c, *the foramen.*

touch. Resting upon it, the brain is borne without a tremor; and, clinging to it, the vital organs are carried without fear of harm.

They become condensed by the weight they bear during the day, so that we are somewhat shorter at evening than in the morning. Their elasticity causes them to resume their usual size during the night, or when we lie down for a time.

The Skull Articulates with (is jointed to) the spine in a peculiar manner. On the top of the upper vertebra (atlas*) are two little hollows (*a*, *b*, Fig. 7), nicely packed and lined with the synovial membrane, into which fit the corresponding projections on the lower part of the skull, and thus the head can rock to and fro. The second vertebra (axis) has a peg, *e*, which projects through a hole, *c*, in the first.

Fig. 8.

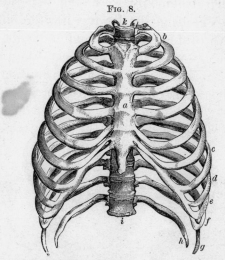

The Thorax, or Chest. a, *the sternum ;* b *to* c, *the true ribs ;* d *to* h, *the false ribs ;* g, h, *the floating ribs ;* i, k, *the dorsal vertebræ.*

The surfaces of both vertebræ are so smooth that they easily glide on each other, and thus, when we move the head sidewise, the atlas turns around the peg, *e*, of the axis.

The Ribs, also twenty-four in number, are ar-

---

* Thus called because, as, in ancient fable, the god Atlas supported the world on his shoulders, so in the body this bone bears the head.

ranged in pairs on each side of the chest. At the back, they are all attached to the spine. In front, the upper seven pairs are tied by cartilages to the breast-bone (sternum); three are fastened to each other and to the cartilage above, and two, the floating ribs, are loose.

The natural form of the chest is that of a cone diminishing upward. But, owing to the tightness of the clothing commonly worn, the reverse is often the case. The long, slender ribs give lightness,* the arched form confers strength, and the cartilages impart elasticity,—properties essential to the protection of the delicate organs within, and to freedom of motion in respiration. (See note, p. 80.)

Fig. 9.

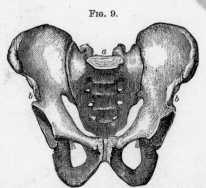

The Pelvis. a, the sacrum; b, b, the right and the left innominatum.

The Hip-bones, called by anatomists the innominata, or nameless bones, form an irregular basin

---

* If the chest-wall were in one bone thick enough to resist a blow, it would be unwieldy and heavy. As it is, the separate bones bound by cartilages yield gradually, and diffuse the force among them all, and so are rarely broken.

styled the *pelvis* (*pelvis*, a basin).   In the upper part, is the foot of the spinal column—a wedge-shaped bone termed the *sacrum** (sacred), firmly planted here between the wide-spreading and solid bones of the pelvis, like the key-stone to an arch, and giving a steady support to the heavy burden above.

3. THE LIMBS.

Two Sets of Limbs branch from the trunk, viz.: the upper, and the lower.   They closely resemble each other.   The arm corresponds to the thigh ; the fore-arm, to the leg ; the wrist, to the ankle ; the fingers, to the toes.   The fingers and the toes are so much alike that they receive the same name, *digits*, while the several bones of both have also the common appellation, *pha-langes*.   The differences which exist grow out of their varying uses.   The foot is characterized by strength ; the hand, by mo-bility.

1. The Upper Limbs.—The Shoulder. — The bones of the shoulder are the collar - bone

FIG. 10.

The Shoulder-joint.   a, the clavicle ; b, the scapula.

(clavicle), and the shoulder-blade (scapula).   The *clavicle* (*clavis*, a key) is a long, slender bone, shaped like the Italic *f*.   It is fastened at one end to the

---

* So called because it was anciently offered in sacrifice.

breast-bone and the first rib, and, at the other, to the shoulder-blade. (See Fig. 1.) It thus holds the shoulder-joint out from the chest, and gives the arm greater play. If it be removed or broken, the head of the arm-bone will fall, and the motions of the arm be greatly restricted.*

The Shoulder-blade is a thin, flat, triangular bone, fitted to the top and back of the chest, and designed to give a foundation for the muscles of the shoulder.

FIG. 11.

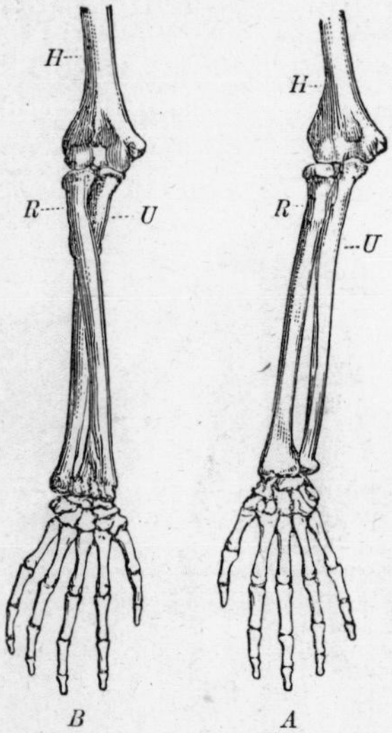

Bones of the right Fore-arm. H, *the humerus;* R, *the radius; and* U, *the ulna.*

The Shoulder - joint.—The arm-bone, or *humerus*, articulates with the shoulder-blade by a ball-and-socket joint. This consists of a cup-like cavity in the latter bone, and a rounded head in the former, to fit it,—thus affording a free rotary motion. The shallowness of the socket accounts for the frequent dislocation of this joint, but a deeper one would diminish the easy swing of the arm.

The Elbow.—At the elbow, the humerus articulates with the *ulna*—a slender bone on the inner side of the fore-arm—by a hinge-joint which admits of motion in

* Animals which use the forelegs only for support (as the horse, ox, etc.), do not possess this bone. "It is found in those that dig, fly, climb, and seize."

only two directions, *i. e.*, backward and forward. The ulna is small at its lower end; the *radius*, or large bone of the fore-arm, on the contrary, is small at its upper end, while it is large at its lower end, where it forms the wrist-joint. At the elbow, the head of the radius is convex and fits into a shallow cavity in the ulna, while at the wrist the ulna plays in a similar socket in the radius. Thus the radius may roll over and even cross the ulna.

The Wrist, or *carpus*, consists of two rows of very irregular bones, one of which articulates with the fore-arm; the other, with the hand. They are placed side to side, and so firmly fastened as to admit of only a gliding motion. This gives little play, but great strength, elasticity, and power of resisting shocks.

Fig. 12.

Bones of the Hand and the Wrist.

The Hand.—The *meta-carpal* (*meta*, beyond; *karpos*, wrist), or bones of the palm, support each a thumb or a finger. Each finger has three bones, while the thumb has only two. The first bone of the thumb, standing apart from the rest, enjoys a special freedom of motion, and adds greatly to the usefulness of the hand.

The first bone (Figs. 11, 12) of each finger is so

attached to the corresponding metacarpal bone as to move in several directions upon it, but the other phalanges form hinge-joints.

The fingers are named in order: the thumb, the index, the middle, the ring, and the little finger. Their different lengths cause them to fit the hollow of the hand when it is closed, and probably enable us more easily to grasp objects of varying size. If the hand clasps a ball, the tips of the fingers will be in a straight line.

The hand in its perfection belongs only to man. Its elegance of outline, delicacy of mold, and beauty of color have made it the study of artists; while its exquisite mobility and adaptation as a perfect instrument have led many philosophers to attribute man's superiority even more to the hand than to the mind.*

2. The Lower Limbs.—The Hip.—The thigh-bone, or *femur*, is the largest and necessarily the strongest in the skeleton, since at every step it has to bear

---

* How constantly the hand aids us in explaining or enforcing a thought! We affirm a fact by placing the hand as if we would rest it firmly on a body; we deny by a gesture putting the false or erroneous proposition away from us; we express doubt by holding the hand suspended, as if hesitating whether to take or reject. When we part from dear friends, or greet them again after long absence, the hand extends toward them as if to retain, or to bring them sooner to us. If a recital or a proposition is revolting, we reject it energetically in gesture as in thought. In a friendly adieu we wave our good wishes to him who is their object; but when it expresses enmity, by a brusque movement we sever every tie. The open hand is carried backward to express fear or horror, as well as to avoid contact; it goes forward to meet the hand of friendship; it is raised suppliantly in prayer toward Him from whom we hope for help; it caresses lovingly the downy cheek of the infant, and rests on its head invoking the blessing of Heaven.—*Wonders of the Human Body.*

the weight of the whole body. It articulates with
the hip-bone by a ball-and-socket joint. Unlike the
shoulder-joint, the cup here is deep, thus affording

FIG. 13.

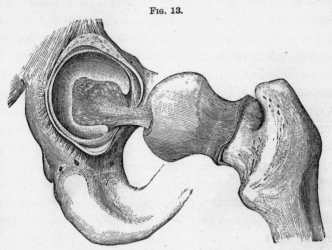

The Mechanism of the Hip-joint.

less play, but greater strength. It fits so tightly that
the pressure of the air largely aids in keeping the
bones in place.* Indeed, when the muscles are cut
away, great force is required to detach the limbs.

The Knee is strengthened by the *patella*, or knee-

---

* In order to test this, a hole was bored through a hip-bone, so as to
admit air into the socket; the thigh-bone at once fell out as far as the
ligaments would permit. An experiment was also devised whereby a suit-
ably-prepared hip-joint was placed under the receiver of an air-pump. On
exhausting the air, the weight of the femur caused it to drop out of the
socket, while the re-admission of the air raised it to its place. Without this
arrangement, the adjacent muscles would have been compelled to bear the
additional weight of the thigh-bone every time it was raised. Now the
pressure of the air rids them of this unnecessary burden, and hence they
are less easily fatigued.—WEBER.

pan (*patella*, little dish), a chestnut-shaped bone firmly fastened over the joint.

The shin-bone, or *tibia*, the large, triangular bone on the inner side of the leg, articulates both with the femur and the foot by hinge-joints. The knee-joint is so made, however, as to admit of a slight rotary motion when the limb is not extended.

The *fibula* (*fibula*, a clasp), the small, outside bone of the leg, is firmly bound at each end to the tibia. (See Fig. 1.) It is immovable, and, as the tibia bears the principal weight of the body, the chief use of this second bone seems to be to give more surface to which the muscles may be attached.*

The Foot.—The general arrangement of the foot is strikingly like that of the hand (Fig. 1). The several parts are the *tarsus*, the *metatarsus*, and the *phalanges*. The graceful arch of the foot, and the numerous bones joined by cartilages, give an elasticity to the step that could never be attained by a single, flat bone.† The toes naturally lie straight forward in the line of the foot. Few persons in civilized nations, however, have naturally-formed feet. The big toe is crowded upon the others, while crossed toes, nails grown-in, enormous joints, corns, and bunions abound.

---

* A young man in the hospital at Limoges had lost the middle part of his tibia. The lost bone was not reproduced, but the fibula, the naturally weak and slender part of the leg, became thick and strong enough to support the whole body.—STANLEY's *Lectures*.

† The foot consists of an arch, the base of which is more extended in front than behind, and the whole weight of the body is made to fall on this arch by means of a variety of joints. These joints further enable the foot to be applied, without inconvenience, to rough and uneven surfaces.—HINTON.

The Cause of these Deformities is found in the shape and size of fashionable boots and shoes. The sole ought to be large enough for full play of motion, the uppers should not crowd the toes, and the heels should be low, flat, and broad. As it is, there is a constant warfare between Nature and our shoe-makers,* and we are the victims. The narrow point in front pinches our toes, and compels them to over-ride one another; the narrow sole compresses the arch; while the high heel, by throwing all the weight forward on the toes, strains the ankle, and, by sending the pressure where Nature did not design it to fall, causes that joint to become enlarged. The body bends forward to meet the demand of this new motion, and thus loses its uprightness and beauty, making our gait stiff and ungraceful. (See p. 271.)

Diseases, etc.—1. *Rickets*, a disease of early life, is caused by a lack of mineral matter in the bones, rendering them soft and pliable, so that they bend under the weight of the body. They thus become permanently distorted, and of course are weaker than if they were straight.† Rickets is most common among children who have inherited a feeble constitu-

---

* When we are measured for boots or shoes, we should *stand* on a sheet of paper, and have the shoemaker mark with a pencil the exact outline of our feet as they bear our whole weight. When the shoe is made, the sole should exactly cover this outline.

† Just here appears an exceedingly beautiful provision. As soon as the disproportion of animal matter ceases, a larger supply of mineral is sent to the weak points, and the bones actually become thicker, denser, harder, and consequently stronger at the very concave part where the stress of pressure is greatest.—WATSON'S *Lectures.* We shall often have occasion to refer to similar wise and providential arrangements whereby the body is enabled to remedy defects, and to prepare for accidents.

3

tion and who are ill fed, or who live in damp, unventilated houses. "Rickety" children should have plenty of fresh air and sunlight, nourishing food, comfortable clothing, and, in short, the best of hygienic care.

2. *A Felon* is a swelling of the finger or thumb, usually of the last joint. It is marked by an accumulation beneath the periosteum and next the bone. The physician will merely cut through the periosteum, and let out the effete matter.

3. *Bow-legs* are caused by children standing on their feet before the bones of the lower limbs are strong enough to bear their weight. The custom of encouraging young children to stand by means of a chair or the support of the hand, while the bones are yet soft and pliable, is a cruel one, and liable to produce permanent deformity. Nature will set the child on its feet when the proper time comes.

4. *Curvature of the Spine.*—When the spine is bent, the packing between the vertebræ becomes compressed on one side into a wedge-like shape. After a time, it will lose its elasticity, and the spine will become distorted. This often occurs in the case of students who bend forward to bring their eyes nearer their books, instead of lifting their books nearer their eyes, or who raise their right shoulder above their left when writing at a desk which is too high. Round shoulders, small, weak lungs, and, frequently, diseases of the spine are the consequences. An erect posture in reading or writing conduces not alone to beauty of form, but also to health of body. We shall learn hereafter that the action of the

muscles bears an important part in preserving the symmetry of the spine. Muscular strength comes from bodily activity; hence, one of the best preventives of spinal curvature is daily exercise in the open air.

5. *Sprains* are produced when the ligaments which bind the bones of a joint are strained, twisted, or torn from their attachments. They are quite as serious as a broken bone, and require careful attention lest they lead to a crippling for life. By premature use a sprained limb may be permanently impaired. Hence, the joint should be kept quiet, even after the immediate pain is gone.

6. *A Dislocation* is the forcible displacement of a bone from its socket. It is, generally, the result of a fall or a violent blow. The tissues of the joint are often ruptured, while the contraction of the muscles prevents the easy return of the bone to its place. A dislocation should be reduced as soon as possible after the injury, before inflammation supervenes.

PRACTICAL QUESTIONS.

1. Why does not a fall hurt a child as much as it does a grown person?
2. Should a young child ever be urged to stand or walk?
3. What is meant by " breaking one's neck "?
4. Should chairs or benches have straight backs?
5. Should a child's feet be allowed to dangle from a high seat?
6. Why can we tell whether a fowl is young by pressing on the point of the breast-bone?
7. What is the use of the marrow in the bones?
8. Why is the shoulder so often put out of joint?
9. How can you tie a knot in a bone?

10. Why are high pillows injurious?

11. Is a stooping posture a healthful position?

12. Should a boot have a heel-piece?

13. Why should one always sit and walk erect?

14. Why does a young child creep rather than walk?

15. What is the natural direction of the big toe?

16. What is the difference between a sprain and a fracture? A dislocation?

17. Does the general health of the system affect the strength of the bones?

18. Is living bone sensitive? *Ans.*—Scrape a bone, and its vessels bleed; cut or bore a bone, and its granulations sprout up; break a bone, and it will heal; cut a piece away, and more bone will readily be produced; hurt it in any way, and it inflames; burn it, and it dies. Take any proof of sensibility but the mere feeling of pain, and it will answer to the proof.—BELL's *Anatomy.* Animal sensibility would be inconvenient; it is therefore not to be found except in diseased bone, where it sometimes exhibits itself too acutely.—TODD's *Cyclopedia of Anatomy.*

19. Is the constitution of bone the same in animals as in man? *Ans.*—The bones of quadrupeds do not differ much from those of man. In general they are of a coarser texture, and in some, as in those of the elephant's head, we find extensive air-cells.—TODD's *Anatomy.*

II.

THE MUSCLES.

———

BEHOLD the outward moving frame,
Its living marbles jointed strong
With glistening band and silvery thong,
And link'd to reason's guiding reins
By myriad rings in trembling chains,
Each graven with the threaded zone
Which claims it as the Master's own."

HOLMES.

ANALYSIS OF THE MUSCLES.

THE MUSCLES.

1. THE USE, STRUCTURE, AND ACTION OF THE MUSCLES.
1. The Use of the Muscles.
2. Contractility of the Muscles.
3. Arrangement of the Muscles.
4. The two Kinds of Muscles.
5. The Structure of the Muscles.
6. The Tendons for Fastening Muscles.
7. The Muscles and Bones as Levers.
8. The Effect of Big Joints.
9. Action of the Muscles in Standing.
10. Action of the Muscles in Walking.

2. THE MUSCULAR SENSE.

3. HYGIENE OF THE MUSCLES.
1. Necessity of Exercise.
2. Time for Exercise.
3. Kinds of Exercise.

4. WONDERS OF THE MUSCLES.

5. DISEASES..........
1. St. Vitus' Dance.
2. Convulsions.
3. Locked-jaw.
4. Gout.
5. Rheumatism.
6. Lumbago.
7. A Ganglion.

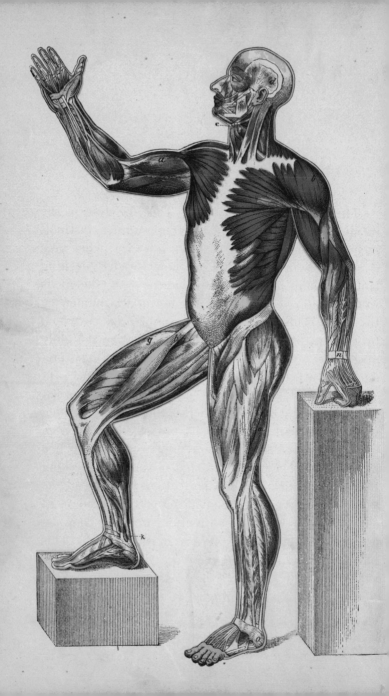

THE MUSCLES.

The Use of the Muscles. — The skeleton is the image of death. Its unsightly appearance instinctively repels us. We have seen, however, what uses it subserves in the body, and how the ugly-looking bones abound in nice contrivances and ingenious workmanship. In life, the frame-work is hidden by the flesh. This covering is a mass of muscles, which by their arrangement and their properties not only give form and symmetry to the body, but also produce its varied movements.

In Fig. 14, we see the large exterior muscles. Beneath these are many others; while deeply hidden within are tiny, delicate ones, too small to be seen with the naked eye. There are, in all, about five hundred, each having its special use, and all working in exquisite harmony and perfection.

Contractility. — The peculiar property of the muscles is their power of contraction, whereby they decrease in length and increase in thickness.* This may be caused by an effort of the will, by cold, by a sharp blow, etc. It does not cease at death, but, in certain cold-blooded animals, a contraction of the

* The maximum force of this contraction has been estimated as high as from eighty-five to one hundred and fourteen pounds per square inch.

muscles is often noticed long after the head has been cut off.

Arrangement of the Muscles.*—The muscles are nearly all arranged in pairs, each with its antagonist, so that, as they contract and expand alternately, the bone to which they are attached is moved to and fro. (See p. 275.)

If you grasp the arm tightly with your hand just above the elbow-joint, and bend the fore-arm, you will feel the muscle on the inside (biceps, *a*, Fig. 14) swell, and become hard and prominent, while the outside muscle (triceps, *f*) will be relaxed. Now straighten the arm, and the swelling and hardness of the inside muscle will vanish, while the outside one will, in turn, become rigid. So, also, if you clasp the arm just below the elbow, and then open and shut the fingers, you can feel the alternate expanding and relaxing of the muscles on opposite sides of the arms.

If the muscles on one side of the face become palsied, those on the other side will draw the mouth that way. Squinting is caused by one of the straight muscles of the eye (Fig. 17) contracting more strongly than its antagonist.

Kinds of Muscles.—There are two kinds of mus-

---

* " Could we behold properly the muscular fibers in operation, nothing, as a mere mechanical exhibition, can be conceived more superb than the intricate and combined actions that must take place during our most common movements. Look at a person running or leaping, or watch the motions of the eye. How rapid, how delicate, how complicated, and yet how accurate, are the motions required! Think of the endurance of such a muscle as the heart, that can contract, with a force equal to sixty pounds, seventy-five times every minute, for eighty years together, without being weary."

cles, the *voluntary*, which are under the control of our will, and the *involuntary*, which are not. Thus our limbs stiffen or relax as we please, but the heart beats on by day and by night The eyelid, however, is both voluntary and involuntary, so that while we wink constantly without effort, we can, to a certain extent, restrain or control the motion.

Structure of the Muscles.—If we take a piece of lean beef and wash out the red color, we can easily detect the fine fibers of which the meat is composed. In boiling corned beef for the table, the fibers often separate, owing to the dissolving of the delicate tissue which bound them together. By means of the microscope, we find that these fibers are made up of minute filaments (*fibrils*), and that each fibril is composed of a row of small cells arranged like a string of beads. This gives the muscles a peculiar striped (striated) appearance.* (See p. 276.)

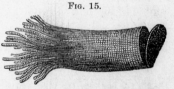

FIG. 15.

Microscopic view of a Muscle, showing, at one end, the fibrillæ; and, at the other, the disks, or cells, of the fiber.

The cells are filled with a fluid or semi-fluid mass of living (protoplasmic) matter.

The binding of so many threads into one bundle †

---

* The involuntary muscles consist generally of smooth, fibrous tissue, and form sheets or membranes in the walls of hollow organs. By their contraction they change the size of cavities which they inclose. Some functions, however, like the action of the heart, or the movements of deglutition (swallowing), require the rapid, vigorous contraction, characteristic of the voluntary muscular tissue.—FLINT.

† We shall learn hereafter how these fibers are firmly tied together by a mesh of fine connective tissue which dissolves in boiling, as just described.

confers great strength, according to a mechanical principle that we see exemplified in suspension bridges, where the weight is sustained, not by bars of iron, but by small wires twisted into massive ropes.

FIG. 16.

Tendons of the Hand.

The Tendons.—The ends of the muscles are generally attached to the bone by strong, flexible, but inelastic tendons.* The muscular fibers spring from the sides of the tendon, so that more of them can act upon the bone than if they went directly to it. Besides, the small, insensible tendon can better bear the exposure of passing over a joint, and be more easily lodged in some protecting groove, than the broad, sensitive muscle. This mode of attachment gives to the limbs strength, and elegance of form. Thus, for example, if the large muscles of the arm extended to the hand, they would make it bulky and clumsy. The tendons, however, reach only to the wrist, whence fine cords pass to the fingers (Fig. 16).

Here we notice two other admirable arrangements. 1. If the long tendons at the wrist on contracting

---

* The tendons may be easily seen in the leg of a turkey as it comes on our table; so we may study Physiology while we pick the bones.

should rise, projections would be made and thus the
beauty of the slender joint be marred. To prevent
this, a stout band or bracelet of ligament holds them
down to their place.   2. In order to allow the tendon
which moves the last joint of the finger to pass
through, the tendon which moves the second joint

FIG. 17.

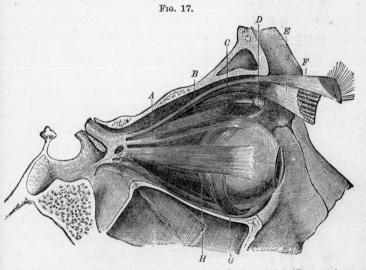

*The Muscles of the Right Eye. A, superior straight ; B, superior oblique passing
through a pulley, D; G, inferior oblique ; H, external straight, and, back of it, the
internal straight muscle.*

divides at its attachment to the bone (Fig. 16). This
is the most economical mode of packing the muscles,
as any other practicable arrangement would increase
the bulk of the slender finger.

Since the tendon can not always pull in the direction of the desired motion, some contrivance is necessary to meet the want. The tendon (B) belonging
to one of the muscles of the eye, for example, passes

through a ring of cartilage, and thus a rotary motion is secured.

FIG. 18.

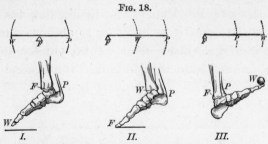

I.   *II.*   *III.*

The three classes of Levers, and also the foot as a Lever.

The Levers of the Body.*—In producing the motions of the body, the muscles use the bones as levers. We see an illustration of the *first class* of

FIG. 19.

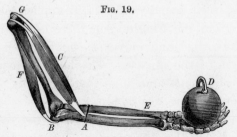

The hand as a Lever of the third class.

levers in the movements of the head. The back or front of the head is the weight to be lifted, the

---

* A *lever* is a stiff bar resting on a point of support, called the *fulcrum* (*F*), and having connected with it a *weight* (*W*) to be lifted, and a *power* (*P*) to move it. There are three classes of levers according to the arrangement of the power, weight, and fulcrum. In the first class, the *F* is between the *P* and *W;* in the second, the *W* is between the *P* and *F;* and in the third, the *P* is between the *W* and *F* (Fig. 18). A pump-handle is an example of the first; a lemon-squeezer, of the second; and a pair of fire-tongs, of the third. See "Popular Physics," pp. 81–83, for a full description of this subject, and for many illustrations.

backbone is the fulcrum on which the lever turns, and the muscles at the back or front of the neck exert the power by which we toss or bow the head.

When we raise the body on tiptoe, we have an instance of the *second class*. Here, our toes resting on the ground form the fulcrum, the muscles of the calf (gas-troc-ne'-mi-us, *j*, and so-le'-us, Fig. 14), acting through the tendon of the heel,* are the power, and the weight is borne by the ankle-joint.

An illustration of the *third class* is found in lifting the hand from the elbow. The hand is the weight, the elbow the fulcrum, and the power is applied by the biceps muscle at its attachment to the radius. (*A*, Fig. 19.) In this form of the lever there is a great loss of force, because it is applied at such a distance from the weight, but there is a gain of velocity, since the hand moves so far by such a slight contraction of the muscle. The hand is required to perform quick motions, and therefore this mode of attachment is here desirable.

The nearer the power is applied to the resistance, the more easily the work is done. In the lower jaw, for example, the jaw is the weight, the fulcrum is the hinge-joint at the back, and the muscles (temporal, *d*, and the mas'-se-ter, *e*, Fig. 14) on each side

---

* This is called the Tendon of Achilles (*k*, Fig. 14), and is so named because, as the fable runs, when Achilles was an infant his mother held him by the heel while she dipped him in the River Styx, whose water had the power of rendering one invulnerable to any weapon. His heel, not being wet, was his weak point, to which Paris directed the fatal arrow.— "This tendon," says Mapother, "will bear one thousand pounds weight before it will break." The horse is said to be "hamstrung," and is rendered useless, when the Tendon of Achilles is cut. (See p. 284.)

are the power.* They act much closer to the resistance than those in the hand, since here we desire force, and there, speed.

The Enlargement of the Bones at the Joints not only affords greater surface for the attachment of the muscles, as we have seen, but also

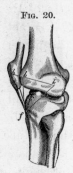

Fig. 20.

enables them to work to better advantage. Thus, in Fig. 20 it is evident that a muscle acting in the line *f b* would not bend the lower limb so easily as if it were acting in the line *f h*, since in the former case its force would be about all spent in drawing the bones more closely together, while in the latter it would pull more nearly at a right angle. Thus the tendon *f*, by passing over the patella, which is itself pushed out by the protuberance *b* of the thigh-bone, pulls at a larger angle,† and so the leg is thrown forward with ease in walking and with great force in kicking.

The Knee-joint; h, *the patella;* f, *the tendon.*

How We Stand Erect.—The joints play so easily, and the center of gravity in the body is so far above the foot, that the skeleton can not of itself hold our bodies upright. Thus it requires the action of many

---

* We may feel the contraction of the masseter by placing our hand on the face when we work the jaw, while the temporal can be readily detected by putting the fingers on the temple while we are chewing. The tendon of the muscle (digastric)—one of those which open the jaw—passes through a pulley (*c*, Fig. 14) somewhat like the one in the eye.

† The chief use of the processes of the spine (Fig. 6) and other bones is, in the same way, to throw out the point on which the power acts as far from the fulcrum as possible. The projections of the ulna ("funny bone") behind the elbow, and that of the heel-bone to which the Tendon of Achilles is attached, are excellent illustrations (Fig. 1).

muscles to maintain this position. The head so rests
upon the spine as to tend to fall in
front, but the muscles of the neck steady
it in its place.* The hips incline forward, but are held erect by the strong
muscles of the back. The trunk is nicely
balanced on the head of the thigh-bones.
The great muscles of the thigh acting
over the knee-pan tend to bend the body
forward, but the muscles of the calf neutralize this action. The ankle, the knee,
and the hip lie in nearly the same line,
and thus the weight of the body rests
directly on the key-stone of the arch of
the foot. So perfectly do these muscles
act that we never think of them until
science calls our attention to the subject,
and yet to acquire the necessary skill to
use them in our infancy needed patient
lessons, much time, and many hard knocks.

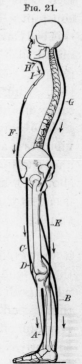

Fig. 21.

Action of the
Muscles which
keep the body
erect.

How We Walk.—Walking is as complex an act as standing. It is really a
perilous performance, which has become
safe only because of constant practice.
We see how violent it is when we run
against a post in the dark, and find with what headlong

---

* In animals the jaws are so heavy, and the place where the head and
spine join is so far back, that there can be no balance as there is in man.
There are therefore large muscles in their necks. We readily find that we
have none if we get on "all fours" and try to hold up the head. On the
other hand, gorillas and apes can not stand erect like man, for the reason
that their head, trunk, legs, etc., are not balanced by muscles, so as to be
in line with one another.

force we were hurling ourselves forward. Holmes has well defined walking as a perpetual falling with a constant self-recovery. Standing on one foot, we let the body fall forward, while we swing the other leg ahead like a pendulum. Planting that foot on the ground, to save the body from falling farther, we then swing the first foot forward again to repeat the same operation.*

The shorter the pendulum, the more rapidly it vibrates; and so short-legged people take quicker and shorter steps than long-legged ones.† We are shorter when walking than when standing still, because of this falling forward to take a step in advance.‡

In running, we incline the body more, and so, as it were, fall faster. When we walk, one foot is on the ground all the time, and there is an instant when both feet are planted upon it; but in running there is an interval of time in each step when both feet are off the ground, and the body is wholly unsupported. As we step alternately with the feet, we are inclined to turn the body first to one side and

---

* It is a curious fact that one side of the body tends to out-walk the other; and so, when a man is lost in the woods, he often goes in a circle, and at last comes round to the spot whence he started.

† In this respect, Tom Thumb was to Magrath, whose skeleton, eight and one half feet high, is now in the Dublin Museum, what a little fast-ticking, French mantel-clock is to a big, old-fashioned, upright, corner time-piece.

‡ Women find that a gown that will swing clear of the ground when they are standing still, will drag the street when they are walking. The length of the step may be increased by muscular effort, as when a line of soldiers keep step in spite of their having legs of different lengths. Such a mode of walking is necessarily fatiguing. (See p. 280.)

then to the other.   This movement is sometimes counterbalanced by swinging the hand on the opposite side.*

The Muscular Sense.—When we lift an object, we feel a sensation of weight, which we can compare with that experienced in lifting another body.† By care we may cultivate this sense so as to form a very precise estimate of the weight of a body by

* In ordinary walking the speed is nearly four miles an hour, and can be kept up for a long period.   But exercise and a special aptitude for it enable some men to walk great distances in a relatively short space of time.   Trained walkers have gone seventy-five miles in twenty hours, and walked the distance of thirty-seven miles at the rate of five miles an hour. The mountaineers of the Alps are generally good walkers, and some of them are not less remarkable for endurance than for speed.   Jacques Balmat, who was the first to reach the summit of Mont Blanc, at sixteen years of age could walk from the hamlet of the Pélerins to the mountain of La Côte in two hours,—a distance which the best-trained travelers required from five to six hours to get over.   At the time of his last attempt to reach the top of Mont Blanc, this same guide, then twenty years old, passed six days and four nights without sleeping or reposing a single moment.   One of his sons, Édouard Balmat, left Paris to join his regiment at Genoa; he reached Chamonix the fifth day at evening, having walked three hundred and forty miles.   After resting two days, he set off again for Genoa, where he arrived in two days.   Several years afterward, this same man left the baths at Louèche at two o'clock in the morning, and reached Chamonix at nine in the evening, having walked a distance equal to about seventy-five miles in nineteen hours.   In 1844, an old guide of De Saussure, eighty years old, left the hamlet of Prats, in the valley of Chamonix, in the afternoon, and reached the Grand-Mulets at ten in the evening; then after resting some hours, he climbed the glacier to the vicinity of the Grand Plateau, which has an altitude of about thirteen thousand feet, and then returned to his village without stopping.—*Wonders of the Body.*

† If a small ivory ball be allowed to roll down the cheek toward the lips, it will appear to increase in weight.   In general, the more sensitive parts of the body recognize smaller differences in weight, and the right hand is more accurate than the left.   We are very apt, however, to judge of the weight of a body from previous conceptions.   Thus, shortly after Sir Humphrey Davy discovered the metal potassium, he placed a piece of it in the hand of Dr. Pierson, who exclaimed: "Bless me! How heavy it is!" Really, however, potassium is so light that it will float on water like cork.

4

balancing it in the hand. The muscular sense is useful to us in many ways. It guides us in standing or moving. We gratify it when we walk erect and with an elastic step, and by dancing, jumping, skating, and gymnastic exercises.

Necessity of Exercise.—The effect of exercise upon a muscle is very marked.* By use it grows larger, and becomes hard, compact, and darker-colored; by disuse it decreases in size, and becomes soft, flabby, and pale.

Violent exercise, however, is injurious, since we then tear down faster than nature can build up. Feats of strength are not only hurtful, but dangerous. Often the muscles are strained or ruptured, and blood-vessels burst in the effort to outdo one's companions.† (See p. 278.)

Two thousand years ago, Isocrates, the Greek rhetorician, said: "Exercise for health, not for strength." The cultivation of muscle for its own sake is a return to barbarism, while it enfeebles the mind, and ultimately the body. The ancient gymnasts are said to have become prematurely old, and the trained performers of our own day soon suffer from the strain they put upon their muscular system. Few men have sufficient vigor to become both

* The greater size of the breast (pectoral muscle) of a pigeon, as compared with that of a duck, shows how muscle increases with use. The breast of a chicken is white because it is not used for flight, and therefore gets little blood.

† Instances have been known of children falling dead from having carried to excess so pleasant and healthful an amusement as jumping the rope, and of persons rupturing the Tendon of Achilles in dancing. The competitive lifting of heavy weights is unwise, sometimes fatal.

athletes and scholars. Exercise should, therefore, merely supplement the deficiency of our usual employment. *A sedentary life needs daily, moderate exercise, which always stops short of fatigue.* This is a law of health. (See p. 280.)

No education is complete which fails to provide for the development of the muscles. Recesses should be as strictly devoted to play as study-hours are to work. Were gymnastics or calisthenics as regular an exercise as grammar or arithmetic, fewer pupils would be compelled to leave school on account of ill health; while spinal curvatures, weak backs, and ungraceful gaits would no longer characterize so many of our best institutions.

Time for Exercise.—We should not exercise after long abstinence from food, nor immediately after a meal, unless the meal or the exercise be very light. There is an old-fashioned prejudice in favor of exercise before breakfast—an hour suited to the strong and healthy, but entirely unfitted to the weak and delicate. On first rising in the morning, the pulse is low, the skin relaxed, and the system susceptible to cold. Feeble persons, therefore, need to be braced with food before they brave the out-door air.

What Kind of Exercise to Take.—For children, games are unequaled. Walking, the universal exercise,* is beneficial, as it takes one into the open air

* The custom of walking, so prevalent in England, has doubtless much to do with the superior physique of its people. It is considered nothing for a woman to take a walk of eight or ten miles, and long pedestrian excursions are made to all parts of the country. The benefits which accrue from such an open-air life are sadly needed by the women of our own

and sunlight. Running is better, since it employs more muscles, but it must not be pushed to excess, as it taxes the heart, and may lead to disease of that organ. Rowing is more effectual in its general development of the system. Swimming employs the muscles of the whole body, and is a valuable acquirement, as it may be the means of saving life. Horseback riding is a fine accomplishment, and refreshes both mind and body. Gymnastic or calisthenic exercises bring into play all the muscles of the body, and when carefully selected, and not immoderately employed, are preferable to any other mode of indoor exercise.* (See p. 280.)

land. A walk of half a dozen miles should be a pleasant recreation for any healthy person.

* The employment of the muscles in exercise not only benefits their especial structure, but it acts on the whole system. When the muscles are put in action, the capillary blood-vessels with which they are supplied become more rapidly charged with blood, and active changes take place, not only in the muscles, but in all the surrounding tissues. The heart is required to supply more blood, and accordingly beats more rapidly in order to meet the demand. A larger quantity of blood is sent through the lungs, and larger supplies of oxygen are taken in and carried to the various tissues. The oxygen, by combining with the carbon of the blood and the tissues, engenders a larger quantity of heat, which produces an action on the skin, in order that the superfluous warmth may be disposed of. The skin is thus exercised, as it were, and the sudoriparous and sebaceous glands are set at work. The lungs and skin are brought into operation, and the lungs throw off large quantities of carbonic acid, and the skin large quantities of water, containing in solution matters which, if retained, would produce disease in the body. Wherever the blood is sent, changes of a healthful character occur. The brain and the rest of the nervous system are invigorated, the stomach has its powers of digestion improved, and the liver, pancreas, and other organs perform their functions with more vigor. By want of exercise, the constituents of the food which pass into the blood are not oxidized, and products which produce disease are engendered. The introduction of fresh supplies of oxygen induced by exercise oxidizes these products, and renders them harmless. As a rule, those who exercise most in the open air will live the longest.—LANKESTER

The Wonders of the Muscles.—The grace, ease, and rapidity with which the muscles contract are astonishing. By practice, they acquire a facility which we call mechanical. The voice may utter one thousand five hundred letters in a minute, yet each requires a distinct position of the vocal organs. We train the muscles of the fingers till they glide over the keys of the piano, executing the most exquisite and difficult harmony. In writing, each letter is formed by its peculiar motions, yet we make them so unconsciously that a skillful penman will describe beautiful curves while thinking only of the idea that the sentence is to express. The mind of the violinist is upon the music which his right hand is executing, while his left determines the length of the string and the character of each note so carefully that not a false sound is heard, although the variation of a hair's breadth would cause a discord. In the arm of a blacksmith, the biceps muscle may grow into the solidity almost of a club; the hand of a prize-fighter will strike a blow like a sledge-hammer; while the engraver traces lines invisible to the naked eye, and the fingers of the blind acquire a delicacy that almost supplies the place of the missing sense.

Diseases, etc.—1. *St. Vitus' Dance* is a disease of the voluntary muscles, whereby they are in frequent, irregular, and spasmodic motion beyond the control of the will. All causes of excitement, and especially of fear, should be avoided, and the general health of the patient invigorated, as this disease is closely connected with a derangement of the nervous system.

2. *Convulsions* are an involuntary contraction of the muscles. Consciousness is wanting, while the limbs may be stiff or in spasmodic action. (See p. 261.)

3. *Locked-jaw* is a disease in which there are spasms and a contraction of the muscles, usually beginning in the lower jaw. It is serious, often fatal, yet it is sometimes caused by as trivial an injury as the stroke of a whip-lash, the lodgment of a bone in the throat, a fish-hook in the finger, or a tack in the sole of the foot.

4. *Gout* is characterized by an acute pain located chiefly in the small joints of the foot, especially those of the great toe, which become swollen and extremely sensitive. It is generally accompanied by an excess of uric acid in the blood, and a deposit of urate of soda about the affected joint. Gout is often the result of high living, and of too much animal food. It is frequently inherited.

5. *Rheumatism* affects mainly the connective, white, fibrous tissue of the larger joints. While gout is the punishment of the rich who live luxuriously, rheumatism afflicts alike the poor and the rich. There are two common forms of rheumatism—the inflammatory or acute, and the chronic. The latter is of long continuance; the former terminates more speedily. The acute form is probably a disease of the blood, which carries with it some poisonous matter that is deposited where the fibrous tissue is most abundant. The disease flies capriciously from one joint to another, and the pain caused by even the slightest

motion deprives the sufferer of the use of the disabled part and its muscles. Its chief danger lies in the possibility of its affecting the vital organs. Chronic rheumatism—the result of repeated attacks of the acute—leads to great suffering, and oftentimes to disorganization of the joints and an interference with the movements of the heart.

6. *Lumbago* is an inflammation of the lumbar muscles and fascia.* It may be so moderate as to produce only a "lame back," or so severe as to disable, as in the case of what is popularly termed a "crick in the back." Strong swimmers who sometimes drown without apparent cause are supposed to be seized in this way.

7. *A Ganglion*, or what is vulgarly called a "weak" or "weeping" sinew, is the swelling of a bursa.† It sometimes becomes so distended by fluid as to be mistaken for bone. If on binding something hard upon it for a few days it does not disappear, a physician will remove the liquid by means of a hypodermic syringe, or perhaps cause it to be absorbed by an external application of iodine.

* Lumbago is really a form of myalgia, a disease which has its seat in the muscles, and may thus affect any part of the body. Doubtless much of what is commonly called "liver" or "kidney complaint" is only, in one case, myalgia of the chest or abdominal walls near the liver, or, in the other, of the back and loins near the kidneys. Chronic liver disease is comparatively rare in the Northern States, and pain in the side is not a prominent symptom; while certain diseases of the kidneys, which are as surely fatal as pulmonary consumption, are not attended by pain in the back opposite these organs.—WEY.

† A bursa is a small sack containing a lubricating fluid to prevent friction where tendons play over hard surfaces. There is one shaped like an hour-glass on the wrist, just at the edge of the palm. By pressing back the liquid it contains, this bursa may be clearly seen.

PRACTICAL QUESTIONS.

1. What class of lever is the foot when we lift a weight on the toes?

2. Explain the movement of the body backward and forward, when resting upon the thigh-bone as a fulcrum.

3. What class of lever do we use when we lift the foot while sitting down?

4. Explain the swing of the arm from the shoulder.

5. What class of lever is used in bending our fingers?

6. What class of lever is our foot when we tap the ground with our toes?

7. What class of lever do we use when we raise ourselves from a stooping position?

8. What class of lever is the foot when we walk?

9. Why can we raise a heavier weight with our hand when lifting from the elbow than from the shoulder?

10. What class of lever do we employ when we are hopping, the thigh-bone being bent up toward the body and not used?

11. Describe the motions of the bones when we are using a gimlet.

12. Why do we tire when we stand erect?

13. Why does it rest us to change our work?

14. Why and when is dancing a beneficial exercise?

15. Why can we exert greater force with the back teeth than with the front ones?

16. Why do we lean forward when we wish to rise from a chair?

17. Why does the projection of the heel-bone make walking easier?

18. Does a horse travel with less fatigue over a flat than a hilly country?

19. Can you move your upper jaw?

20. Are people naturally right or left-handed?

21. Why can so few persons move their ears by the muscles?

22. Is the blacksmith's right arm healthier than the left?

23. Boys often, though foolishly, thrust a pin into the flesh just above the knee. Why is it not painful?

24. Will ten minutes' practice in a gymnasium answer for a day's exercise?

25. Why would an elastic tendon be unfitted to transmit the motion of a muscle?

26. When one is struck violently on the head, why does he instantly fall?

27. What is the cause of the difference between light and dark meat in a fowl?

III.

THE SKIN.

A PROTECTION from the outer world, it is our only means of communicating with it. Insensible itself, it is the organ of touch. It feels the pressure of a hair, yet bears the weight of the body. It yields to every motion of that which it wraps and holds in place. It hides from view the delicate organs within, yet the faintest tint of a thought shines through, while the soul paints upon it, as on a canvas, the richest and rarest of colors.

ANALYSIS OF THE SKIN.

THE SKIN.

1. **THE STRUCTURE OF THE SKIN.**
   1. The Cutis; its Composition and Character.
   2. The Cuticle; its Composition and Character.
   3. The Value of the Cuticle.
   4. The Complexion.

2. **THE HAIR AND THE NAILS.**
   1. The Hair
      - a. *Description.*
      - b. *Method of Growth.*
      - c. *As an Instrument of Feeling.*
      - d. *Indestructibility of the Hair.*
   2. The Nails
      - a. *Uses.*
      - b. *Method of Growth.*

3. **THE MUCOUS MEMBRANE.**
   1. The Structure.
   2. Connective Tissue.
   3. Fat.

4. **THE TEETH.**
   1. Number and Kinds of Teeth.
   1. The Two Sets
      1. *The Milk Teeth.*
      2. *The Permanent Teeth.*
   2. Structure of the Teeth.
   3. The Setting of the Tooth in the Jaw.
   4. The Decay of the Teeth.
   5. The Preservation of the Teeth.

5. **THE GLANDS.**
   1. The Two Kinds
      1. *Oil Glands.*
      2. *Perspiratory Glands.*
   2. The Perspiration.
   3. The Absorbing Power of the Skin. (See Lymphatics.)

6. **HYGIENE**
   1. About Washing and Bathing.
   2. The Reaction.
   3. Sea-bathing.
   4. Clothing
      - a. *General Principles.*
      - b. *Linen.*
      - c. *Cotton.*
      - d. *Woolen.*
      - e. *Flannel.*
      - f. *Color of Clothing.*
      - g. *Structure of Clothing.*
      - h. *Insufficient Clothing.*

7. **DISEASES.**
   1. Erysipelas.
   2. Salt Rheum.
   3. Corns.
   4. In-growing Nails.
   5. Warts.
   6. Chilblains.

THE SKIN.

The Skin is a tough, thin, close-fitting garment for the protection of the tender flesh. Its perfect elasticity beautifully adapts it to every motion of the body. We shall learn hereafter that it is more than a mere covering, being an active organ, which does its part in the work of keeping in order the house in which we live. It oils itself to preserve its smoothness and delicacy, replaces itself as fast as it wears out, and is at once the perfection of use and beauty.

I. STRUCTURE OF THE SKIN.

Cutis and Cuticle.—What we commonly call the skin—viz., the part raised by a blister—is only the cuticle* or covering of the cutis or true skin. The latter is full of nerves and blood-vessels, while the former neither bleeds† nor gives rise to pain, neither suffers from heat nor feels the cold.

---

* *Cuticula*, little skin. It is often styled the scarf-skin, and also the epidermis (*epi*, upon ; and *derma*, skin).

† We notice this in shaving; for if a razor goes below the cuticle, it is followed by pain and blood. So insensible is this outer layer that we can run a pin through the thick mass at the roots of the nails without discomfort.

The cuticle is composed of small, flat cells or scales. These are constantly shed from the surface in the form of scurf, dandruff, etc., but are as constantly renewed from the cutis* below.

Under the microscope, we can see the round cells of the cuticle, and how they are flattened and hardened as they are forced to the surface. The immense

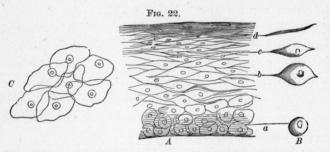

Fig. 22.

A *represents a vertical section of the Cuticle.* B, *lateral view of the Cells.* C, *flat side of scales like* d, *magnified 250 diameters, showing the nucleated cells transformed into broad scales.*

number of these cells surpasses comprehension. In one square inch of the cuticle, counting only those in a single layer, there are over a billion horny scales, each complete in itself.—HARTING.

Value of the Cuticle.—In the palm of the hand, the sole of the foot, and other parts especially liable to injury, the cuticle is very thick. This is a most admirable provision for their protection.† By use, it

---

* We see how rapidly this change goes on by noticing how soon a stain of any kind disappears from the skin. A snake throws off its cuticle entire, and at regular intervals.

† We can hold the hand in strong brine with impunity, but the smart will quickly tell us when there is even a scratch in the skin. Vaccine matter must be inserted beneath the cuticle to take effect. This membrane doubtless prevents many poisonous substances from entering the system.

becomes callous and horny. The boy who goes out barefoot for the first time, "treading as if on eggs," can soon run where he pleases among thistles and over stones. The blacksmith handles hot iron without pain, while the mason lays stones and works in lime, without scratching or corroding his flesh.

The Complexion.— In the freshly-made cells on the lower side of the cuticle, is a pigment composed of tiny grains.* In the varying tint of this coloring-matter, lies the difference of hue between the blonde and the brunette, the European and the African. In the purest complexion, there is some of this pigment, which, however, disappears as the fresh, round, soft cells next the cutis change into the old, flat, horny scales at the surface.

Scars are white, because this part of the cuticle is not restored. The sun has a powerful effect upon the coloring-matter, and so we readily "tan" on exposure to its rays. If the color gathers in spots, it forms freckles.†

* These grains are about $\frac{1}{1000}$ of an inch in diameter, and, curiously enough, do not appear opaque, but transparent and nearly colorless.— MARSHALL.

† This action of the sun on the pigment of the skin is very marked. Even among the Africans, the skin is observed to lose its intense black color in those who live for many months in the shades of the forest. It is said that Asiatic and African women confined within the walls of the harem, and thus secluded from the sun, are as fair as Europeans. Among the Jews who have settled in Northern Europe, are many of light complexion, while those who live in India are as dark as the Hindoos. Intense heat also increases this coloring-matter, and thus a furnace-man's skin, even where protected by clothing, becomes completely bronzed. The black pigment has been known to disappear during severe illness, and a lighter color to be developed in its place. Among the negroes, are sometimes found people who have no complexion, i. e., there is no coloring-matter in their skin, hair, or the iris of their eyes. These persons are called Albinos.

II. HAIR AND NAILS.

THE Hair and the Nails are modified forms of the cuticle.

The Hair is a protection from heat and cold, and shields the head from blows.   It is found on nearly

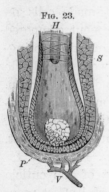

FIG. 23.

all parts of the body, except the palms of the hands and the soles of the feet.   The outside of a hair is hard and compact, and consists of a layer of colorless scales, which overlie one another like the shingles of a house ; the interior is porous,* and probably conveys the liquids by which it is nourished.

A Hair, magnified 600 diameters. S, *the sac (follicle);* P, *the papilla, showing the cells and the bloodvessels* (V).

Each hair grows from a tiny bulb (papilla), which is an elevation of the cutis at the bottom of a little hollow in the skin.   From the surface of this bulb, the hair is produced, like the cuticle, by the constant formation of new cells at the bottom.   When the hair is pulled out, this bulb, if uninjured, will produce a new one ; but, when once destroyed, it will never grow again.† The hair has been known to whiten in a single

* In order to examine a hair, it should be put on the slide of the microscope, and covered with a thin glass, while a few drops of alcohol are allowed to flow between the cover and the slide.   This causes the air, which fills the hair and prevents our seeing its structure, to escape.

† Hair grows at the rate of about five to seven inches in a year.   It is said to grow after death.   This appearance is due to the fact that by the shrinking of the skin the part below the surface is caused to project, which is especially noticeable in the beard.

night by fear, fright, or nervous excitement. When
the color has once changed, it
can not be restored.* (See p.
285.)

Fig. 24.

Wherever hair exists, tiny
muscles are found, interlaced
among the fibers of the skin.
These, when contracting under
the influence of cold or electricity, pucker up the skin,
and cause the hair to stand on
end.† The hairs themselves
are destitute of feeling. Nerves,
however, are found in the hollows in which the hair is
rooted, and so one feels pain
when it is pulled.‡ Thus the
insensible hairs become won-
derfully delicate instruments
to convey an impression of even
the slightest touch.

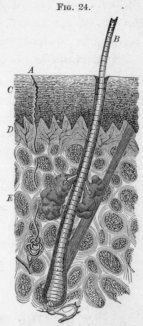

A, *a perspiratory tube with its
gland ;* B, *a hair with a muscle
and two oil-glands ;* C, *cuticle ;*
D, *the papillæ ; and* E, *fat-cells.*

---

* Hair dyes, or so-called "hair restorers," are almost invariably deleterious substances, depending for their coloring properties upon the action
of lead or lunar caustic. Frequent instances of hair-poisoning have occurred, owing to the common use of such dangerous articles. If the growth
of the hair be impaired, the general constitution or the skin needs treatment. This is the work of a skillful physician, and not of a patent remedy.
Dame Fashion has her repentant freaks as well as her ruinous follies, and
it is a healthful sign that the era of universal hair-dyeing has been blotted
out from her present calendar, and the gray hairs of age are now honored
with the highest place in "style" as well as in good sense and cleanliness.

† In horses and other animals which are able to shake the whole skin,
this muscular tissue is much more fully developed than in man.

‡ These nerves are especially abundant in the whiskers of the cat,
which are used as feelers.

Next to the teeth and bones, the hair is the least destructible part of the body, and its color is often preserved for many years after the other portions have gone to decay.*

The Nails protect the ends of the tender finger, and toe, and give us power more firmly to grasp and easily to pick up any object we may desire. They enable us to perform a hundred little, mechanical acts which else were impossible. At the same time, their delicate color and beautiful outline give a finish of ornament to that exquisite instrument, the hand. The nail is firmly set in a groove (matrix) in the cuticle, from which it grows at the root in length †️ and from beneath in thickness. So long as the matrix at the root is uninjured, the nail will be replaced after any accident. (See p. 288.)

III. THE MUCOUS MEMBRANE.

Structure.—At the edges of the openings into the body, the skin seems to stop and give place to a tissue which is redder, more sensitive, more liable to bleed, and is moistened by a fluid, or mucus, as it is called. Really, however, the skin does not cease, but passes into a more delicate covering of the same

* Fine downy hairs, such as are general upon the body, have been detected in the little fragments of skin found beneath the heads of the nails by which, centuries ago, certain robbers were fastened to the church doors, as a punishment for their sacrilege.

† By making a little mark on the nail near the root we can see, week by week, how rapidly this process goes on, and so form some idea of what a multitude of cells must be transformed into the horny matter of the nail.

general structure, viz., an outer, hard, bloodless, insensible layer, and an inner, soft, sanguine, nervous one.* Thus every part of the body is wrapped in a kind of double bag, made of tough skin on the outside, and tender mucous membrane on the inside.

Connective Tissue.—The cutis and the corresponding layer of the mucous membrane consist chiefly of a fibrous substance interlaced like felt. It is called connective tissue, because it connects all the different parts of the body. It spreads from the cutis, invests muscles, bones, and cartilages, and thence passes into the mucous membrane. So thoroughly does it permeate the body, that, if the other tissues were destroyed, it would give a perfect model of every organ.† It can be seen in a piece of meat as a delicate substance lying between the layers of muscle, where it serves to bind together the numerous fibers of which they are composed.

* With a dull knife, we can scrape from the mucous membrane which lines the mouth some of the cuticle for examination under the microscope. In a similar way, we can obtain cuticle from the surface of the body for study and comparison.

† It is curious to notice how our body is wrapped in membrane. On the outside, is the skin protecting from exterior injury, and, on the inside, is the mucous membrane reaching from the lips to the innermost air-cell of the lungs. Every organ is enveloped in its membrane. Every bone has its sheath. Every socket is lined. Even the separate fibers of muscles have their covering tissue. The brain and the spinal cord are triply wrapped, while the eye is only a membranous globe filled with fluid. These membranes protect and support the organs they enfold, but, with that wise economy so characteristic of nature every-where, they have also an important function to perform. They are the *filters* of the body. Through their pores pass alike the elements of growth, and the returning products of waste. On one side, bathed by the blood, they choose from it suitable food for the organ they envelop, and many of them in their tiny cells, by some mysterious process, form new products,—put the finishing touches, as it were, upon the material ere it is deposited in the body.

5

Connective tissue yields gelatine on boiling, and is the part which tans when hides are manufactuerd into leather. It is very elastic, so that when you remove your finger after pressing upon the skin, no indentation is left.* It varies greatly in character,— from the mucous membrane, where it is soft and tender, to the ligaments and tendons which it largely composes, where it is strong and dense.†

Fat is deposited as an oil in the cells‡ of this tissue, just beneath the skin (Fig. 24), giving roundness and plumpness to the body, and acting as an excellent non-conductor for the retention of heat. It collects as pads in the hollows of the bones, around the joints, and between the muscles, causing them to glide more easily upon each other. As marrow, it nourishes the skeleton, and also distributes the shock of any jar the limb may sustain.

It is noticeable, however, that fat does not gather within the cranium, the lungs, or the eyelids, where its accumulation would clog the organs.

* In dropsy, this elasticity is lost by distension, and there is a kind of "pitting," as it is called, produced by pressure.

† The leather made from this tissue varies as greatly, from the tough, thick ox-hide, to the soft, pliable kid and chamois skin.

‡ So tiny are these cells, that there are over sixty-five million in a cubic inch of fat. As they are kept moist, the liquid does not ooze out; but, on drying, it comes to the surface, and thus a piece of fat feels oily when exposed to the air. The quantity of fat varies with the state of nutrition. In corpulent persons, the masses of fat beneath the skin, in the mesentery, on the surface of the heart and great vessels, between the muscles, and in the neighborhood of the nerves, are considerably increased. Conversely, in the emaciated we sometimes find beneath the skin nucleated cells, which contain only one oil-drop. Many masses of fat which have an important relation to muscular actions—such as the fat of the orbit or the cheek—do not disappear in the most emaciated object. Even in starvation the fatty substances of the brain and spinal cord are retained.—VALENTIN.

IV. THE TEETH.

The Teeth[*] are thirty-two in all,—there being eight in each half-jaw, similarly shaped and arranged. In each set of eight, the two nearest the middle of the jaw have wide, sharp, chisel-like edges, fit for cutting, and hence are called *incisors*. The next one corresponds to the great tearing or holding tooth of the dog, and is styled the *canine*, or eye-tooth. The next two have broader crowns, with two points, or cusps, and are hence termed the *bicuspids*. The remaining three are much broader, and, as they are used to crush the food, are called the *grinders*, or *molars*. The incisors and eye-teeth have one fang, or root; the others have two or three fangs.

The Milk-teeth.—We are provided with two sets of teeth. The first, or milk-teeth, are small and only twenty in number. In each half-jaw there are two incisors, one canine, and two molars. The middle incisors are usually cut about the age of seven months, the others at nine months, the first molars at twelve months, the canines at eighteen months, and the remaining molars at two or three years of age. The lower teeth precede the corresponding

---

[*] Although the teeth are always found in connection with the skeleton, and are, therefore, figured as a part of it (Fig. 1), yet they do not properly belong to the bones of the body, and are merely set in the solid jaw to insure solidity. They are hard, and resemble bony matter, yet they are neither true bone nor are they formed in the same manner. "They are properly appendages of the mucous membrane, and are developed from it." —LEIDY. "They belong to the Tegumentary System, which, speaking generally of animals, includes teeth, nails, horns, scales, and hairs."—MARSHALL. They are therefore classed with the mucous membrane, as are the nails and hair with the skin.

upper ones. The time often varies, but the order seldom.

The Permanent Teeth.—At six years, when the first set is usually still perfect, the jaws contain the crowns of all the second, except the wisdom-teeth. About this age, to meet the wants of the growing body, the crowns of the permanent set begin to press against the roots of the milk-teeth, which, becoming absorbed, leave the loosened teeth to drop out, while the new ones rise and occupy their places.*

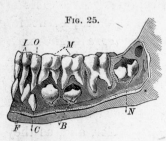

Fig. 25.

The Teeth at the age of six and one half years. I, *the incisors ;* O, *the canine ;* M, *the molars ; the last molar is the first of the permanent teeth ;* F, *sacs of the permanent incisors ;* C, *of the canine ;* B, *of the bicuspids ;* N, *of the second molar ; the sac of the third molar is empty.* —MARSHALL.

The central incisors appear at about seven years of age; the others at eight; the first bicuspids at nine, the second at ten; the canines at eleven or twelve; the second † molars at twelve or thirteen, and the last, or wisdom-teeth, are sometimes delayed until the twenty-second year, or even later.

Structure of the Teeth.—The interior of the tooth consists principally of *dentine*, a dense substance resembling bone.‡ The crown of the tooth,

---

* If the milk-teeth do not promptly loosen on the appearance of the second set, the former should be at once removed to permit the permanent teeth to assume their natural places. If any fail to come in regularly, or if they crowd the others, a competent dentist should be consulted.

† The first molar appears much earlier. (See Fig. 25.)

‡ In the tusk of the elephant this is known as ivory.

which is exposed to wear, is protected by a sheath of *enamel.* This is a hard, glistening, white substance, containing only two and a half per cent. of animal matter. The fang is covered by a thin layer of true bone (cement).

At the center of the tooth is a cavity filled with a soft, reddish-white, pulpy substance full of blood-vessels and nerves. This pulp is very sensitive, and toothache is caused by its irritation.

The Fitting of the Tooth into the Jaw is a most admirable contrivance. It is not set like a nail in wood, having the fang in contact with the bone; but the socket is lined with a membrane which forms a soft cushion. While this is in a healthy state, it deadens the force of any shock, but, when inflamed, it becomes the seat of excruciating pain.

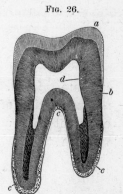

Fig. 26.

Vertical section of a Molar Tooth, moderately magnified. a, enamel of the crown, the lines of which indicate the arrangement of its columns; b, dentine; c, cement; d, pulp cavity.

The Decay of the Teeth* is commonly caused (1) by portions of the food which become entangled

---

* Unlike the other portions of the body, there is no provision made for any change in the permanent teeth. That part, however, which is thus during life most liable to change, after death resists it the longest. In deep-sea dredgings teeth are found when all traces of the frame to which they belonged have disappeared. Yet hard and incorruptible as they seem, their permanence is only relative. Exposed to injury and disease, they break or decay. Even if they escape accident, they yet wear at the crown, are absorbed at the fang, and, in time, drop out, thus affording another of the many signs of the limitations Providence has fixed to the endurance of our bodies and the length of our lives.

between them, and, on account of the heat and moisture, quickly decompose; and (2) by the saliva, as it evaporates, leaving on the teeth a sediment, which we call *tartar*. This collects organic matter that rapidly changes, and also affords a soil in which a sort of fungus speedily springs up. From both these causes, the breath becomes offensive, and the teeth are injured.

Preservation of the Teeth.—Children should early be taught to brush their teeth at least every morning with tepid water, and twice a week with white castile soap and powdered orris-root, or with some dentifrice recommended by a responsible dentist. They should also be instructed to remove the particles of food from between the teeth, after each meal, by means of a quill or wooden tooth-pick.

The enamel once injured is never restored, and the whole interior of the tooth is exposed to decay. We should not, therefore, crack hard nuts, bite thread, or use metal tooth-picks, gritty tooth-powders, or any acid which "sets the teeth on edge," *i. e.*, that acts upon the enamel. It is well also to have the teeth examined yearly by a dentist, that any small orifice may be filled, and further decay prevented.

V. THE GLANDS OF THE SKIN.

I. The Oil Glands are clusters of tiny sacs which secrete an oil that flows along the duct to the root of the hair, and thence oozes out on the cuticle (Fig.

24).* This is nature's efficient hair-dressing, and also keeps the skin soft and flexible. These glands are not usually found where there is no hair, as on the palm of the hand, and hence at those points only can water readily soak through the skin into the body. They are of considerable size on the face, especially about the nose. When obstructed, their contents become hard and dark-colored, and are vulgarly called "worms." †

II. The Perspiratory Glands are fine tubes about $\frac{1}{300}$ of an inch in diameter, and a quarter of an inch in length, which run through the cutis, and then coil up in little balls (Fig. 24). They are found in all parts of the body, and in almost incredible numbers. In the palm of the hand, there are about two thousand eight hundred in a single square inch. On the back of the neck and trunk, where they are fewest, there are yet four hundred to the square inch. The total number on the body of an adult is estimated at about two and a half million. If they were laid end to end, they would extend nearly ten miles.‡ The mouths of these glands—"pores," as we commonly call them—may be seen with a pocket

---

* This secretion is said to vary in different persons, and on that account the dog is enabled to trace his master by the scent.

† Though they are not alive, yet, under the microscope, they are sometimes found to contain a curious parasite, called the pimple-mite, which is supposed to consume the superabundant secretion.

‡ The current statement, that they would extend twenty-eight miles, is undoubtedly an exaggeration. Krause estimates the total number at 2,381,248, and the length of each coil, when unraveled, at $\frac{1}{16}$ of an inch, which would make the total length much less than even the statement in the text. Seguin states that the proportion of impurities thrown off by the skin and the lungs, is eleven to seven.

lens along the fine ridges which cover the palm of
the hand.

The Perspiration. — From these openings, there
constantly passes a vapor, forming what we call the
insensible perspiration. Exercise or heat causes it
to flow more freely, when it condenses on the surface in drops. The perspiration consists of about
ninety-nine parts water, and one part solid matter.
The amount varies greatly, but on the average is,
for an adult, not far from two pounds per day. Any
suppression of this constant drainage will lead to
disagreeable and even dangerous results. If it be
entirely and permanently checked, death will inevitably ensue.*

The Absorbing Power of the Skin. — We have
already described two uses of the skin : (1) Its *pro-
tective,* (2) its *exhaling,* and now we come to (3) its
absorbing power. This is not so noticeable as the
others, and yet it can be illustrated. Persons frequently poison their hands with the common wood-
ivy. Contagious diseases are taken by touching a
patient, or even his clothing, especially if there be a
crack in the cuticle.† Painters absorb so much lead

---

* Once, on an occasion of great solemnity at Rome, a child was, it is
said, completely covered with gold-leaf, closely applied to the skin, so as
to represent, according to the idea of that age, the golden glory of an angel
or seraph. In a few hours, after contributing to this pageant, the child
died; the cause being suffocation, from stopping the exhalation of the
skin; although, in the ignorance of the common people of those days, the
death was attributed to the anger of the Deity, and looked upon as a circumstance of evil omen.

† If one is called upon to handle a dead body, it is well, especially if
the person has died of a contagious disease, to rub the hand with lard or
olive-oil. Poisonous matter has been fatally absorbed through the breaking

through the pores of their hands that they are attacked with colic.* Snuff and lard are frequently rubbed on the chest of a child suffering with the croup, to produce vomiting. It is said that seamen in want of water drench their clothing in salt spray, when the skin will absorb enough moisture to quench thirst (see Lymphatic System).

By carefully conducted experiments, it has been found that the skin acts in the same way as the lungs (see Respiration) in absorbing oxygen from the air, and giving off carbonic acid to a small but appreciable amount. Indeed, the skin has not inaptly been styled the third lung. Hence, the importance of absolute cleanliness and a frequent ablution of the entire body.

VI. HYGIENE.

Hints about Washing and Bathing.—The moment of rising from bed is the proper time for the full wash or bath with which one should commence the day. The body is then warm, and can endure moderately cold water better than at any other time;

of the cuticle by a hang-nail, or a simple scratch. There is a story that Buonaparte, when a lieutenant of artillery, in the heat of battle, seized the rammer and worked the gun of an artillery-man who had fallen. From the wood which the soldier had used, Buonaparte absorbed a poison that gave him a skin-disease, by which he was annoyed the remainder of his life.

   * Cosmetics, hair-dyes, etc., are exceedingly injurious, not only because they tend to fill the pores of the skin, but because they often contain poisonous matters that may be absorbed into the system, especially if they are in a solution.

it is relaxed, and needs bracing; and the nerves, deadened by the night's repose, require a gentle stimulus. If the system be strong enough to resist the shock, cold water is the most invigorating; if not, a tepid bath will answer.*

Before dressing, the whole body should be thoroughly rubbed with a coarse towel or flesh-brush. At first, the friction may be unpleasant, but this sensitiveness will soon be overcome, and the keenest pleasure be felt in the lively glow which follows. A bath should not be taken just before nor immediately after a meal, as it will interfere with the digestion of the food. Soap should be employed occasionally, but its frequent use tends to make the skin dry and hard.

Reaction.— After taking a cold bath, there should be a prompt reaction. When the surface is chilled by cold water, the blood sets to the heart and other vital organs, exciting them to more vigorous action,

* Many persons have not the conveniences for a bath. To them, the following plan, which the author has daily employed for years, is commended. The necessities are: a basin full of soft water, a mild soap, a large sponge or a piece of flannel, and two towels—one soft, the other rough. The temperature of the water should vary with the season of the year—cold in summer and tepid in winter. Rub quickly the entire body with the wet sponge or flannel. (If more agreeable, wash and wipe only a part at a time, protecting the rest in cold weather with portions of clothing.) Dry the skin gently with a soft towel, and when quite dry, with the rough towel or flesh-brush rub the body briskly four or five minutes till the skin is all aglow. The chest and abdomen need the principal rubbing. The roughness of the towel should be accommodated to the condition of the skin. Enough friction, however, must be given to produce at least a gentle warmth, indicative of the reaction necessary to prevent subsequent chill or languor. An invalid will find it exceedingly beneficial if a stout, vigorous person produce the reaction by rubbing with the hands.

and then, being thrown back to the surface, it reddens, warms, and stimulates the skin to an unwonted degree. This is called the reaction, and in it lies the invigorating influence of the cold bath. When, on the contrary, the skin is heated by a hot bath, the blood is drawn to the surface, less blood goes to the heart, the circulation decreases, and languor ensues. A dash of cold water is both necessary and refreshing at the close of a hot bath.*

If, after a cold bath, there be felt no glow of warmth, but only a chilliness and depression, we are thereby warned that either proper means were not taken to bring on this reaction, or that the circulation is not vigorous enough to make such a bath beneficial. The general effect of a cool bath is exhilarating, and that of a warm one depressing.† Hence the latter should not ordinarily be taken oftener than once a week, while the former may be enjoyed daily. (See p. 289.)

Sea-bathing is exceedingly stimulating, on account of the action of the salt and the exciting surround-

---

* The Russians are very fond of vapor-baths, taken in the following manner. A large room is heated by stoves. Red-hot stones being brought in, water is thrown upon them, filling the room with steam. The bathers sit on benches until they perspire profusely, when they are rubbed with soap-suds and dashed with cold water. Sometimes, while in this state of excessive perspiration, they run out-of-doors and leap into snow-banks.

† The sudden plunge into a cold bath is good for the strong and healthy, but too severe for the delicate. One should always wet first the face, neck. and chest. It is extremely injurious to stand in a bath with only the feet and the lower limbs covered by the water, for the blood is thus sent from the extremities to the heart and internal organs, and they become so burdened that reaction may be out of their power. A brisk walk, or a thorough rubbing of the skin, before a cold bath or swim, adds greatly to its value and pleasure.

ings. Twenty minutes is the utmost limit for bathing or swimming in salt or fresh water. A chilly sensation should be the signal for instant removal. It is better to leave while the glow and buoyancy which follow the first plunge are still felt. Gentle exercise after a bath is beneficial.

Clothing in winter, to keep us warm, should repel the external cold and retain the heat of the body. In summer, to keep us cool, it should not absorb the rays of the sun, and should permit the passage of the heat of the body. At all seasons, it should be porous, to give ready escape to the perspiration, and a free admission of air to the skin. We can readily apply these essential conditions to the different kinds of clothing.

Linen is soft to the touch, and is a good conductor of heat. Hence it is pleasant for summer wear, but, being apt to chill the surface too rapidly, it should not be worn next the skin.

Cotton is a poorer conductor of heat and absorber of moisture, and is therefore warmer than linen. It is sufficiently cool for summer wear, and affords better protection against sudden changes.

Woolen absorbs moisture slowly, and contains much air in its pores. It is therefore a poor conductor of heat, and guards the wearer against the vicissitudes of our climate.

The outer clothing may be adapted largely to ornament, and may be varied to suit our fancy and the requirements of society. The under-clothing should always be sufficient to keep us warm. Woolen should be worn next the skin at all times; light gossamer garments in the heat of summer, and warm, porous flannels in mid-winter.

Light-colored clothing is not only cooler in summer, but warmer in winter. As the warmth of clothing depends greatly on the amount of air contained in its fibers, fine, loose, porous cloth with a plenty of nap is best for winter wear. Firm and heavy goods are not necessarily the warmest. Furs are the perfection of winter clothing, since they combine warmth with lightness. Two light woolen garments are warmer than one heavy one, as there is between them a layer of non-conducting air.

All the body except the head should be equally protected by clothing. Whatever fashion may dictate, no part covered to-day can be uncovered to-night or to-morrow, except at the peril of health. It is a most barbarous and cruel custom to leave the limbs of little children unprotected, when adults would shiver at the very thought of exposure. Equally so is it for children to be thinly clad for the purpose of hardening them. To go shivering with cold is not the way to increase one's power of endurance. The system is made more vigorous by exercise and food; not by exposure. In winter, we should wear warm shoes with thick soles, and rubbers when it is damp. At night, and after exercise, we require extra clothing. (See p. 295.)

Diseases, etc.—1. *Erysipelas* is an inflammation (see Inflammation) of the skin, and often begins in a spot not larger than a pin-head. which spreads with great rapidity. It is very commonly checked by the application of a solution of iodine. The burning and contracting sensation may be relieved by cloths wrung out of hot water.

2: *Eczema* (Salt Rheum, etc.) is of constitutional origin. It is characterized by an itching, burning, reddened eruption, in which a serous discharge exudes and dries into crusts or scales. The skin thickens in patches, and painful fissures are formed, which are irritated by exposure to air or water. Eczema denotes debility. It occurs in various forms, and, like erysipelas, should be treated by a physician.

3. *Corns* are thickened cuticle, caused by pressure or friction. They most frequently occur on the feet; but are produced on the shoemaker's knee by constant hammering, and on the soldier's shoulder by the rubbing of his musket. This hard portion irritates the sensitive cutis beneath, and so causes pain. A corn will soften in hot water, when it may be pared with a sharp knife. If the cause be removed, the corn will not return.

4. *In-growing Nails* are caused by pressure, which forces the edge of the toe-nail into the flesh. They may be cured by carefully cutting away the part which has mal-grown, and then scraping the back of the nail till it is thin, making a small incision in the center, at the top. The two portions, uniting, will draw away the nail from the flesh at the edge. In-growing nails may be prevented by wearing broad-toed shoes.

5. *Warts* are overgrown papillæ (Fig. 24). They

may generally be removed by the application of glacial acetic acid, or a drop of nitric acid, repeated until the entire structure is softened. Care must be taken to keep the acid from touching the neighboring skin. The capricious character of warts has given rise to the popular delusion concerning the influence of charms upon them.

6. *Chilblain* is a local inflammation affecting generally the feet, the hands, or the lobes of the ear. Liability to it usually passes away with manhood. It is not caused by "freezing the feet," as many suppose, though attacks are brought on, or aggravated, by exposure to cold, followed by sudden warming. Chilblain is subject to daily congestion (see Congestion), manifested by itching, soreness, etc., commonly occurring at night. The best preventive is a uniform temperature, and careful protection against the cold by warm clothing, especially for the feet.

PRACTICAL QUESTIONS.

1. If a hair be plucked out, will another grow in its place?
2. What causes the hair to "stand on end" when we are frightened?
3. Why is the skin roughened by riding in the cold?
4. Why is the back of a washer-woman's hand less water-soaked than the palm?
5. What would be the length of the perspiratory tubes in a single square inch of the palm, if placed end to end?
6. What colored clothing is best adapted to all seasons?
7. What is the effect of paint and powder on the skin?
8. Is water-proof clothing healthful for constant wear?
9. Why are rubbers cold to the feet?
10. Why does the heat seem oppressive when the air is moist?
11. Why is friction of the skin invigorating after a cold bath?
12. Why does the hair of domestic animals become roughened in winter?

13. Why do fowls spread their feathers before they perch for the night?

14. How can an extensive burn produce congestion of the lungs?

15. Why do we perspire so profusely after drinking cold water?

16. How can we best prevent skin-diseases, colds, and rheumatism?

17. What causes the difference between the hard hand of a blacksmith and the soft hand of a woman?

18. Why should a painter avoid getting paint on the palm of his hand?

19. Why should we not use the soap or the soiled towel at a hotel?

20. Which teeth cut like a pair of scissors?

21. Which teeth cut like a chisel?

22. Which should be clothed the warmer, a merchant or a farmer?

23. Why should we not crack nuts with our teeth?

24. Do the edges of the upper and the lower teeth meet?

25. When fatigued, would you take a cold bath?

26. Why is the outer surface of a kid glove finer than the inner?

27. Why will a brunette endure the sun's rays better than a blonde?

28. Does patent leather form a healthful covering for the feet?

29. Why are men more frequently bald than women?

30. On what part of the head does baldness commonly occur? Why?

31. What does the combination in our teeth of canines and grinders suggest as to the character of our food?

32. Is a staid, formal promenade suitable exercise?

33. Is there any danger in changing the warm clothing of our daily wear for the thin one of a party?

34. Should we retain our overcoat, shawl, or furs when we come into a warm room?

35. Which should bathe the oftener, students or out-door laborers?

36. Is abundant perspiration injurious?

37. How often should the ablution of the entire body be performed?

38. Why is cold water better than warm, for our daily ablution?

39. Why should our clothing always fit loosely?

40. Why should we take special pains to avoid clothing that is colored by poisonous dye-stuffs? (See p. 296.)

41. What general principles should guide us as to the length and frequency of baths in salt or fresh water?

42. What is the beneficial effect of exercise upon the functions of the skin?

43. How can we best show our admiration and respect for the human body?

44. Why is the scar of a severe wound upon a negro sometimes white?

IV.

RESPIRATION AND THE VOICE

"THE smooth soft air with pulse-like waves
Flows murmuring through its hidden caves,
Whose streams of brightening purple rusn,
Fired with a new and livelier blush;
While all their burden of decay
The ebbing current steals away."

ANALYSIS OF RESPIRATION AND THE VOICE.

RESPIRATION AND THE VOICE.

1. ORGANS OF VOICE.....
   1. The Larynx.
   2. The Vocal Cords.
   3. Different Tones of Voice.
   4. Speech.
   5. Formation of Vocal Sounds.

2. ORGANS OF RESPIRA-TION.
   1. The Trachea.
   2. The Bronchial Tubes.
   3. The Cells.
   4. The Lung-wrapping.
   5. The Cilia.

3. HOW WE BREATHE....
   1. Inspiration.
   2. Expiration.

4. MODIFICATIONS OF THE BREATH.
   1. Sighing.
   2. Coughing.
   3. Sneezing.
   4. Snoring.
   5. Laughing, and Crying.
   6. Hiccough.
   7. Yawning.

5. CAPACITY OF THE LUNGS.

6. HYGIENE..............
   1. The Need of Air.
   2. Action of Air in the Lungs.
   3. Tests of the Breath.
   4. Analysis of Expired Air.
   5. Effect of Re-breathed Air.
   6. Concerning the Need of Ventilation.
      a. *The Sources of Impurity.*
      b. *The Sick-room.*
      c. *The Sitting-room.*
      d. *The Bed-room.*
      e. *The Church.*
      f. *The School-room.*
      g. *How we should Ventilate.*

7. THE WONDERS OF RESPIRATION.

8. DISEASES...............
   1. Constriction of the Lungs.
   2. Bronchitis.
   3. Pleurisy.
   4. Pneumonia.
   5. Consumption.
   6. Asphyxia.
   7. Diphtheria.
   8. Croup.
   9. Stammering.

RESPIRATION AND THE VOICE.

THE Organs of Respiration and the Voice are the *larynx*, the *trachea*, and the *lungs*.

Description of the Organs of the Voice.—1. *The Larynx.*—In the neck, is a prominence sometimes called Adam's apple. It is the front of the *larynx.* This is a small triangular, cartilaginous box, placed just below the root of the tongue, and at the top of the windpipe. The opening into it from the throat is called the *glottis;* and the cover, the *epiglottis* (*epi*, upon ; *glōtta*, the tongue). The latter is a spoon-shaped lid, which opens when we breathe, but, by a nice arrangement, shuts when we try to swallow, and so lets our food slip over it into the *œsophagus* (e-sŏf'-a-gŭs), the tube leading from the pharynx to the stomach (Fig. 27).

If we laugh or talk when we swallow, our food is apt to "go the wrong way," *i. e.*, little particles pass into the larynx, and the tickling sensation which they produce forces us to cough in order to expel the intruders.

2. *The Vocal Cords.*—On each side of the *glottis* are the so-called *vocal cords.* They are not really cords, but merely elastic membranes projecting from

the sides of the box across the opening.* When not
in use, they spread apart and leave a V-shaped orifice
(Fig. 28), through which the air passes to and from
the lungs.   If the cords are tightened, the edges

FIG. 27.

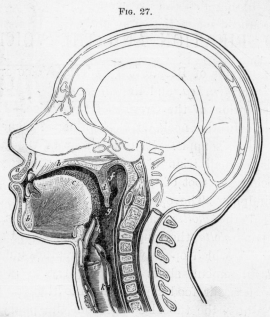

Passage to the Œsophagus and Windpipe. c, *the tongue;* d, *the soft palate,
ending in* g, *the uvula;* h, *the epiglottis;* i, *the glottis;* I, *the œsophagus;* f, *the
pharynx.*

approach sometimes within $\frac{1}{100}$ of an inch of each
other, and, being thrown into vibration, cause corresponding vibrations in the current of air.   Thus
sound is produced in the same manner as by the

* The cartilages and vocal cords may be readily seen in the larynx of
an ox or sheep. If the flesh be cut off, the cartilages will dry, and will
keep for years.

vibrations of the tongues of an accordion, or the strings of a violin, only in this case the strings are scarcely an inch long.

Different Tones of the Voice. —The higher tones of the voice are produced when the cords are short, tight, and closely in contact; the lower, by the opposite conditions. Loudness is regulated by the quantity of air and force of expulsion. A falsetto voice is thought to be the result of a peculiarity in the pharynx (Fig. 27) at the back part of the nose; it is more probably produced by some muscular

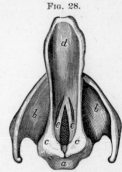

Fig. 28.

e, e, *the vocal cords;* d, *the epiglottis.*

maneuver not yet fully understood. When boys are about fourteen years of age, the larynx enlarges, and the cords grow proportionately longer and coarser; hence, the voice becomes deeper, or, as we say, "changes." The peculiar harshness of the voice at this time seems to be due to a congestion of the mucous membrane of the cords. The change may occur very suddenly, the voice breaking in a single night.

Speech is voice modulated by the lips, tongue,*

---

* The tongue is styled the "unruly member," and held reponsible for all the tattling of the world; but when the tongue is removed, the adjacent organs in some way largely supply the deficiency, so that speech is still possible. Huxley describes the conversation of a man who had two and one half inches of his tongue preserved in spirits, and yet could converse intelligibly. Only the two letters *t* and *d* were beyond his power; the articulation of these involves the employment of the tip of the tongue; hence, "tin" he converted into "fin," and "dog" into "thog."

palate, and teeth.*   Speech and voice are commonly
associated, but speech may exist without the voice;

FIG. 29.

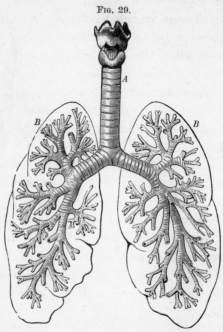

The Lungs, showing the Larynx. A, *the windpipe;* B, *the bronchial tubes.*

for when we whisper we articulate the words,
although there is no vocalization, *i. e.*, no action of
the larynx.†   (See p. 297.)

* An artificial larynx may be made by using elastic bands to represent
the vocal cords, and by placing above them chambers which by their reso-
nance will produce the same effect as the cavities lying above the larynx.
An artificial speaking-machine was constructed by Kempelen, which could
pronounce such sentences as, "I love you with all my heart," in different
languages, by simply touching the proper keys.

† We can observe this by placing the hand on the throat, and noticing
the absence of vibrations when we whisper, and their presence when we

Formation of Vocal Sounds.—The method of modulating voice into speech may be seen by producing the pure vowel sounds *a*, *e*, etc., from one expiration, the mouth being kept open while the form of the aperture is changed for each vowel by the tongue and the lips. *H* is only an explosion, or forcible throwing of a vowel sound from the mouth.*

The consonants, or short sounds, may also be made without interrupting the current of air, by various modifications of the vocal organs. In sounding singly any one of the letters, we can detect its peculiar requirements. Thus *m* and *n* can be made only by blocking the air in the mouth and sending it through the nose; *l* lets the air escape at the sides of the tongue; *r* needs a vibratory movement of the tongue; *b* and *p* stop the breath at the lips; *k* and *g* (hard), at the back of the palate. Consonants like *b* and *d* are abrupt, or, like *l* and *s*, continuous. Those made by the lips are termed *labials;* those by pressing the tongue against the teeth, *dentals;* those by the tongue, *linguals.*

The child gains speech slowly, first learning to pronounce the vowel *a*, the consonants *b*, *m*, and *p*, and then their unions—*ba, ma, pa.*

---

talk. The difference between vocalization and non-vocalization is seen in a sigh and a groan, the latter being the former vocalized. Whistling is a pure mouth-sound, and does not depend on the voice. Laughter is vocal, being the aspirated vowels, a, e, or o, convulsively repeated.

* When, in sounding a vowel, the sound coincides with a sudden change in the position of the vocal cords from one of divergence to one of approximation, the vowel is pronounced with the *spiritus asper.* When the vocal cords are brought together before the blast of air begins, the vowel is pronounced with the *spiritus lenis.*—FOSTER.

Description of the Organs of Respiration.—Beneath the larynx is the windpipe, or *trachea* (see Fig. 29), so called because of its roughness. It is strengthened by *C* - shaped cartilages with the openings behind, where they are attached to the œsophagus. At the lower end, the trachea divides into two branches, called the right and left *bronchi.* These subdivide in the small bronchial tubes, which ramify through the lungs like the branches of a tree, the tiny twigs of which at last end in clusters of cells so small that there are six hundred million in all. This cellular structure renders the lungs exceedingly soft, elastic, and sponge-like.*

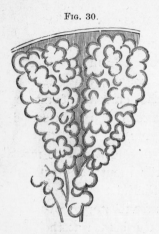

Fig. 30.

Bronchial Tubes, with clusters of cells.

The stiff, cartilaginous rings, so noticeable in the rough surface of the trachea and the bronchi, disappear as we reach the smaller bronchial tubes, so that while the former are kept constantly open for the free admission of air, the latter are provided with elastic fibers by which they may be almost closed.

---

* The lungs of slaughtered animals are vulgarly called "lights," probably on account of their lightness. They are similar in structure to those of man. They will float on water, and if a small piece be forcibly squeezed between the fingers (notice the creaking sound it gives), it will retain sufficient air to make it buoyant.

Wrappings of the Lungs.—The lungs are invested with a double covering—the *pleura*—one layer being attached to the lungs and the other to the walls of the chest. It secretes a fluid which lubricates it, so that the layers glide upon each other with perfect ease.* The lungs are lined with mucous membrane, exceedingly delicate and sensitive to the presence of any thing except pure air. We have all noticed this when we have breathed any thing offensive.

The Cilia.—Along the air passages are minute filaments (*cilia*, Fig. 32), which are in constant motion, like a field of

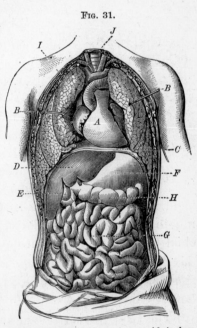

Fig. 31.

A, *the heart* ; B, *the lungs drawn aside to show the internal organs* ; C, *the diaphragm* ; D, *the liver* ; E, *the gall cyst* ; F, *the stomach* ; G, *the small intestines* ; H, *the transverse colon.*

grain stirred by a gentle breeze. They serve to fan the air in the lungs, and produce an outward current, which is useful in catching dust and fine particles swept inward with the breath.

* These pleural sacs are distinct and closed; hence, when the ribs are raised, a partial vacuum being formed in the sacs, air rushes in, and distends the pulmonary lobules.

How we Breathe.—Respiration consists of two acts—taking in the air, or *inspiration*, and expelling the air, or *expiration*.

FIG. 32.

A   *B*

B, *a section of the mucous membrane, showing the cilia rising from the peculiar epithelial cells on the outside of the mucous membrane lining the tubes;* A, *a single cell more highly magnified.*

1. *Inspiration.*—When we draw in a full breath, we straighten the spine and throw the head and shoulders back, so as to give the greatest advantage to the muscles.* At the same time, the diaphragm † descends and presses the walls of the abdomen outward. Both these processes increase the size of the chest. Thereupon, the elastic lungs expand to occupy the extra space, while the air, rushing in through the windpipe, pours along the bronchial tubes and crowds into every cell.‡

---

* If we examine the bony cage of the thorax or chest in Fig. 8, we shall see that the position of the ribs may alter its capacity in two ways. 1. As they run obliquely downward from the spine, if the sternum or breast-bone be lifted in front, the diameter of the chest will be increased. 2. The ribs are fastened by elastic cartilages, which stretch as the muscles that lift the ribs contract, and so increase the breadth of the chest.

† The diaphragm is the muscular partition between the chest and the abdomen. It is always convex toward the former, and concave toward the latter (Fig. 31). Long muscular fibers extend from its center toward the ribs in front and the spine at the back. When these contract, they depress and flatten the diaphragm; when they relax, it becomes convex again. In the former case, the bowels are pressed downward and the abdomen pushed outward; in the latter, the bowels spring upward, and the abdomen is drawn inward.

‡ It is said that in drawing a full breath, the muscles exert a force equal to raising a weight of seven hundred and fifty pounds. When we are about to make a great effort, as in striking a heavy blow, we naturally take a deep inspiration, and shut the glottis. The confined air makes the chest tense and firm, and enables us to exert a greater force. As we let slip the blow, the glottis opens and the air escapes, often with a curious aspirated sound,

2. *Expiration.*—When we forcibly expel the air from our lungs, the operation is reversed. We bend forward, draw in the walls of the abdomen, and press the diaphragm upward, while the ribs are pulled downward,—all together diminishing the size of the chest, and forcing the air outward.

Ordinary, quiet breathing is performed mainly by the diaphragm,—one breath to every four beats of the heart, or eighteen per minute. (See p. 299.)

Modifications of the Breath.—*Sighing* is merely a prolonged inspiration followed by an audible expiration. *Coughing* is a violent expiration in which the air is driven through the mouth. *Sneezing* differs from coughing, the air being forced through the nose. *Snoring* is produced by the passage of the breath through the pharynx when the tongue and soft palate are in certain positions.* *Laughing* and *crying* are very much alike. The expression of the face is necessary to distinguish between them. The sounds are produced by short, rapid contractions of the diaphragm. *Hiccough* is confined to inspiration.

as is noticeable in workmen. To make a good shot with a rifle, we should take aim with a full chest and tight breath, since then the arms will have a steadier support.

* The soft palate must have fallen back in such a manner as nearly or quite to close the entrance to the nasal cavity from the throat, and the tongue must also be thrown back so far as to leave only a narrow opening between it and the soft palate. The noise is produced by the air being forced either inward or outward through this opening. A snore results also when, with a closed mouth, the air is forced between the soft palate and the back wall of the pharynx into the nasal cavity. With deep breathing, perhaps accompanied by a variation in the position of the soft palate, a rattling noise may be heard in addition to the snoring, which is due to a vibration of the soft palate.—F. A. FERNALD, in "How we Sneeze, Laugh, Stammer, and Sigh."—*Popular Science Monthly*, Feb., 1884.

It is caused by a contraction of the diaphragm and
a constriction of the glottis; the current of air just
entering, as it strikes the closed glottis, gives rise
to the well-known sound. *Yawning*, or *gaping*, is
like sighing.* It is distinguished by a wide opening
of the mouth and a deep, profound inspiration. Both
processes furnish additional air, and therefore probably meet a demand of the system for more oxygen.
Frequently, however, they are like laughing, sobbing,
etc., merely a sort of contagion, which runs through
an audience, and seems almost irresistible.

The Capacity of the Lungs.—If we take a deep
inspiration, and then forcibly exhale all the air we
can expel from the lungs, this amount, which is
termed the *breathing capacity*, will bear a very close
correspondence to our stature. For a man of medium
height (five feet eight inches) it will be about two
hundred and thirty cubic inches,† or a gallon, and
for each inch of height between five and six feet
there will be an increase of eight cubic inches. In
addition, it is found that the lungs contain about
one hundred cubic inches which can not be expelled,
thus making their entire contents about three hun-

* The usefulness of a yawn lies in bringing up the arrears, as it
were, of respiration, when it has fallen behindhand, either through
fatigue or close attention to other occupation. The stretching of the
jaws and limbs may also serve to equalize the nervous influence, certain
muscles having become uneasy on account of being stretched or contracted
for a long time.

† Of this amount, one hundred cubic inches can be forced in only by
an extra effort, and is available for emergencies, or for purposes of training, as in singing, climbing, etc. It is of great importance, since, if the
capacity of the lungs only equaled our daily wants, the least obstruction
would prove fatal.

dred and thirty cubic inches, or eleven pints. The extra amount always on hand in the lungs is of great value, since thereby the action of the air goes on continuously, even during a violent expiration. In ordinary breathing, only about twenty or thirty cubic inches (less than a pint) of air pass in and out.

The Need of Air.—The body needs food, clothing, sunshine, bathing, and drink; but none of these wants is so pressing as that for air. The other demands may be met by occasional supplies, but air must be furnished every moment or we die. Now the vital element of the atmosphere is oxygen gas.* This is a stimulating, life-giving principle. No tonic will so invigorate as a few full, deep breaths of cold, pure air. Every organ will glow with the energy of the fiery oxygen.

Action of the Air in the Lungs.—In the delicate cells of the lungs, the air gives up its oxygen to the blood, and receives in turn carbonic-acid gas and water, foul with waste matter which the blood has picked up in its circulation through the body. The blood, thus purified and laden with the inspiring oxygen, goes bounding through the system, while the air we exhale carries off the impurities. In this process, the blood changes from purple to red. If we examine our breath, we can readily see what it has removed from the blood.

---

* See "Steele's Popular Chemistry," p. 30. The atmosphere consists of one fifth oxygen and four fifths nitrogen. The former is the active element; and the latter, the passive. Oxygen alone would be too stimulating, and must be restrained by the neutral nitrogen. Separately, either element of the air would kill us.

Tests of the Breath.—1. Breathe into a jar, and on lowering into it a lighted candle, the flame will be instantly extinguished; thus indicating the presence of carbonic-acid gas. 2. Breathe upon a mirror, and a film of moisture will show the vapor.* 3. If breath be confined in a bottle, the animal matter will decompose and give off an offensive odor.

Analysis of the Expired Air shows that it has lost about twenty-five per cent. of its oxygen, and gained an equal amount of carbonic-acid gas, besides moisture, and organic impurities. Our breath, then, is air robbed of its vitality, and containing in its place a gas as fatal to life† as it is to a flame, and effete matter which is disagreeable to the smell, injurious to the health, and which may contain the germs of serious disease.

The Evil Effect of Re-breathing the air can not be overestimated. We take back into our bodies that which has just been rejected. The blood thereupon leaves the lungs, bearing, not the invigorating oxygen, but refuse matter to obstruct the whole system. We soon feel the effect. The muscles become in-

---

* There is a close relation between the functions of the skin, the lungs, and the kidneys—the scavengers of the body. They all carry off water from the blood, and when the function of one of the three is, in this respect, interfered with, the others are called upon to perform its functions. When the function of perspiration is deranged, the lungs and kidneys are required to perform heavier duty, and this may lead to disease (see p. 62).

† Carbonic-acid gas can not be breathed when undiluted, as the glottis closes and forbids its passage into the lungs. Air containing only three or four per cent. acts as a narcotic poison (MILLER), and a much smaller proportion will have an injurious effect. The great danger, however, lies in the organic particles constantly exhaled from the lungs and the skin, which, it is believed, are often direct and active poisons.

active. The blood stagnates. The heart acts slowly. The food is undigested. The brain is clogged. The head aches. Instances of fatal results are only too frequent.* The constant breathing of even the slightly-impure air of our houses can not but tend to undermine the health. The blood is not purified, and is thus in a condition to receive the seeds of disease at any time. The system uninspired by the energizing oxygen is sensitive to cold. The pale cheek, the lusterless eye, the languid step, speak but too plainly of oxygen starvation. In such a soil, catarrh, scrofula, and kindred diseases run riot.†

Concerning the Need of Ventilation.—The foul air which passes off from the lungs and through the pores of the skin does not fall to the floor, but diffuses itself through the surrounding atmosphere. A single breath will to a trifling but certain extent taint the air of a whole room.‡ A light will vitiate

* During the English war in India, in the last century, one hundred and forty-six prisoners were shut up in a room scarcely large enough to hold them. The air could enter only by two narrow windows. At the end of eight hours, but twenty-three persons remained alive, and these were in a most deplorable condition. This prison is well called "The Black Hole of Calcutta."—Percy relates that after the battle of Austerlitz, three hundred Russian prisoners were confined in a cavern, where two hundred and sixty of them perished in a few hours.—The stupid captain of the ship *Londonderry*, during a storm at sea, shut the hatches. There were only seven cubic feet of space left for each person, and in six hours ninety of the passengers were dead.

† One not very strong, or unable powerfully to resist conditions unfavorable to health, and with a predisposition to lung disease, will be sure, sooner or later, by partial lung-starvation and blood-poisoning, to develop pulmonary consumption. *The lack of what is so abundant and so cheap—good, pure air—is unquestionably the one great cause of this terrible disease.* — BLACK'S *Ten Laws of Health.*

‡ This grows out of a well-known philosophical principle called the Diffusion of Gases, whereby two gases tend to mix in exact proportions, no

as much air as a dozen persons. Many breaths and lights therefore rapidly unfit the air for our use.

The perfection of ventilation is reached when the air of a room is as pure as that out-of-doors. To accomplish this result, it is necessary to allow for each person six hundred cubic feet of space, while ventilation is still going on in the best manner known.

In spite of these well-known facts, scarcely any pains are taken to supply fresh air, while the doors and windows where the life-giving oxygen might creep in are hermetically stopped.

How often is this true of the sick-room. Yet here the danger of bad air is intensified. The expired breath of the patient is peculiarly threatening to himself as well as to others. Nature is seeking to throw off the poison of the disease. The scavengers of the body are all at work. The breath and the insensible perspiration are loaded with impurities.* The odor is oftentimes exceedingly offensive. Sick and well alike need an abundance of fresh air. But, too often, it is the only want not supplied.

Our sitting-rooms, heated by furnaces or red-hot stoves, generally have no means of ventilation, or,

matter what may be the quantity of each.—STEELE's *Popular Chemistry*, p. 86, and *Popular Physics*, p. 52.

* The floating dust in the air, revealed to us by the sunbeam shining through a crack in the blinds, shows the abundance of these impurities, and also the presence of germs which, lodging in the lungs, may implant disease, unless thrown off by a vigorous constitution. "On uncovering a scarlet-fever patient, a cloud of fine dust is seen to rise from the body—contagious dust that for days will retain its poisonous properties."—YOUMANS. (See p. 300.)

if provided, they are seldom used. A window is occasionally dropped to give a little relief, as if pure air were a rarity, and must be doled out to the suffering lungs in morsels, instead of full and constant draughts. The inmates are starved by scanty lung-food, and stupefied by foul air. The process goes on year by year. The weakened and poisoned body at last succumbs to disease, while we, in our blindness and ignorance, talk of the mysterious Providence which thus untimely cuts down the brightest intellects. The truth is, death is often simply the penalty for violating nature's laws. Bad air begets disease; disease begets death.

In our churches, the foul air left by the congregation on Sunday is shut up during the week, and heated for the next Lord's day, when the people assemble to re-breathe the polluted atmosphere. They are thus forced, with every breath they take, to violate the physical laws of Him whom they meet to worship,—laws written not three thousand years ago upon Mount Sinai on tables of stone, but to-day engraved in the constitution of their own living, breathing bodies. On brains benumbed and starving for oxygen, the purest truth and the highest eloquence fall with little force.

We sleep in a small bedroom from which every breath of fresh air is excluded, because we believe night air to be unhealthy,* and so we breathe its

* There is a singular prejudice against the night air. Yet, as Florence Nightingale aptly says, what other air can we breathe at night? We then have the choice between foul air within and pure air without. For, in

7

dozen hogsheads of air over and over again, and then wonder why we awaken in the morning so dull and unrefreshed! Return to our room after inhaling the fresh, morning air, and the fetid odor we meet on opening the door, is convincing proof how we have poisoned our lungs during the night.

Each room should be supplied with two thousand feet of fresh air per hour for every person it contains.   Our ingenuity ought to find some way of doing this advantageously and pleasantly. A moiety of the care we devote to delicate articles of food, drink, and dress would abundantly meet this prime necessity of our bodies.

Open the windows a little at the top and the bottom. Put on plenty of clothing to keep warm by day and by night, and then let the inspiring oxygen come in as freely as God has given it.   Pure air is the cheapest necessity and luxury of life. Let it not be the rarest!

School-room Ventilation.—Who, on going from the open air of a clear, bracing winter's day, into a crowded school-room, late in the session, has not noticed the disagreeable odor, and been for a moment nauseated and half-stifled by the oppressive atmosphere!   It is not strange. See how many causes here combine to pollute the air. If the room is heated by a stove, quantities of carbonic-oxide and carbonic-acid gases, as well as other products

large cities especially, the night air is far more wholesome than that of the day-time.   To secure fresh air all night, we must open the windows of our bedroom.

of combustion, driven by downward drafts in the
flue, escape through seams and cracks and the occasionally-opened door of the stove. In the case of a
furnace, the same effect is too often experienced,
and the odor of coal-gas is a common one, especially
when the fire is replenished. The insensible perspiration is more active in children than in adults; they,
moreover, rush in with their clothing saturated with
the perspiration induced by their sports; so that, on
the average, each pupil, during school-hours, loads
the air with about half a pint of aqueous vapor.
The children come, oftentimes, from homes that are
close, ill-ventilated, and uncleanly; and frequently
from sick-rooms, bringing in their clothing the germs
of disease. (See p. 304.) Some of the pupils may
even bear traces of illness, or have unsound organs,
and so their breath and exhalations be poisonous.

In addition to all this, the air is filled with dust
brought in and kept astir by many busy feet; with
ashes floating from the stove or furnace; and especially with chalk-dust. The modern method of teaching requires a large amount of blackboard work, and
the air of the school-room is thus loaded with chalk
particles. These collect in the nasal passages, and
the upper part of the larynx, and irritate the membrane, perhaps laying the foundation of catarrh.

The usual school-room atmosphere bears in the
pupils the natural fruit of frequent headaches, inattention, weariness, and stupor; but in the teacher
its frightful influence is most apparent. His labor
is severe, his worry of mind is constant, and, when

he finishes his day's work, he is generally too tired to take proper physical exercise. He consequently labors on with impaired health, or is forced to abandon his profession.

Instead of six hundred feet of space being allowed for each pupil, as perfect ventilation demands—the lowest estimate being two hundred and fifty feet—often not over one hundred feet are afforded. Instead of two thousand cubic feet of fresh air being supplied every hour for each person, and as much foul air removed, which, all physiologists assert, is needed for perfect health, perhaps no means of ventilation at all are provided, and none is secured except what an occasionally-opened door, or the benevolent cracks and chinks in the building furnish the suffering lungs.*

How shall We Ventilate ?—The usual method of ventilation depends upon the fact that hot air is lighter than cold air, and so the cold air tends, by the force of gravity, to fall and compel the warm air to rise. Thus, if we open the door of a heated room, and hold a lighted candle first at the top, and then at the bottom, we can see, by the deflection of the flame, that there is a current of air setting out-

---

* Imagine fifty pupils put into a class-room thirty feet long, twenty-five feet wide, and ten feet high. This would generally be considered a very liberal provision. Such a room contains seven thousand five hundred cubic feet of air. But it furnishes only one hundred and fifty feet of space for each pupil. Allowing ten cubic feet of air per pupil each minute, in fifteen minutes after assembling, the entire atmosphere of the room is tainted, and unfit to be re-breathed. The demand of health is that at least one thousand five hundred cubic feet of pure air should be admitted into this room every minute, and as much be removed.

ward at the top, and another setting inward at the bottom of the opening. A handkerchief held loosely, or the smoke of a smoldering match, in front of a fire-place will show a current of air passing up the chimney ; this is caused by the difference of temperature between the air in the room and the outside atmosphere. *Upon this difference of temperature, all ordinary ventilation is based.** A proper treatment of this subject and its practical applications, would require a book by itself. There is room here for only a few general statements and suggestions.

1. Two openings are always necessary to produce a thorough change of air. (See "Popular Chemistry," p. 70.) Put a lighted candle in a bottle. The flame will soon be extinguished. The oxygen of the little air in the bottle is burned out, and carbonic-acid has taken its place. Now place over the mouth of the bottle a lamp-chimney, and insert in the chimney a strip of card-board, thus dividing the passage. On relighting the candle, it will burn freely. The smoke of a bit of smoldering paper will show that two opposite currents of air are established, one setting into the bottle, the other outward.

2. In the winter, when our school-rooms, churches, public halls, etc., are heated artificially, ventilation is comparatively easy if properly arranged.† The

---

* Public buildings are sometimes ventilated by mechanical means, *i. e.*, immense fans which are turned by machinery, and thus set the air in motion. Such methods are, however, expensive, and rarely adopted, except where power is also used for other purposes.

† For the escape of bad air, Dr. Bell suggests that an efficient foul-air shaft may be fitted to the commonest of stoves by simply inclosing the

required difference of temperature is kept up with
little difficulty. The fresh air admitted to the room
should then be heated* either by a furnace, or by
passing over a stove, or through a coil of steam-
pipes. This cold air should always be taken directly
from out-of-doors, and not from a cellar, or from
under a piazza, where contamination is possible.

3. In order to remove the impure air, there should
be ventilators provided at or near the floor, opening
into air-shafts, or pipes leading upward through the
roof, with proper orifices at the top. These ventilating-pipes should be heated artificially so as to
produce a draught. They may form one of the flues
of a chimney in which there is a constant fire; or be
carried upward in a large flue through the center of
which runs the smoke-pipe of the furnace or stove;†

stove-pipe in a jacket—that is, in a pipe two or three inches greater in
diameter. This should be braced round the stove-pipe and left open at the
end next the stove. At its entrance into the chimney, a perforated collar
should separate it from the stove-pipe

* Ventilation is change of air, and, unless scientifically arranged, and
especially unless the incoming volume of air be warmed in cold weather,
such change of atmosphere means cold currents, with their attendant train
of catarrhs, bronchitis, neuralgia, rheumatism, and all the evils that spring
from these diseases. The raw, damp, frosty air of our ever-changing winter
temperature ought not to have uncontrolled and constant ingress to our
dwellings. Air out-of-doors is suited to out-of-door habits. It is healthy
and bracing when the body is coated and wrapped, and prepared to meet
it, and when exercise can be taken to keep up the circulation; but to live
under cover is to live artificially, and such essential conditions must be
observed as suit an abnormal state. All the evils attaching to ventilation, as it is generally effected, spring from the neglect of this consistency.—*Westminster Review.*

† This plan has been adopted in the newer school-buildings of Elmira,
N. Y. The older buildings were provided with ventilating-pipes, not heated
artificially, and hence of no service. These pipes are rendered effective,
however, by conducting them into a small room in the garret, heated by a

or the ventilating-pipe be itself conveyed through the center of the larger chimney-flue. If the register for hot air be on the floor at one side of the room, two or more ventilators may be placed near the floor on the opposite side. The warm air will thus make the complete circuit of the room, and thoroughly warm it before passing out.

If the ventilating-shaft be not heated artificially, the ventilator must be placed at the top of the room in order that the hot air may escape through it, thus producing an upward draught. But the objection to this method is that it allows the warmer air to escape, while economy requires that the cooler air at the bottom of the room should be removed and the warm air be made to descend, thus securing uniformity of temperature.

4. In the summer, ventilation may be commonly provided for by opening windows *at the top and the bottom*, on the sheltered side of the building, so as to avoid draughts of air injurious to the occupants. On a dull, still, hot day, when there is little difference of temperature between the inner and the outer air, ventilation can be secured only by having a fire provided in the ventilating-shaft; this, by exhausting the air from the room, will cause a fresh current to

coal-stove. From this room, a large exit-pipe leads to the roof, where it terminates in an Emerson's ventilator. So strong a draught is thus established that throughout the building air is taken from the floors, and consequently the cooler portion of the rooms, at a velocity of three to five feet per second or one hundred and eighty to three hundred cubic feet per minute for each square foot of flue-opening. In perpendicular flues, heated throughout with a smoke-flue from the furnace, ten feet per second is attained.

pour in through the open windows. At recess, all the children should, if the weather permit, be sent out-of-doors, to allow their clothing to be exposed to the purifying influence of the open air; meantime, the windows should be thrown wide open, that the room may be thoroughly ventilated during their absence. In bad weather, rapid marching or calisthenic exercises will furnish exercise, and also permit the airing of the room.

5. The school and the church are the centers for spreading contagious diseases. The former offers especially dangerous facilities for scattering disease-germs. Great pains, therefore, should be taken to exclude pupils attacked by or recovering from diphtheria, scarlet-fever, whooping-cough, etc., and even those who live in houses where such sickness exists.

6. In our houses,* open fire-places are efficient ventilators, and they should never be closed for any cause. Fresh air admitted by a hot-air register and impure air passed out by a chimney, form a simple and thorough system. Our sleeping-apartments demand especial care. As soon as the occupants leave the room, the bed-clothes should be removed, and

* The air of our homes is often contaminated by decaying vegetables and other filth in the cellar; by bad air drawn up from the soil into the cellar, by the powerful draughts that our fires create; by defective gas and waste pipes that let the foul air from cess-pool or sewer spread through the house; and by piles of refuse, or puddles of slops emptied at the back-door. Too often, also, the water in our wells, or in the streams that supply our towns and cities, receives the drainage from out-houses and barn-yards, and so introduces into our systems, in the liquid—and thus easily-assimilated— form, the most dangerous poisons. The question of sanitary precautions is one that presses upon every observant mind, and demands constant and thoughtful attention. (See p. 305.)

laid on the backs of chairs to air; the bed be shaken up; and the windows thrown open. In the summer, the windows may be closed before the sun is high; the house is then left filled with the cool morning air. In damp and cold weather, a fire should be lighted in sleeping-apartments, particularly if used by children* or delicate persons, to dry the bed-clothing, and also to prevent a chill on the part of the occupants. It is not necessary to go shivering to bed in order to harden one's constitution.

Wonders of Respiration.—The perfection of the organs of respiration challenges our admiration. So delicate are they that the least pressure would cause exquisite pain, yet tons of air surge to and fro through their intricate passages, and bathe their innermost cells. We yearly perform at least seven million acts of breathing, inhaling one hundred thousand cubic feet of air, and purifying over three thousand five hundred tons of blood. This gigantic process goes on constantly, never wearies or worries us, and we wonder at it only when science reveals to us its magnitude. In addition, by a wise economy, the process of respiration is made to subserve a second

* In winter, children should always be given a moderately warm, well-ventilated bedroom, with light, fleecy bed-coverings. Says a recent English writer: "The loving care which prescribes for children a cold bedroom and a hot, sweltering bed is of the nature that kills. Buried in blankets, their delicate skins become overheated and relaxed, while they are irritated by perspiration; at the same time, the most delicate tissues of all, in the lungs, are dealing with air abnormally frigid. The poor little victims of combined ignorance and kindness thus toss and dream, feverish and troubled, under a mass of bed-clothes, while the well-meaning mother, soothed by a bedroom-fire, slumbers peacefully through this working out of the sad process of the 'survival of the fittest.'"

use no less important, and the air we exhale, passing through the organs of voice, is transformed into prayers of faith, songs of hope, and words of social cheer.

FIG. 33.

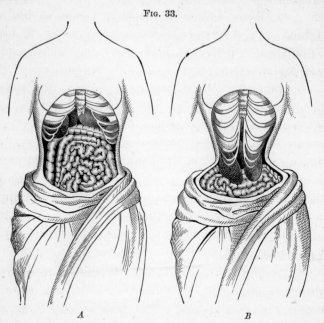

A, *the natural position of the internal organs.* B, *when deformed by tight lacing. Marshall says that the liver and the stomach have, in this way, been forced downward almost as low as the pelvis.*

Diseases, etc.— 1. *Constriction of the Lungs* is produced by tight clothing. The ribs are thus forced inward, the size of the chest is diminished, and the amount of inhaled air decreased. Stiff clothing, and especially a garment that will not admit of a full breath without inconvenience, will prevent that free movement of the ribs so essential to health. Any infraction of the laws of respiration, even though it be fashionable, will result in diminished vitality and vigor, and will be fearfully punished by sickness and weakness through the whole life.

2. *Bronchitis* (brŏn-kī'-tis) is an inflammation (see Inflammation) of the mucous membrane of the bronchial tubes. It is accompanied by an increased secretion of mucus, and consequent coughing.

3. *Pleurisy* is an inflammation of the pleura. It is sometimes caused by an injury to the ribs, and results in a secretion of water within the membrane.

4. *Pneumonia* (*pneuma*, breath) is an inflammation of the lungs, affecting chiefly the air-cells.

5. *Consumption* is a disease which destroys the substance of the lungs. Like other lung difficulties, it is caused largely by a want of pure air, a liberal supply of which is the best treatment that can be prescribed for it.*

6. *Asphyxia* (as-fĭx'-ĭ-a). — When a person is drowned, strangled, or choked in any way, what is called asphyxia occurs. The face turns black; the veins become turgid; insensibility and often convulsions ensue. If relief is not secured within a few minutes, death will be inevitable.† (See p. 264.)

---

* If I were seriously ill of consumption, I would live out-doors day and night, except in rainy weather or mid-winter; then I would sleep in an unplastered log-house. Physic has no nutriment, gaspings for air can not cure you, monkey capers in a gymnasium can not cure you, stimulants can not cure you. What consumptives want is pure air, not physic, plenty of meat and plenty of bread.—Dr. MARSHALL HALL.

† The lack of oxygen, and the presence of carbonic-acid gas, are the combined causes. Oxygen starvation and carbonic-acid poisoning, each fatal in itself, work together to destroy life.

7. *Diphtheria* (*diphthera*, a membrane) is characterized by fever, debility, and a peculiar sore throat, in which exuding fibrinous matter forms a grayish white membrane, which afterward decomposes with a fetid odor. Its sudden and insidious approach, contagious character, and frequent fatality, render it an exceedingly dreaded disease. A diphtheritic patient should be quarantined, and every thing connected with the sick-room thoroughly disinfected.

8. *Croup*, which often attacks young children, is an inflammation of the mucous membrane of the larynx and trachea. It is commonly preceded by a cold. The child sneezes, coughs, and is hoarse, but the attack frequently comes on suddenly, and usually in the night. It is accompanied by a peculiar " brassy," ringing cough, which, once heard, can never be mistaken. It may prove fatal within a few hours. (See p. 260.)

9. *Stammering* depends, not on defects of the muscles, but on a want of due control of the mind. When a stammerer is not too conscious of his lack, and tries to form his words slowly, he speaks plainly, and may sing well, for then his words must follow one another in rhythmic time. Many persons who stammer in common conversation can talk with fluency when making a speech. The stammerer should seek to discover the cause of his difficulty, and to overcome it by vocal and respiratory exercise, especially by speaking only after a full inspiration, and during a long, slow expiration.

PRACTICAL QUESTIONS.

1. What is the philosophy of "the change of voice" in a boy?

2. Why can we see our breath on a frosty morning?

3. When a law of health and a law of fashion conflict, which should we obey?

4. If we use a "bunk" bed, should we pack away the clothes when we first rise in the morning?

5. Why should a clothes-press be well ventilated?

6. Should the weight of our clothing hang from the waist, or the shoulder?

7. Describe the effects of living in an overheated room.

8. What habits impair the power of the lungs?

9. For full, easy breathing in singing, should we use the diaphragm and lower ribs, or the upper ribs alone?

10. Why is it better to breathe through the nose than the mouth?

11. Why should not a speaker talk while returning home on a cold night after a lecture:

12. What part of the body needs the loosest clothing?

13. What part needs the warmest?

14. Why is a "spare bed" generally unhealthful?

15. Is there any good in sighing?

16. Should a hat be thoroughly ventilated? How?

17. Why do the lungs of people who live in cities become of a gray color?

18. How would you convince a person that a bedroom should be aired?*

19. What persons are most liable to catarrhs, consumption, etc.?

20. If a person is plunged under water, will it enter his lungs?

21. Are bed-curtains healthful?

22. Why do some people take "short breaths" after a meal?

23. What is the special value of public parks?

24. Can a person become used to bad air, so that it will not injure him?

25. Why do we gape when we are sleepy?

26. Is a fashionable waist a model of art in sculpture or painting?

27. Should a fire-place be closed?†

---

* "If the condensed breath collected on the cool window-panes of a room where a number of persons have been assembled, be burned, a smell as of singed hair will show the presence of organic matter; and if the condensed breath be allowed to remain on the windows for a few days, it will be found, on examination by the microscope, that it is alive with animalculæ."

† Thousands of lives would be saved if all fire-places were kept open. If you are so fortunate as to have a fire-place in your room, paint it when not in use, put a bouquet of fresh flowers in it every morning, if you please, or do any thing to make it attractive,

28. Why does embarrassment or fright cause a stammerer to stutter still more painfully?

29. In the organs of voice, what parts have somewhat the same effect as the case of a violin and the sounding-board of a piano?

30. Why should we be careful not to "take the breath of a sick person"?

31. What special care should be taken with regard to keeping a cellar clean?

32. How is the air strained as it passes into the lungs?

33. Can one really "draw the air into his lungs"?

34. How often do we breathe?

35. Describe some approved method of ventilation.

36. What is at once the floor of the chest and the roof of the abdomen?

37. What would you do in a case of apparent death by drowning, or by coal-gas? (See p. 264.)

38. What would you do in a case of croup, while the doctor was coming? (See p. 260.)

39. How would you treat a severe burn? (See p. 257.)

40. Describe the various ways in which the water in a well is liable to become unwholesome.

---

but never *close it ;* better use the fire-boards for kindling-wood. It would be scarcely less absurd to take a piece of elegantly-tinted court-plaster and stop up the nose, trusting to the accidental opening and shutting of the mouth for fresh air, because you thought it spoiled the looks of your face to have two such great, ugly holes in it, than to stop your fire-place with elegantly-tinted paper, or a Japanese fan, because it looks better.—LEEDS.

V.

THE CIRCULATION.

" No rest this throbbing slave may ask,
  Forever quivering o'er his task,
  While far and wide a crimson jet
  Leaps forth to fill the woven net,
  Which in unnumber'd crossing tides
  The flood of burning life divides,
  Then, kindling each decaying part,
  Creeps back to find the throbbing heart."

HOLMES.

ANALYSIS OF THE CIRCULATION.

THE CIRCULATION.

1. THE BLOOD
   1. Its Composition.
   2. Its Uses.
   3. Transfusion.
   4. Coagulation.

2. ORGANS OF THE CIRCULATION.
   1. The Heart.
      1. *Description.*
      2. *Movements.*
      3. *Auricles and Ventricles.*
      4. *The Valves.*
         a. Need of.
         b. Tricuspid **and** Bicuspid.
         c. The Strengthening of the Valves.
         d. Semi-lunar Valves.
   2. The Arteries.
      1. *Description.*
      2. *The Arterial System.*
      3. *The Pulse.*
   3. The Veins.
      1. *General Description.*
      2. *Valves.*
   4. The Capillaries.
      1. *Description.*
      2. *Use.*
      3. *Under the Microscope.*

3. THE CIRCULATION
   1. The Lesser.
   2. The Greater.
   3. The Velocity of the Blood.

4. THE HEAT OF THE BODY.
   1. Distribution.
   2. Regulation.

5. LIFE BY DEATH.

6. CHANGE OF OUR BODIES.

7. THE THREE VITAL ORGANS.

8. WONDERS OF THE HEART.

9. THE LYMPHATIC CIRCULATION.
   1. Description.
   2. The Glands.
   3. The Lymph.
   4. The Office of the Lymphatics.

10. DISEASES
    1. Congestion.
    2. Inflammation.
    3. Bleeding.
    4. Scrofula.
    5. A Cold.
    6. Catarrh.

11. ALCOHOLIC DRINKS AND NARCOTICS.
    1. Effect of Alcohol upon the Circulation.
    2. Effect of Alcohol upon the Heart.
    3. Effect of Alcohol upon the Membrane.
    4. Effect of Alcohol upon the Blood.
    5. Effect of Alcohol upon the Lungs.

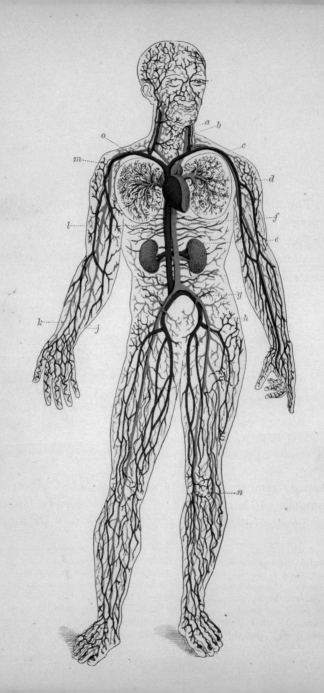

THE CIRCULATION.

The Organs of the Circulation are the *heart*, the *arteries*, the *veins*, and the *capillaries*.

The Blood is the liquid by means of which the circulation is effected. It permeates every part of the body, except the cuticle, nails, hair, etc. The

Fig. 35.

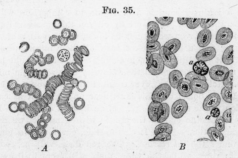

A

B

A, *corpuscles of human blood, highly magnified ;* B, *corpuscles in the blood of an animal (a non-mammal).*

average quantity in each person is about eighteen pounds.* It is composed of a thin, colorless liquid, the *plasma*, filled with red disks or cells,† so small

---

* It is difficult to estimate the exact amount, and therefore authorities disagree. Foster places it at about one thirteenth of the body-weight.

† There is also one white globular cell to every three or four hundred red ones. The blood is no more red than the water of a stream would be if you were to fill it with little red fishes. Suppose the fishes to be very, very small — as small as a grain of sand — and closely crowded together through the whole depth of the stream; the water would look quite red, would it not? And this is the way in which blood looks red — only observe

that about three thousand five hundred placed side by side would measure only an inch, and it would take sixteen thousand laid flatwise upon one another to make a column of that height. Under the microscope, they are found to be rounded at the edge and concave on both sides.* They have a tendency to collect in piles like rolls of coin. The size and shape vary in the blood of different animals.† Disks are continually forming in the blood, and as constantly dying—twenty millions at every breath.—DRAPER.

The plasma also contains fibrin,‡ albumen—which

one thing; a grain of sand is a mountain in comparison with the little red fishes in the blood. If I were to tell you they measured about $\frac{1}{3500}$ of an inch in diameter, you would not be much wiser; so I prefer saying (by way of giving you a more perfect idea of their minuteness) that there would be about a million in such a drop of blood as would hang on the point of a needle. I say so on the authority of a scientific microscopist— M. Bouillet. Not that he has ever counted them, as you may suppose, any more than I have done; but this is as near an approach as can be made by calculation to the size of $\frac{1}{3500}$ part of an inch in diameter.—JEAN MACE.

* By pricking the end of the finger with a needle, we can obtain a drop for examination. Place it on the slide, cover with a glass, and put it at once under the microscope. The red disks will be seen to group themselves in rows, while the white disks will seem to draw apart, and to be constantly changing their form. After a gradual evaporation, the crystals (Fig. 36) may be seen. In animals, they have various, though distinctive forms.

† Authorities differ greatly in their estimate of the size of the disks (corpuscles) in human blood. The fact is that the size varies in different persons, probably also in the same individual. Many of the best microscopists therefore hesitate to state whether a particular specimen of blood belonged to a human being or to an animal. Others claim that they can distinguish with accuracy. Evidently, the question is one of great uncertainty. The following statement of the size of the cells in different animals is taken from Gulliver's tables: Cat, $\frac{1}{7404}$ of an inch in diameter; whale, $\frac{1}{3100}$; mouse, $\frac{1}{3817}$; hog, $\frac{1}{4236}$; camel, $\frac{1}{3123}$; sheep, $\frac{1}{6366}$; horse, $\frac{1}{4600}$; Virginia deer, $\frac{1}{6036}$; dog-faced baboon, $\frac{1}{3181}$; brown baboon, $\frac{1}{3193}$; red monkey, $\frac{1}{3393}$; black monkey, $\frac{1}{3535}$.

‡ It is usual to say that fibrin is contained in the blood. It probably does not exist as such, but there are present in the blood certain sub-

is found nearly pure in the white of an egg—and various mineral substances, as iron,* lime, magnesia, phosphorus, potash, etc.

Uses of the Blood.—The blood has been called "liquid flesh"; but it is more than that, since it contains the materials for making every organ. The plasma is rich in mineral matter for the bones, and in albumen for the muscles. The red disks are the air-cells of the blood. They contain the oxygen so essential to every operation of life. Wherever there is work to be done or repairs to be made, there the oxygen is needed. It stimulates to action, and tears down all that is worn out. In this process, it combines with and actually burns out parts of the muscles and other tissues, as wood is burned in the stove.† The blood, now foul

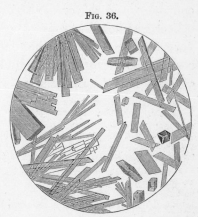

Fig. 36.

Blood Crystals.

stances known as *paraglobulin* and *fibrinogen*, which, by the action of a third substance, *fibrin-ferment*, under certain circumstances, form fibrin and so cause coagulation. The exact nature of the process by which fibrin is produced by these three factors is not understood.—See FOSTER'S *Text Book of Physiology*, p. 22.

* Enough iron has been found in the ashes of a burned body to form a mourning ring.

† For the sake of simplicity, perhaps to conceal our own ignorance, we call this process "burning." The simile of a fire is good so far as it goes. But as to the real nature of the change which the physiologist briefly terms "oxidation," we know nothing. This much only can be asserted

with the burned matter, the refuse of this fire, is caught up by the circulation, and whirled back to the lungs, where it is purified, and again sent bounding on its way.

There are, then, two different kinds of the blood in the body : the red or arterial, and the dark or venous.

Transfusion. — As the blood is really the "vital fluid," it would seem that feeble persons might be restored to vigor by infusing healthy blood into their veins. This hypothesis, so valuable in its possible

positively. A stream of oxygen is carried by the blood to the muscles (in fact to every tissue in the body), while, from the muscles the blood carries away a stream of carbonic acid and water. But what takes place in the muscles, when and what chemical change occurs, no one can tell. We see the first and the last stage. We know that contraction of the muscles somehow comes about, oxygen disappears, carbonic acid appears, energy is released, and force is exhibited as motion, heat, and electricity. But the intermediate step is hidden.

There are certain theories advanced, however, that are worth considering. Some physiologists hold that the muscle has the power of taking up the oxygen from the *hæmaglobin* (a body that comprises ninety per cent. of the red corpuscles when dried, and is the oxygen-carrier of the blood), and fixing it, as well as the raw material (food) furnished by the blood, thus forming a true contractile substance. The breaking-down or decomposition of this contractile substance in the muscle, sets free its potential energy. The process is gentle so long as the muscle is at rest, but becomes excessive and violent when contraction occurs. (See "Foster's Physiology," p. 118.) It is also believed by some that the chemical change in the muscle partakes of a fermentive character; that, under the influence of the proper ferments, the substances break up into other and simpler products, thus setting free heat and force; and that this chemical change is followed by a secondary oxidation by the oxygen in the arterial blood, thereby forming carbonic acid and water, as in all putrefactive processes. But these and other views are not as yet fully understood; while they utterly fail to tell us how a collection of simple cells, filled merely with a semi-fluid mass of matter, can contract and set free muscular power. The commonness of this act hides from us its wonderful nature. But here, hidden in the cell— Nature's tiny laboratory—lies the mystery of life. Before its closed door we ponder in vain, confessing the unskillfulness of our labor, and fearing all the while lest the *Secret of the Cell* will always elude our search.

results in prolonging human life, has been carefully tested. Animals which have ceased to breathe have thus had their vitality recalled. In the seventeenth century the theory became a subject of special investigation. A maniac was restored to reason by the blood of a calf, and the most extravagant hopes were entertained. But many fatal accidents occurring, experiments upon human beings were forbidden by law, and transfusion soon fell into disuse. It has, however, been successfully practiced in several cases within the last few years, and is a method still in repute for saving life.

Coagulation.—When blood is exposed to the air, it coagulates. This is caused by the solidifying of the fibrin, which, entangling the disks, forms the "clot." The remaining clear, yellow liquid is the *serum*. The value of this peculiar property of the blood can hardly be overestimated. The coagulation soon checks all ordinary cases of bleeding.* When a wound is made, and bleeding commences, the fibrin forms a temporary plug, as it were, which is absorbed when the healing process is finished. Thus we see how a Divine foresight has provided not only for the ordinary wants of the body, but also for the accidents to which it is liable.†

---

* In the case of the lower animals, which have no means of stopping hemorrhages as we have, the coagulation is generally still more rapid. In some species of birds it takes place almost instantaneously.

† The fibrin is not an essential ingredient of the blood. All the functions of life are regularly performed in people whose blood lacks fibrin; and, in cases of transfusion, where blood deprived of its fibrin was used, the vivifying influence seemed to be the same. Its office, therefore, must mainly be to stanch any hemorrhage which may occur.—FLINT.

The Heart is the engine which propels the blood. It is a hollow, pear-shaped muscle, about the size of

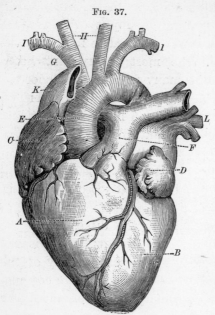

FIG. 37.

the fist. It hangs, point downward, just to the left of the center of the chest. (See Fig. 31.) It is inclosed in a loose sac of serous membrane,* called the pericardium (*peri*, about; and *kardia*, the heart). This secretes a lubricating fluid, and is smooth as satin.

The Movements of the Heart consist of an alternate contraction and expansion. The former is called the *sys'-to-le*, and the latter the *di-as'-to-le*. During the diastole, the blood

The Heart. A, *the right ventricle;* B, *the left ventricle;* C, *the right auricle;* D, *the left auricle.*

---

* The mucous membrane lines the open cavities of the body; the serous, the closed. The pericardium is a sac composed of two layers—a fibrous membrane on the outside, and a serous one on the inside. The latter covers the external surface of the heart, and is reflected back upon itself in order to form, like all the membranes of this nature, a sac without an opening. The heart is thus covered by the pericardial sac, but not contained inside its cavity. A correct idea may be formed of the disposition of the pericardium around the heart by recalling a very common and very convenient, though now discarded head-dress, the cotton night-cap. The pericardium incloses the heart exactly as this cap covered the heads of our forefathers.—*Wonders of the Human Body.*

flows into the heart, to be expelled by the systole. The alternation of these movements constitutes the beating of the heart which we hear so distinctly between the fifth and sixth ribs.*

The Auricles and Ventricles.—The heart is divided into four chambers. In an adult, each holds about a wine-glassful. The upper ones, from appendages on the outside resembling the ears of a dog, are called *auricles* (*aures*, ears); the lower ones are termed *ventricles*.

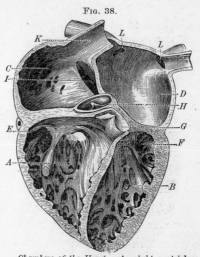

Fig. 38.

Chambers of the Heart. A, *right ventricle;* B, *left ventricle;* C, *right auricle;* D, *left auricle;* E, *tricuspid valve;* F, *bicuspid valve;* G, *semi-lunar valves;* H, *valve of the aorta;* I, *inferior veni cava;* K, *superior veni cava;* L, L, *pulmonary veins.*

The auricle and ventricle on each side communicate with each other, but the right and left halves of the heart are entirely distinct, and perform different offices. The left side propels the red blood ; and the right, the dark.

* Two sounds are heard if we put our ear over the heart,—the first and longer as the blood is leaving the organ, the second as it falls into the pockets of the two arteries, and the valves then striking together cause it. The first sound is mainly the noise made by the muscular tissue. During the first, the two ventricles contract; during the second, the two auricles do so. The hand may feel the heart striking the ribs as it contracts,—a feeling called the impulse, or, if quicker and stronger than usual, palpitation. This is not always a sign of disease, but in hypochondriacs is often an effect of the mind on the nerves of the heart.—MAPOTHER.

The auricles are merely reservoirs to receive the blood (the left auricle, as it filters in bright and pure from the lungs; the right, as it returns dark and foul from the tour of ·the body), and to furnish it to the ventricles as they need. Their work being so light, their walls are comparatively thin and weak. On the other hand, the ventricles force the blood (the left, to all parts of the body; the right, to the lungs), and are, therefore, made very strong. As the left ventricle drives the blood so much farther than the right, it is correspondingly thicker and stronger.

Need of Valves in the Heart.—As the auricles do not need to contract with much force simply to empty their contents into the ventricles below them, there is no demand for any special contrivance to prevent the blood from setting back the wrong way. Indeed, it would naturally run down into the ventricle, which is at that moment open to receive it. But, when the strong ventricles contract, especially the left one, which must drive the blood to the extremities, some arrangement is necessary to prevent it from returning into the auricle. Besides, when they expand, the "suction power" would tend to draw back again from the arteries all the blood just forced out. This difficulty is obviated by means of little doors, or valves, which will not let it go the wrong way.*

---

* The heart of an ox or a sheep may be used to show the chambers and valves. The aorta should be cut as far as possible from the heart, and then by pumping in water the perfection of these valves will be finely exhibited. Cutting the heart across near the middle will show the greater thickness of the left ventricle.

The Tricuspid and Bicuspid Valves. — At the opening into the right ventricle, is a valve consisting of three folds or flaps of membrane, whence it is called the *tri-cuspid* valve (*tri*, three ; and *cuspides*, points), and in the left ventricle, one containing two flaps, and named the *bi-cuspid* valve. These hang so loosely as to oppose no resistance to the passage

FIG. 39.

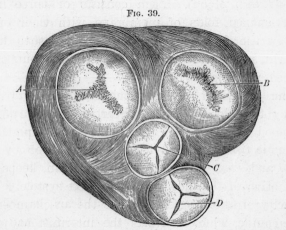

Diagram showing the peculiar Fibrous Structure of the Heart and the Shape of the Valves. A, *triscupid valve ;* B, *bicuspid valve ;* C, *semi-lunar valves of the aorta ;* D, *semi-lunar valves of the pulmonary artery.*

of the blood into the ventricles ; but, if any attempts to go the other way, it gets between the flaps and the walls of the heart, and, driving them outward, closes the orifice.

These Flaps are Strengthened like sails by slender cords, which prevent their being pressed back through the opening. If the cords were attached directly to the walls of the heart, they would be loosened in the systole, and so become useless when most needed.   They are, therefore, fastened to little muscular pillars projecting from the sides of the ventricle; when that contracts, the pillars contract also, and thus the cords are held tight.

The Semi-lunar Valves.—In the passages outward from the ventricles, are valves, called from their peculiar half-moon shape *semi-lunar* valves (*semi*, half; *Luna*, Moon).   Each consists of three little pocket-shaped folds of membrane, with their openings in the direction which the blood is to take. When it sets back, they fill, and, swelling out, close the passage (Fig. 40).

The Arteries* are the tube-like canals which convey the blood *from* the heart.   They carry the red blood (see note, p. 119).   They are composed of an elastic tissue, which yields at every throb of the heart, and then slowly contracting again, keeps up the motion of the blood until the next systole.   The elasticity of the arteries acts like the air-chamber of a fire-engine, which converts the intermittent jerks of the brakes or pump into the steady stream of the hose-nozzle.

The arteries sometimes communicate by means of branches or by meshes of loops, so that if the blood be blocked in one, it can pass round through another, and so get by the obstacle.†   When an artery pene-

---

* *Aer*, air; and *tereo*, I contain — so named because after death they contain air only, and hence the ancients supposed them to be air-tubes leading through the body.

† This occurs especially about the joints, where it serves to maintain the circulation during the bending of a limb, or when the main artery is obstructed by disease or injury, or has been tied by the surgeon.   In the

trates a muscle, it is often protected by a sheath or by fibrous rings, which prevent its being pulled out of place or compressed by the play of the muscles.

The arteries are generally located as far as possible beneath the surface, out of harm's way, and hence are found closely hugging the bones or creeping through safe passages provided for them. They are generally nearly straight, and take the shortest routes to the parts which they are to supply with blood.

The Arterial System starts from the left ventricle by a single trunk—the *aorta*—which, after giving off branches to the head, sweeps back of the chest with a bold curve—the *arch of the aorta* (*c*, Fig. 34)—and thence runs downward (*f*), dividing and subdividing, like a tree, into numberless branches, which, at last, penetrate every nook and corner of the body.

The Pulse.—At the wrist (*k*, radial artery) and on the temple (temporal artery) we can feel the expansion of the artery by each little wave of blood set in motion by the contraction of the heart. In health, there are about seventy-two* pulsations per minute. They increase with excitement or inflammation, weaken with loss of vigor, and are modified by

last case, the small adjacent arteries gradually enlarge, and form what is called a collateral circulation.

* This number varies much with age, sex, and individuals. Napoleon's pulse is said to have been only forty, while it is not infrequent to find a healthy pulse at one hundred or over. In general, the pulse is quicker in children and in old people than in the middle-aged ; in short persons than in tall ; in women than in men. Shame makes the heart send more blood to the blushing cheek, and fear almost stops it. The will can not check the heart. There is said, however, to have been a notable exception to this in the case of one Colonel Townsend, of Dublin, who, after having succeeded several times in stopping the pulsation, at last lost his life in the act.

nearly every disease. The physician, therefore, finds the pulse a good index of the state of the system and the character of the disorder. (See p. 314.)

The Veins are the tube-like canals which convey the blood *to* the heart.* They carry the dark or venous blood (note, p. 119). As they do not receive the direct impulse of the heart, their walls are made much thinner and less elastic than those of the arteries. At first small, they increase in size and diminish in number as they gradually pour into one another, like tiny rills collecting to form two rivers, the vena cava ascending and the vena cava descending (*l, m*, Fig. 34), which empty into the right auricle.

Some of the veins creep along under the skin, where they can be seen, as in the back of the hand; while others accompany the arteries, some of which have two or more of these companions.

Valves similar in construction to those already described (the semi-lunar valves of the heart, page 114) are placed at convenient intervals, in order to guide the blood in its course, and prevent its setting backward.† We can easily examine the working of

---

* There is one exception to the general course of the veins. The *portal* vein carries the blood from the digestive organs to the liver, where it is acted upon, thence poured into the ascending vena cava, and goes back to the heart.

† Too much standing, or tight elastics, often cause the veins in the leg to swell, so that the valves can not work ; the veins then become *varicose*, or permanently enlarged, and, if they burst, the bleeding may be profuse and even dangerous. Raising the leg and pressing the finger on the bleeding spot will stay it. Walking does not encourage this disease, for the active muscles force on the venous blood. Clerks who are subject to varicose veins should have seats behind the counters where they may rest when not actually employed. A deep breath helps the flow in the veins, and a

these valves. On baring the arm, blue veins may be
seen running along the arm toward the hand. Their
diameter is tolerably even, and they gradually decrease in size. If now the
finger be pressed on the upper part of one of these veins,
and then passed downward
so as to drive its blood backward, swellings like little
knots will make their appear-

Fig. 40.

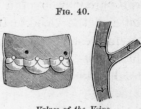

Valves of the Veins.

ance. Each of these marks the location of a valve,
which is closed by the blood we push before our
finger. Remove the pressure, and the valve will
swing open, the blood set forward, and the vein col-
lapse to its former size.

The Capillaries (*capillus*, a hair) form a fine net-
work of tubes, connecting the ends of the arteries
with the veins. They blend, however, with the extremities of these two systems, so that it is not easy
to tell just where an artery ends and a vein begins.
So closely are they placed, that we can not prick the
flesh with a needle without injuring, perhaps, hundreds of them. The air-cells of the blood deposit
there their oxygen, and receive carbonic acid, while
in the delicate capillaries of the lungs* they give

wound may suck in air with fatal effect. A maimed horse is most merci-
fully killed by blowing a bubble of air into the veins of his neck. As the
deep-sea pressure would burst valves, the whale has none ; hence a small
wound by the harpoon causes him to bleed to death.—MAPOTHER.

　* The capillary tubes are there so fine that the disks of the blood have
to go one by one, and are sadly squeezed at that. However, their elasticity
enables them to resume their old shape as soon as they have escaped from
this labyrinth.

up their load of carbonic acid in exchange for oxygen.

If, by means of a microscope, we examine the transparent web of a frog's foot, we can trace the route of the blood.* It is an experiment of wonderful interest. The crimson stream, propelled by the

Fig. 41.

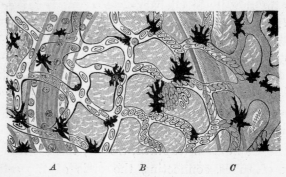

A   B   C

Circulation of the Blood in the Web of a Frog's Foot, highly magnified. A, *an artery;* B, *capillaries crowded with disks, owing to a rupture just above, where the disks are jammed into an adjacent mesh;* C, *a deeper vein; the black spots are pigment cells.*

heart, rushes through the arteries, until it reaches the intricate meshes of the capillaries. Here it breaks into a thousand tiny rills. We can see the disks winding in single file through the devious passages, darting hither and thither, now pausing, swaying to and fro with an uncertain motion, and anon dashing ahead, until, at last, gathered in the veins, the blood sets steadily back on its return to the heart.

* With small splints and twine, a frog's foot can be easily stretched and tied so that the transparent web can be placed on the table of the microscope.

The Circulation* consists of two parts—the *lesser*, and the *greater*.

1. *The Lesser Circulation.* — The dark blood from the veins collects in the right auricle, and, going through the tricuspid valve, empties into the right ventricle. Thence it is driven past the semi-lunar valves, through the pulmonary artery, to the lungs. After circulating through the fine capillaries of the air-cells contained in the lungs, it is returned, bright and red, through the four pulmonary veins,† to the left auricle.

Fig. 42.

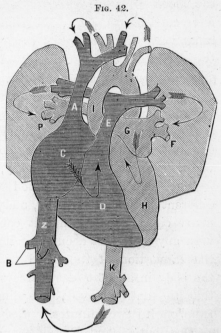

Diagram illustrating the Circulation of the Blood. —MARSHALL. A, *vena cava descending (superior);* Z, *vena cava ascending (inferior);* C, *right auricle;* D, *right ventricle;* E, *pulmonary artery;* F P, *lungs and pulmonary veins;* G, *left auricle;* H, *left ventricle;* I, K, *aorta.*

* The circulation of the blood was discovered by Harvey in 1619. For several years, he did not dare to publish his belief. When it became known, he was bitterly persecuted, and his practice as a physician greatly decreased in consequence. He lived, however, to see his theory universally adopted, and his name honored. Harvey is said to have declared that no man over forty years of age accepted his views.

† It is noticeable that the pulmonary set of veins circulates red blood, and the pulmonary set of arteries circulates dark blood. Both are connected with the lungs.

2. *The Greater Circulation.*—From the left auricle, the blood is forced past the bicuspid valve to the left ventricle; thence it is driven through the semi-lunar valves into the great aorta, the main trunk of the arterial system. Passing through the arteries, capillaries, and veins, it returns through the venæ cavæ, ascending and descending, gathers again in the right auricle, and so completes the "grand round" of the body. Both these circulations are going on constantly, as the two auricles contract, and the two ventricles expand simultaneously, and *vice versa*.

The Velocity of the Blood varies so much in different parts of the body, and is influenced by so many circumstances, that it can not be calculated with any degree of accuracy. It has been estimated that a portion of the blood will make the tour of the body in about twenty-three seconds (FLINT), and that the entire mass passes through the heart in from one to two minutes.* (See p. 314.)

Distribution and Regulation of the Heat of the Body.—1. *Distribution.*—The natural temperature is not far from 98°.† This is maintained, as we have

---

* The total amount of blood in an adult of average weight is about eighteen pounds. Dividing this by five ounces, the quantity discharged by the left ventricle at each systole, gives fifty-eight pulsations as the number necessary to transmit all the blood in the body. This, however, is an extremely unreliable basis of calculation, as the rapidity of the blood is itself so variable. Chauvreau has shown by experiments with his instrument that, corresponding to the first dilation of the vessels, the blood moves with immense rapidity; following this, the current suddenly becomes nearly arrested; this is succeeded by a second acceleration in the current, not quite so rapid as the first; and after this there is a gradual decline in the rapidity to the time of the next pulsation.

† The average temperature is, however, easily departed from. Through some trivial cause the cooling agencies may be interfered with, and then,

already seen, by the action of the oxygen within us. Each capillary tube is a tiny stove, where oxygen is combining with the tissues of the body (see note, p. 107). Every contraction of a muscle develops heat, the latent heat being set free by the breaking up of the tissue. The warmth so produced is distributed by the circulation of the blood. Thus the arteries, veins, and capillaries form a series of hot-water pipes, through which the heated liquid is forced by a pump—the heart—while the heat is kept up, not by a central furnace and boiler, but by a multitude of little fires placed here and there along its course.

2. *Regulation.*—The temperature of the body is regulated by means of the pores of the skin and the mucous membrane in the air-passages. When the system becomes too warm, the blood-vessels on the surface expand, the blood fills them, the fluid exudes into the perspiratory glands, pours out upon the exterior, and by evaporation cools the body.* When the temperature of the body is too low, the vessels contract, less blood goes to the surface, the perspiration decreases, and the loss of heat by evaporation diminishes.†

the heating processes getting the superiority, a high temperature or fever comes on. Or the reverse may ensue. In Asiatic cholera, the constitution of the blood is so changed that its disks can no longer carry oxygen into the system, the heat-making processes are put a stop to, and, the temperature declining, the body becomes of a marble coldness, characteristic of that terrible disease.—DRAPER.

* Just as water sprinkled on the floor cools a room.—*Popular Physics*, p. 255.

† Thus one is enabled to go into an oven where bread is baking, or into the arctic regions where the mountains are snow and the rivers ice. Even by these extremes the temperature of the blood will be but slightly

9

Life by Death. — The body is being incessantly corroded, and portions borne away by the tireless oxygen. The scales of the epidermis are constantly falling off and being replaced by secretion from the cutis. The disks of the blood die, and new ones spring into being. On the continuance of this interchange depend our health and vigor. Every act is a destructive one. Not a bend of the finger, not a wink of the eye, not a thought of the brain but is at some expense of the machine itself. Every process of life is thus a process of death. The more rapidly this change goes on, and fresh, vigorous tissue takes the place of the old, the more elasticity and strength we possess.

Change of our Bodies. — There is a belief that our bodies change once in seven years. From the nature of the case, the rate must vary with the labor we perform; the organs most used altering oftenest. Probably the parts of the body in incessant employment are entirely reorganized many times within a single year.*

The Three Vital Organs. — Death is produced by the stoppage of the action of any one of the three organs — the heart, the lungs, or the brain. They have, therefore, been termed the "Tripod of Life." Really, however, as Huxley has remarked, "Life has

---

affected. In the one case, the flood-gates of perspiration will be opened and the superfluous heat expended in turning the water to vapor; and, in the other, they will be tightly closed and all the heat retained.

* To use a homely simile, our bodies are like the Irishman's knife, which, after having had several new blades, and at least one new handle, was yet the same old knife.

but two legs to stand upon." If respiration and circulation be kept up artificially, the removal of the brain will not produce death.*

Wonders of the Heart.—The ancients thought the heart to be the seat of love. There were located the purity and goodness as well as the evil passions of the soul.† Modern science has found the seat of the mental powers to be in the brain. But while it has thus robbed the heart of its romance, it has revealed wonders which eclipse all the mysteries of the past. This marvelous little engine throbs on continually at the rate of one hundred thousand beats per day, forty millions per year, often three billions without a single stop. It is the most powerful of machines. "Its daily work is equal to one third that of all the muscles. If it should expend its entire force in lifting its own weight vertically, it would rise twenty thousand feet in an hour."‡ Its vitality is amazing. The most tireless of organs while life exists, it is one of the last to yield when life expires. So long as a flutter lingers at the heart, we know the spark of being is not quite extinguished, and there is hope

---

* When death really does take place, *i. e.*, when the vital organs are stopped, it is noticeable that the tissues do not die for some time thereafter. If suitable stimulants be applied, as the galvanic battery, transfusion of blood, etc., the muscles may be made to contract, and many of the phenomena of life be exhibited. Dr. Brown-Sequard thus produced muscular action in the hand of a criminal, fourteen hours after his execution.

† Our common words, hearty, large-hearted, courage (*cor*, the heart), are remains of this fanciful theory.

‡ "The greatest exploit ever accomplished by a locomotive, was to lift itself through less than one eighth of that distance." Vast and constant as is this process, so perfect is the machinery, that there are persons who do not even know where the heart lies until disease or accident reveals its location.

of restoration. During a life such as we sometimes
see, it has propelled half a million tons of blood, yet
repaired itself as it has wasted, during its patient
unfaltering labor.   The play of its valves and the

FIG. 43.

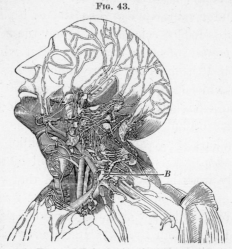

*Lymphatics of the Head and Neck, showing the Glands, and, B, the thoracic duct
as it empties into the left innominate vein at the junction of the left jugular and sub-
clavian veins.*

rhythm of its throb have never failed until, at the
command of the great Master-Workman, the " wheels
of life have stood still." *

The Lymphatic Circulation is intimately connected
with that of the blood. It is, however, more delicate

* Our brains are seventy-five-year clocks. The Angel of Life winds
them up once for all, then closes the case, and gives the key into the hand
of the Angel of the Resurrection. Tic-tac! tic-tac! go the wheels of
thought; our will can not stop them, they can not stop themselves; sleep
can not stop them; madness only makes them go faster; death alone can
break into the case, and, seizing the ever-swinging pendulum which we call
the heart, silence at last the clicking of the terrible escapement we have
carried so long beneath our wrinkled foreheads.—HOLMES.

in its organization, and less thoroughly understood. Nearly every part of the body is permeated by a second series of capillaries, closely interlaced with the blood-capillaries already described, and termed the Lymphatic system. The larger number converge into the thoracic duct—a small tube, about the size of a goose-quil. which empties into the great veins of the neck (Fig. 43). Along their course the lymphatics frequently pass through *glands*, — hard, pinkish bodies of all sizes, from that of a hemp-seed to an almond. These glands are often enlarged by disease, and then are easily felt.

FIG. 44.

Lymphatics in the Leg, with Glands at the Hip.

The Lymph, which circulates through the lymphatics like blood through the veins, is a thin, colorless liquid, very like the serum. This fluid, probably in great measure an overflow from the blood-vessels, is gathered up by the lymphatics, undergoes in the glands some process of preparation not well understood, and is then returned to the circulation.

Office of the Lymphatics.—It is thought that portions of the waste matter of the body capable of further use are thus, by a wise economy, retained and elaborated in the system.

The *lacteals*, a class of lymphatics which will be described under Digestion (p. 166), aid in taking up the food ; after a meal they become milk-white. In the lungs, the lymphatics are abundant ; sometimes absorbing the poison of disease, and diffusing it through the system.*

The lymphatics of the skin we have already spoken of as producing the phenomena of absorption.† Nature in her effort to heal a cut deposits an excess of matter to fill up the breach. Soon, the lymphatics go to work and remove the surplus material to other parts of the body.

Animals that hibernate are supported during the winter by the fat which their absorbents carry into the circulation from the extra supply they have laid up during the summer. In famine or in sickness, a man unconsciously consumes his own flesh.

Diseases, etc.—1. *Congestion* is an unnatural accumulation of blood in any part of the body. The excess is indicated by the redness. If we put our feet in hot water, the capillaries will expand by the heat, and the blood will set that way to fill them. The red nose and purplish face of the drunkard show a congestion of the capillaries. Those vessels have lost their power of contraction, and so are permanently

* Persons have thus been poisoned by tiny particles of arsenic which evaporate from green wall-paper, and float in the air.

† Pain is often relieved by injecting under the cuticle a solution of morphine, which is taken up by the absorbents, and so carried through the system.

increased in size and filled with blood.   Blushing is
a temporary congestion.   The capillaries being expanded only for an instant by the nervous excitement, contract again and expel the blood.*

2. *Inflammation* means simply a burning.   If there
is irritation or an injury at any spot, the blood sets
thither and reddens it.   This extra supply, both by
its presence and the friction of the swiftly-moving
currents, produces heat.   The pressure of the distended vessels upon the nerves frets them, and produces pain.   The swelling stretches the walls of the
blood-vessels, and the serum or lymph oozes through.
The four characteristics of an inflammation are redness, heat, pain, and swelling.

3. *Bleeding*, if from an artery, will be of red
blood, and will come in jets;† if from the veins, it

* Blushing is a purely local modification of the circulation of this
kind, and it will be instructive to consider how a blush is brought about.
An emotion—sometimes pleasurable, sometimes painful—takes possession
of the mind; thereupon a hot flush is felt, the skin grows red, and according to the intensity of the emotion these changes are confined to the
cheeks only, or extend to the "roots of the hair," or "all over."   What is
the cause of these changes?   The blood is a red and a hot fluid; the skin reddens and grows hot, because its vessels contain an increased quantity of
this red and hot fluid; and its vessels contain more, because the small
arteries suddenly dilate, the natural moderate contraction of their muscles
being superseded by a state of relaxation.   In other words, the action of
the nerves which cause this muscular contraction is suspended.   On the
other hand, in many people, extreme terror causes the skin to grow cold,
and the face to appear pale and pinched.   Under these circumstances, in
fact, the supply of blood to the skin is greatly diminished, in consequence
of an excessive stimulation of the nerves of the small arteries, which
causes them to contract and so to cut off the supply of blood more or less
completely.—HUXLEY's *Physiology.*

† The elasticity of the arteries (p. 114) is a physical property, as may
easily be shown by removing one from a dead body.   If they were rigid
and unyielding, a considerable portion of the heart's force would be use-
lessly expended against their walls.   Their expansion is a passive state, and

will be of dark blood, and will flow in a steady stream. If only a small vessel be severed, it may be checked by a piece of cloth held or bound firmly upon the wound. If a large trunk be cut, especially in a limb, make a knot in a handkerchief and tie it loosely about the limb; then, placing the knot on the wound, with a short stick twist the handkerchief tightly enough to stop the flow. If you have a piece of cloth to use as a pad, the knot will be unnecessary. If it be an artery that is cut, the pressure should be applied between the wound and the heart; if a vein, beyond the wound. If you are alone, and are severely wounded, or in an emergency, like a railroad accident, use the remedy which has saved many a life upon the battle-field—bind or hold a handful of dry earth upon the wound, elevate the part, and await surgical assistance.

4. *Scrofula* is generally inherited. It is a disease affecting the lymphatic glands, most commonly those of the neck, forming "kernels," as they are called. It is, however, liable to attack any organ. Persons inheriting this disease can hope to ward off its in-

---

depends on the pressure of the blood within them; but their vital contractility is an active property.—The intermittent movement of the blood through the arteries is strikingly shown in the manner in which they bleed when wounded. When an artery is cut across, the blood spurts out with great force to a distance of several feet, but the flow is not continuous. It escapes in a series of jets, the long, slender scarlet stream rising and falling with each beat of the heart, and this pulsation of the blood-stream tells at once that it comes from a wounded artery. But as the blood traverses these elastic tubes, the abruptness of the heart's stroke becomes gradually broken and the current equalized, so that the greater the distance from the heart the less obvious is the pulsation, until at length in the capillaries the rate of the stream becomes uniform.

sidious approaches only by the utmost care in diet and exercise; by the use of pure air and warm clothing, and by avoiding late hours and undue stimulus of all kinds. Probably the most fatal and common excitants of the latent seeds of scrofula are insufficient or improper food, and want of ventilation.

5. *A Cold.*—We put on a thinner dress than usual, or, when heated, sit in a cool place. The skin is chilled, and the perspiration checked. The blood, no longer cleansed and reduced in volume by the drainage through the pores, sets to the lungs for purification. That organ is oppressed, breathing becomes difficult, and the extra mucus secreted by the irritated surface of the membrane is thrown off by coughing. The mucous membrane of the nasal chamber sympathizes with the difficulty, and we have "a cold in the head," or a catarrh. In general, the excess of blood seeks the weakest point, and develops there any latent disease.* Where one person has been killed in battle, thousands have died of colds.

To restore the equipoise must be the object of all treatment. We put the feet in hot water and they soon become red and gorged with the blood which is

* A party go out for a walk and are caught in a rain, or, coming home heated from some close assembly, throw off their coats to enjoy the deliciously-cool breeze. The next day, one has a fever, another a slight headache, another pleurisy, another pneumonia, another rheumatism, while some of the number escape without any ill-feeling whatever. The last had vital force sufficient to withstand the disturbance, but in the others there were various weak points, and to these the excess of blood has gone, producing congestion.

thus called from the congested organs. Hot foot-
baths have saved multitudes of lives. It is well in
case of a sudden cold to go immediately to bed, and
with hot drinks and extra clothing open the pores,
and induce free perspiration. This calls the blood to
the surface, and, by equalizing and diminishing the
volume of the circulation, affords relief.*

6. *Catarrh* commonly manifests itself by the
symptoms known as those of a "cold in the head,"
and is produced by the same causes. It is an inflammation of the mucous membrane lining the
nasal and bronchial passages. One going out from
the hot dry air of a furnace-heated room into the
cold damp atmosphere of our climate can hardly
avoid irritating and inflaming this tender membrane.
If our rooms were heated less intensely, and ventilated more thoroughly, so that we had not the present hot-house sensitiveness to cold air, this disease
would be far less universal, and perhaps would disappear entirely.† (See p. 315.)

* Severe colds may often be relieved in their first stages by using
lemons freely during the day, and taking at night fifteen or twenty grains
of sodium bromide. Great care, however, should be observed in employing
the latter remedy, except under the advice of a physician.

† Dr. Gray gives the following table:

Rooms Occupied by Letter-press Printers.	Number per cent. Spitting Blood.	Subject to Catarrh.
104 men having less than 500 cubic feet of air to breathe......................................	12.50	12.50
115 men having from 500 to 600 cubic feet of air to breathe.................................	4.35	3.58
101 men having more than 600 cubic feet of air to breathe.................................	3.96	1.98

ALCOHOLIC DRINKS AND NARCOTICS.

1. ALCOHOL.

THAT we may understand fully the effect of alcohol upon the human system, let us first consider its nature and the process by which harmless fruits and grains are made to produce a substance so unlike themselves in its deleterious effects.

How Alcohol is Made.—When any substance containing sugar, as fruit-juice, is caused to ferment, the elements of which the sugar is composed, viz., hydrogen, carbon, and oxygen, so re-arrange themselves as to form carbon dioxide (carbonic acid), alcohol, and certain volatile oils and ethers.* The carbonic acid partly evaporates and partly remains in the liquor; the alcohol is the poisonous or intoxicating principle, while the oils and ethers impart the peculiar flavor and odor. Thus wine is fermented grape-juice, and cider is fermented apple-juice, each having its distinctive taste and smell, and each containing, as one product of fermentation, more or less of the inebriating alcohol. Wines are also made from other fruits and vegetables, such as oranges, currants, tomatoes, and rhubarb, but the alcohol which they contain is of the same nature in all cases, whether the fermented liquor has been manufactured in great quantities, by large presses, or by

---

* The precise relation between chemical phenomena and the physiological functions of the organic ferment is still to be discovered; and all that has been said, written, and brought forward to decide the question, needs experimental proof.—SCHÜTZENBERGER.

a simple domestic process for home consumption. It
is important to remember this fact, as many people
do not associate alcohol with such beverages as domestic wines and home-brewed ales, whereas it is
always present with the same treacherous qualities
which attach to it every-where. An apple is a wholesome and useful fruit, and its simple juice, fragrant
and refreshing, is a delight to the palate; but apple-
juice converted into cider and allowed to enter upon
alcoholic fermentation, loses its innocence, and becomes a dangerous drink, because it is the nature of
the alcohol it now contains to create an appetite for
more alcohol. (See p. 185.)

What is a Ferment?—Ferments, of which there
are many varieties in nature, are minute living organisms analogous to the microscopic objects called
bacteria or microbes,* of which we have heard much
in late years, especially in connection with the famous researches and experiments of the great French
investigator, M. Pasteur. He tells us that "Every
fermentation has its specific ferment. This minute
being produces the transformation which constitutes
fermentation by breathing the oxygen of the substance to be fermented, or by appropriating for an
instant the whole substance, then destroying it by
what may be termed the secretion of the fermented

---

* There is no well-defined limit between ferments and bacteria, any
more than between ferments and fungi, or again, between fungi and bacteria. Their smaller size is the principal difference which separates bacteria from ferments, although there are bacteria of large size, such as are so
frequently found in the mouth of even a healthy man, and which much
resemble in their mode of growth some of the lower fungi.—TROUESSART.

products."* The effect, therefore, of fermentation is to change entirely the character of the substance upon which it acts; hence it is an error to assume that fermented liquors, as beer, wine, and cider, are safe drinks because the grains or fruits from which they are produced are healthful foods.

Yeast is a ferment which causes alcoholic fermentation. It consists of microscopic plants, which increase by the formation of multitudes of tiny cells not more than $\frac{1}{2400}$ of an inch in diameter. In the brewing of beer they grow in great abundance, making common brewer's yeast. Ferments or their spores float in the air ready to enter any fermentable liquid, and under favorable conditions they multiply with great activity and energy. The favorable conditions include the presence of oxygen or sugar;† oxygen being, as we know, necessary for the development and the reproduction of all cell life (p. 107), and ferments having the power to resolve sugar,

---

* What we call spontaneous fermentation often occurs, as when apple-juice turns to hard cider by simple exposure to the air. Science teaches us, however, that this change is always effected by the action of the busy little ferments which, wandering about, drop into the liquid, begin their rapid propagation, and, in the act of growing, evolve the products of the fermentation. "If the above liquids be left only in contact with air which has been passed through a red-hot platinum tube, and thus the living sporules destroyed; or if the air be simply filtered by passing through cotton wool, and the sporules prevented from coming into the liquid, it is found that these fermentable liquids may be preserved for any length of time without undergoing the slightest change."—ROSCOE.

† Yeast, like ordinary plants, buds and multiplies even in the absence of fermentable sugar, when it is furnished with free oxygen. This multiplication, however, is favored by the presence of sugar, which is a more appropriate element than non-fermentable hydrocarbon compounds. Yeast is also able to bud and multiply in the absence of free oxygen, but in this case a fermentable substance is indispensable.—SCHÜTZENBERGER's *Fermentation.*

which penetrates by endosmose into the interior of the cell, into alcohol, carbonic acid, glycerine, succinic acid, and oxygen.

Beer.—The barley used for making beer is first malted, *i. e.*, sprouted, to turn a part of its starch into sugar. When this process has gone far enough, it is checked by heating the grain in a kiln until the germ is destroyed. The malt is then crushed, steeped, and fermented with hops and yeast. The sugar gradually disappears, alcohol is formed, and carbonic acid escapes into the air. The beer is then put into casks, where it undergoes a second, slower fermentation, and the carbonic acid gathers; when the liquor is drawn, this gas bubbles to the surface, giving to the beer its sparkling, foamy look.

Wine is generally made from the juice of the grape. The juice, or *must*, as it is called, is placed in vats in the cellar, where the low temperature favors a slow fermentation. If all the sugar be converted into alcohol and carbonic-acid gas, a dry wine will remain; if the fermentation be checked, a sweet wine will result; and if the wine be bottled while the change is still going on, a brisk effervescing liquor like champagne, will be formed. All these are dangerous beverages because of the alcohol they contain.

Distillation.—Alcohol is so volatile that, by the application of heat, it can be driven off as a vapor from the fermented liquid in which it has been produced. Steam and various fragrant substances will accompany it, and, if they are collected and condensed in a cool receiver, a new and stronger liquor will be formed, having a distinctive odor.

In this way whiskey is distilled from fermented corn, rye, barley, or potatoes; the alcohol of commerce is distilled from whiskey; brandy, from wine; rum, from fermented molasses; and gin, from fermented barley and rye, afterward distilled with juniper berries.

Varieties and Properties of Alcohol.—There are several varieties of alcohol produced from distillation of various substances. Thus Methyl Alcohol is obtained from the decomposition of hard wood when exposed to intense heat with little or no oxygen present. It is a light, volatile liquid, which closely resembles ordinary alcohol in all its properties. It is used in the manufacture of aniline dyes, in making varnishes, and for burning in spirit lamps. Amyl Alcohol* is the chief constituent of "fusel oil," found in whiskey distilled from potatoes. It is often present in common alcohol, giving a slightly unpleasant odor when it evaporates from the hand. Fusel oil is extremely poisonous and lasting in its effects, so that when contained in liquors it greatly increases their destructive and intoxicating properties.

---

* The odor of amylic alcohol is sweet, nauseous, and heavy. The sensation of its presence remains long. In taste it is burning and acrid, and it is itself practically insoluble in water. When it is diluted with common alcohol it dissolves freely in water, and gives a soft and rather unctuous flavor, I may call it a fruity flavor, something like that of ripe pears. Amyl alcohol, introduced as an adulterant, is an extremely dangerous addition to ordinary alcohol, in whatever form it is presented. From the quantities of it imported into this country, it is believed to be employed largely in the adulteration of wines and spirits.—RICHARDSON.

Ethyl Alcohol, which is that which we have described as obtained from fermentation of fruits and grains, is the ordinary alcohol of commerce. We have spoken of its volatility. This property permits it to pass into vapor at 56° Fahr. It boils at 173° Fahr. (Water boils at 212°.) Like Methyl Alcohol, it burns without smoke and with great heat,* and is therefore of much value in the arts. Its great solvent power over fats and mixed oils renders it a useful agent in many industrial operations. It is also a powerful antiseptic, and no one who visits a museum of natural history will be likely to forget the rows of bottles within which float reptilian and batrachian specimens, preserved in alcohol.

To alcohol, also, we are indebted for various anæsthetic agents, which, when not abused (p. 340), are of inestimable value. Thus, if certain proportions of alcohol and nitric acid be mixed together and heated, nitrite of amyl, so serviceable in relieving the agonizing spasms peculiar to that dread disease, angina pectoris, will be obtained. If, instead of nitric, we use sulphuric acid, we shall get ether; if

* Pour a little alcohol into a saucer and apply an ignited match. The liquid will suddenly take fire, burning with intense heat, but feeble light. In this process, alcohol takes up oxygen from the air, forming carbonic-acid gas, and water.—Hold a red-hot coil of platinum wire in a goblet containing a few drops of alcohol, and a peculiar odor will be noticed. It denotes the formation of *aldehyde*—a substance produced in the slow oxidation of alcohol. Still further oxidized, the alcohol would be changed into *acetic acid*—the sour principle of vinegar.—Put the white of an egg—nearly pure albumen—into a cup, and pour upon it some alcohol, or even strong brandy; the fluid albumen will coagulate, becoming hard and solid. In this connection, it is well to remember that albumen is contained in our food, while the brain is largely an albuminous substance.

chlorine be passed through alcohol, hydrate of chloral is the result; and, if chloride of lime and alcohol be treated together, the outcome is chloroform.

One of the most striking properties of alcohol, and one which we shall hereafter consider in its disastrous effects upon the tissues of our body, is its affinity for water.* When strong alcohol is exposed

* Suppose, then, a certain measure of alcohol be taken into the stomach, it will be absorbed there, but, previous to absorption, it will have to undergo a proper degree of dilution with water; for there is this peculiarity respecting alcohol when it is separated by an animal membrane from a watery fluid like the blood, that it will not pass through the membrane until it has become charged, to a given point of dilution, with water. Alcohol is itself, in fact, so greedy for water that it will pick it up from watery textures, and deprive them of it until, by its saturation, its power of reception is exhausted, after which it will diffuse into the current of circulating fluid.

To illustrate this fact of dilution I perform a simple experiment. Into a bladder is placed a mixture consisting of equal parts of alcohol and distilled water. Into the neck of the bladder a long glass tube is inserted and firmly tied. Then the bladder is immersed in a saline fluid representing an artificial serum of blood. The result is, that the alcohol in the bladder absorbs water from the surrounding saline solution, and thereby a column of fluid passes up into the glass tube. A second mixture of alcohol and water, in the proportion this time of one part of alcohol to two of water, is put into another bladder immersed in like manner in an artificial serum. In this instance a little fluid also passes from the outside into the bladder, so that there is a rise of water in the tube, but less than in the previous instance. A third mixture, consisting of one part of alcohol with three parts of water, is placed in another little bladder, and is also suspended in the artificial serum. In this case there is, for a time, a small rise of fluid in the tube connected with the bladder; but after awhile, owing to the dilution which took place, a current from within outward sets in, and the tube becomes empty. Thus each bladder charged originally with the same quantity of fluid contains at last a different quantity. The first contains more than it did originally, the second only a little more, the third a little less. From the third, absorption takes place, and if I keep changing and replacing the outer fluid which surrounds the bladder with fresh serum, I can in time, owing to the double current of water into the bladder through its coats, and of water and alcohol out of the bladder into the serum, remove all the alcohol. In this way it is removed from the stomach into the circulating blood after it has been swallowed. When we

10

to the air, it absorbs moisture and becomes diluted; at the same time, the spirit itself evaporates. The commercial or proof-spirit is about one half water; the strongest holds ten per cent.; and to obtain absolute or waterless alcohol, requires careful distillation in connection with some substance, as lime, that has a still greater affinity for water, and so can despoil the alcohol.

Alcohol in its Destructive Relation to Plant and Animal Life.—If we pour a little quantity of strong spirits upon a growing plant in our garden or conservatory, we shall soon see it shrivel and die. If we apply it to insects or small reptiles which we may have captured for specimens in our cabinet, the same potent poison will procure for them a speedy death. If we force one of our domestic animals to take habitual doses of it, the animal will not only strongly protest against the unnatural and nauseous potion, but it will gradually sicken and lose all power for usefulness. "If I wished," says a distinguished English physician, "by scientific experiment to spoil for work the most perfect specimen of a working animal, say a horse, without inflicting mechanical injury, I could choose no better agent for the purpose of the experiment than alcohol."*

dilute alcohol with water before drinking it, we quicken its absorption. If we do not dilute it sufficiently, it is diluted in the stomach by transudation of water in the stomach, until the required reduction for its absorption; the current then sets in toward the blood, and passes into the circulating canals by the veins.—RICHARDSON.

* "The effects produced by alcohol are common, so far as I can discover, to every animal. Alcohol is a universal intoxicant, and in the higher orders of animals is capable of inducing the most systematic phe-

Alcohol in Wine, Beer, and Cider Identical with Alcohol in Ardent Spirits.—In all liquors the active principle is alcohol. It comprises from six to eight per cent. of ale and porter, seven to seventeen per cent. of wine, and forty to fifty per cent. of brandy and whiskey. All these may therefore be considered as alcohol more or less diluted with water and flavored with various aromatics. The taste of different liquors—as brandy, gin, beer, cider, etc.—may vary greatly, but they all produce certain physiological effects, due to their common ingredient—alcohol. "In whatever form it enters," says Dr. Richardson, "whether as spirit, wine, or ale, matters little when its specific influence is kept steadily in view. To say this man only drinks ale, that man only drinks wine, while a third drinks spirits, is merely to say, when the apology is unclothed, that all drink the same danger." In other words, the poisonous nature of alcohol, and the effects which result when it is taken into the stomach, are definite and immutable facts, which are not dependent upon any particular name or disguise under which the poison finds entrance.

We shall learn, as we study the influence of alcohol upon the human system, that one of its most subtle characteristics is the progressive appetite for

nomena of disease. But it is reserved for man himself to exhibit these phenomena in their purest form, and to present, through them, in the morbid conditions belonging to his age, a distinct pathology. Bad as this is, it might be worse; for if the evils of alcohol were made to extend equally to animals lower than man, we should soon have none that were tamable, none that were workable, and none that were eatable."

itself (p. 185) which it induces, an appetite which, in many cases, is formed long before its unhappy subject is aware of his danger. The intelligent pupil, who knows how to reason from cause to effect, needs hardly to be told, in view of this physical truth, of the peril that lies in the first draught of *any* fermented liquor, even though it be so seemingly harmless as a glass of home-brewed beer or "slightly-beaded" cider. Few of us really understand our own inherent weakness or the hereditary proclivities (p. 186) that may be lurking in our blood, ready to master us when opportunity invites; but we may be tolerably certain that if we resolutely refuse to tamper with cider, beer, or wine, we shall not fall into temptation before rum, gin, or brandy. Since we know that in all fermented beverages there is present the same treacherous element, alcohol, we are truly wise only when we decline to measure arms in any way with an enemy so seductive in its advances, so insidious in its influence, and so terrible in its triumph.*

---

* Aside from all considerations of physical, mental, and moral injury wrought by the use of alcoholic drinks, every young man may well take into account the damaging effect of such a dangerous habit upon his business prospects. Careful business men are becoming more and more unwilling to take into their employ any person addicted to liquor-drinking. Within the past few years the officers of several railroads, having found that a considerable portion of their losses could be directly traced to the drinking habits of some one or more of their employés, have ordered the dismissal of all persons in their service who were known to use intoxicants, with the additional provision that persons thus discharged should never be re-instated. Many Eastern manufactories have adopted similar rules. All mercantile agencies now report the habits of business men in this respect, and some life-insurance companies refuse to insure habitual drinkers, regarding such risks as "extra-hazardous."

Let us now consider the physiological effects of alcohol upon the organs immediately connected with the circulation of the blood.

General Effect of Alcohol upon the Circulation.— During the experiment described on page 118, the influence of alcohol upon the blood may be beautifully tested. Place on the web of the frog's foot a drop of dilute spirit. The blood-vessels immediately expand—an effect known as *"Vascular enlargement."* Channels before unseen open, and the blood-disks fly along at a brisker rate. Next, touch the membrane with a drop of pure spirit. The blood channels quickly contract; the cells slacken their speed; and, finally, all motion ceases. The flesh shrivels up and dies. The circulation thus stopped is stopped forever. The part affected will in time slough off. Alcohol has killed it.

The influence of alcohol upon the human system is very similar. When strong, as in spirits, it acts as an irritant, narcotic poison (p. 142, note). Diluted, as in fermented liquors, it dilates the blood-vessels, quickens the circulation, hastens the heart-throbs, and accelerates the respiration.

The Effect of Alcohol upon the Heart.—What means this rapid flow of the blood? It shows that the heart is overworking. The nerves that lead to the minute capillaries and regulate the passage of the vital current through the extreme parts of the body, are paralyzed by this active narcotic. The tiny blood-vessels at once expand. This "Vascular enlargement" removes the resistance to the passage of the blood, and a rapid beating of the heart results.*

Careful experiments show that two ounces of alcohol—an amount contained in the daily potations of a very moderate ale or whiskey drinker—increase the heart-beats six thousand in twenty-four hours;— a degree of work represented by that of lifting up a weight of seven tons to a height of one foot. Reducing this sum to ounces and dividing, we find that the heart is driven to do extra work equivalent to lifting seven ounces one foot high one thousand four hundred and ninety-three times each hour! No wonder that the drinker feels a reaction, a physical languor, after the earliest effects of his indulgence have passed away. The heart flags, the brain and the muscles feel exhausted, and rest and sleep are imperatively demanded. During this time of excitement, the machinery of life has really been "running

* Dr. B. W. Richardson's experiments tend to prove that this apparently stimulating action of alcohol upon the heart is due to the paralysis of the nerves that control the capillaries (Note, p. 208), which ordinarily check the flow of the blood (p. 117). The heart, like other muscles under the influence of alcohol, really loses power, and contracts less vigorously (p. 183). Dr. Palmer, of the University of Michigan, also claims that alcohol, in fact, diminishes the strength of the heart. Prof. Martin, of Johns Hopkins University, from a series of carefully conducted experiments upon dogs, concludes that blood containing one fourth per cent. of alcohol almost invariably diminishes within a minute the work done by the heart; blood containing one half per cent. always diminishes it, and may reduce the amount pumped out by the left ventricle so that it is not sufficient to supply the coronary arteries. One hundred years ago, alcohol was always spoken of as a stimulant. Modern experiment and investigation challenged that definition, and it is now classified as a narcotic. There are, however, able physicians who maintain that, taken in small doses, and under certain physical conditions, it has the effect of a stimulant. All agree that, when taken in any amount, it tends to create an appetite for more.

down." "It is hard work," says Richardson, "to fight against alcohol; harder than rowing, walking, wrestling, coal-heaving, or the tread-mill itself."

All this is only the first effect of alcohol upon the heart. Long-continued use of this disturbing agent causes a "Degeneration of the muscular fiber,"* so that the heart loses its old power to drive the blood, and, after a time, fails to respond even to the spur of the excitant that has urged it to ruin.

Influence upon the Membranes.—The flush of the face and the blood-shot eye, that are such noticeable effects of even a small quantity of liquor, indicate the condition of all the internal organs. The delicate linings of the stomach, heart, brain, liver, and lungs are reddened, and every tiny vein is inflamed, like the blushing nose itself. If the use of liquor is habitual, this "Vascular enlargement," that at first slowly passed away after each indulgence, becomes permanent, and now the discolored, blotched skin reveals the state of the entire mucous membrane.

---

* This "Degeneration" of the various tissues of the body, we shall find, as we proceed, is one of the most marked effects of alcoholized blood. The change consists in an excess of liquid, or, more commonly, in a deposit of fat. This fatty matter is not an increase of the organ, but it takes the place of a part of its fiber, thus weakening the structure, and reducing the power of the tissue to perform its function. Almost every-where in the body we thus find cells—muscle-cells, liver-cells, nerve-cells, as the case may be—changing one by one, under the influence of this potent disorganizer, into unhealthy fat-cells. "Alcohol has been well termed," says the *London Lancet*, "the 'Genius of Degeneration.'"

The cause of this degeneration can be easily explained. The increased activity of the circulation compels a correspondingly-increased activity of the cell-changes: but the essential condition of healthful change—the presence of additional oxygen—is wanting (see p. 143), and the operation is imperfectly performed.—BRODIE.

We learned on page 55 what a peculiar office the membrane fills in nourishing the organs it enwraps. Any thing that disturbs its delicate structure must mar its efficiency. Alcohol has a wonderful affinity for water. To satisfy this greed, it will absorb moisture from the tissues with which it comes in contact, as well as from their lubricating juices. The enlargement of the blood-vessels and their permanent congestion must interfere with the filtering action of the membrane. In time, all the membranes become dry, thickened, and hardened; they then shrink upon the sensitive nerve, or stiffen the joint, or enfeeble the muscle. The function of these membranes being deranged, they will not furnish the organs with perfected material, and the clogged pores will no longer filter their natural fluids. Every organ in the body will feel this change.

Effect upon the Blood.*—From the stomach, alcohol passes directly into the circulation, and so, in a few minutes, is swept through the entire system. If it be present in sufficient amount and strength, its eager desire for water will lead it to absorb moisture from the red corpuscles, causing them to shrink, change their form, harden, and lose some of their ability to carry oxygen; it may even make them adhere in masses, and so hinder their passage through the tiny capillaries.—RICHARDSON.

---

* Alcohol acts upon the oxygen-carrier, the coloring matter of the red corpuscles, causing it to settle in one part of the globule, or even to leave the corpuscle, and deposit itself in other elements of the blood. Thus the red corpuscle may become colorless, distorted, shrunken, and even entirely broken up.—DR. G. B. HARRIMAN.

With most persons who indulge freely in alcoholic drinks, the blood is thin, the avidity of alcohol for water causing the burning thirst so familiar to all drinkers, and hence the use of enormous quantities of water, oftener of beer, which unnaturally dilutes the blood. The blood then easily flows from a wound, and renders an accident or surgical operation very dangerous.

When the blood tends, as in other cases of an excessive use of spirits, to coagulate in the capillaries,* there is a liability of an obstruction to the flow of the vital current through the heart, liver, lungs, etc., that may cause disease, and in the brain may lay the foundation of paralysis, or, in extreme cases, of apoplexy.

Wherever the alcoholized blood goes through the body, it bathes the delicate cells with an irritating narcotic poison, instead of a bland, nutritious substance.

Effect upon the Lungs.—Here we can see how certainly the presence of alcohol interferes with the red corpuscles in their task of carrying oxygen. "Even so small a quantity as one part of alcohol to

---

* The blood is rendered unduly thin, or is coagulated, according to the amount of alcohol that is carried into the circulatory system. "The spirit may fix the water with the fibrin, and thus destroy the power of coagulation; or it may extract the water so determinately as to produce coagulation. This explains why, in acute cases of poisoning by alcohol, the blood is sometimes found quite fluid, at other times firmly coagulated in the vessels."—B. W. RICHARDSON.

Reckless persons have sometimes drunk a large quantity of liquor for a wager, and, as the result of their folly, have died instantly. The whole of the blood in the heart having coagulated, the circulation was stopped, and death inevitably ensued.

five hundred of the blood will materially check the absorption of oxygen in the lungs."

The cells, unable to take up oxygen, retain their carbonic-acid gas, and so return from the lungs, carrying back, to poison the system, the refuse matter the body has sought to throw off. Thus the lungs no longer furnish properly oxygenized blood.

The rapid stroke of the heart, already spoken of, is followed by a corresponding quickening of the respiration. The flush of the cheek is repeated in the reddened mucous membrane lining the lungs.

When this "Vascular enlargement" becomes permanent, and the highly-albuminous membrane of the air-cells is hardened and thickened as well as congested, the Osmose of the gases to and fro through its pores can no longer be prompt and free as before. Even when the effect passes off in a few days after the occasional indulgence, there has been, during that time, a diminished supply of the life-giving oxygen furnished to the system; weakness follows, and, in the case of hard drinkers, there is a marked liability to epidemics.*

Physicians tell us, also, that there is a peculiar form of consumption known as Alcoholic Phthisis caused by long-continued and excessive use of

---

* There is no doubt that alcohol alters and impairs tissues so that they are more prone to disease. — Dr. G. K. Sabine. A volume of statistics could be filled with quotations like the following: "Mr. Huber, who saw in one town in Russia two thousand one hundred and sixty persons perish with the cholera in twenty days, said: 'It is a most remarkable circumstance that persons given to drink have been swept away like flies. In Tiflis, with twenty thousand inhabitants, every drunkard has fallen,—all are dead, not one remaining."

liquor. It generally attacks those whose splendid physique has enabled them to "drink deep" with apparent impunity. This type of consumption appears late in life and is considered incurable. Severe cases of pneumonia are also generally fatal with inebriates.*

PRACTICAL QUESTIONS.

1. Why does a dry, cold atmosphere favorably affect catarrh?

2. Why should we put on extra covering when we lie down to sleep?

3. Is it well to throw off our coats or shawls when we come in heated from a long walk?

4. Why are close-fitting collars or neck-ties injurious?

5. Which side of the heart is the more liable to inflammation?

6. What gives the toper his red nose?

7. Why does not the arm die when the surgeon ties the principal artery leading to it?

8. When a fowl is angry, why does its comb redden?

9. Why does a fat man endure cold better than a lean one?

10. Why does one become thin during a long sickness?

11. What would you do if you should come home "wet to the skin"?

12. When the cold air strikes the face, why does it first blanch and then flush?

13. What must be the effect of tight lacing upon the circulation of the blood?

14. Do you know the position of the large arteries in the limbs, so that in case of accident you could stop the flow of blood?

15. When a person is said to be good-hearted, is it a physical truth?

16. Why does a hot foot-bath relieve the headache?

17. Why does the body of a drowned or strangled person turn blue?

18. What are the little "kernels" in the arm-pits?

19. When we are excessively warm, would the thermometer show any rise of temperature in the body?

20. What forces besides that of the heart aid in propelling the blood?

21. Why can the pulse be best felt in the wrist?

22. Why are starving people exceedingly sensitive to any jar?

23. Why will friction, an application of horse-radish leaves, or a blister, relieve internal congestion?

24. Why are students very liable to cold feet?

---

* The Influence of Alcohol is continued in the chapter on Digestion.

25. Is the proverb that "blood is thicker than water" literally true?

26. What is the effect upon the circulation of "holding the breath"?

27. Which side of the heart is the stronger?

28. How is the heart itself nourished?*

29. Does any venous blood reach the heart without coming through the venæ cavæ?

30. What would you do, in the absence of a surgeon, in the case of a severe wound?   (See p. 258.)

31. What would you do in the case of a fever?   (See p. 263.)

32. What is the most injurious effect of alcohol upon the blood?

33. Are our bodies the same from day to day?

34. Show how life comes by death.

35. Is not the truth just stated as applicable to moral and intellectual, as to physical life?

36. What vein begins and ends with capillaries? *Ans.* The portal vein commences with capillaries in the digestive organs, and ends with the same kind of vessels in the liver. (See p. 166.)

37. By what process is alcohol always formed? Does it exist in nature?

38. What percentage of alcohol is contained in the different kinds of liquor?

39. Does cider possess the same intoxicating principle as brandy?

40. Describe the general properties of alcohol.

41. Show that alcohol is a narcotic poison.

42. If alcohol is not a stimulant, how does it cause the heart to over-work?

43. Why is the skin of a drunkard always red and blotched?

44. What danger is there in occasionally using alcoholic drinks?

45. What is meant by a fatty degeneration of the heart?

46. What keeps the blood in circulation between the beats of the heart?

47. What is the office of the capillaries? (See note, p. 373.)

48. Does alcohol interfere with this function?

49. How does alcohol interfere with the regular office of the membranes?

50. How does it check the process of oxidation?

---

* The coronary artery, springing from the aorta just after its origin, carries blood to the muscular walls of the heart ; the venous blood comes back through the coronary veins, and empties directly into the right auricle.

VI

DIGESTION AND FOOD.

"A MAN puts some ashes in a hill of corn and thereby doubles its yield. Then he says, 'My ashes have I turned into corn.' Weak from his labor, he eats of his corn, and new life comes to him. Again, he says, 'I have changed my corn into a man.' This also he feels to be the truth.

"It is the problem of the body, remember, that we are discussing. A man is more than the body; to confound the body and the man is worse than confounding the body and the clothing."--JOHN DARBY.

ANALYSIS OF DIGESTION AND FOOD.

DIGESTION AND FOOD.

1. WHY WE NEED FOOD.

2. WHAT FOOD DOES.

3. KINDS OF FOOD
   1. Nitrogenous.
   2. Carbonaceous.
      - a. *The Sugars.*
      - b. *The Fats.*
   3. Minerals.

4. ONE KIND IS INSUFFICIENT

5. OBJECT OF DIGESTION.

6. PROCESS OF DIGESTION.
   - — General Description.
   1. Mastication and Insalivation.
      - a. *The Saliva.*
      - b. *Process of Swallowing.*
   2. Gastric Digestion
      - a. *The Stomach.*
      - b. *The Gastric Juice.*
      - c. *The Chyme.*
   3. Intestinal Digestion.
      - — Description.
      - a. *The Bile.*
      - b. *The Pancreatic Juice.*
      - c. *The Small Intestine.*
   4. Absorption.
      - a. *By the Veins.*
      - b. *By the Lacteals.*

7. COMPLEXITY OF THE PROCESS OF DIGESTION.

8. HYGIENE
   1. Length of Time required.
   2. Value of different kinds of Food.
      - a. *Beef.*
      - b. *Mutton.*
      - c. *Lamb.*
      - d. *Pork.*
      - e. *Fish.*
      - f. *Milk.*
      - g. *Cheese.*
      - h. *Eggs, etc.*
   3. The Stimulants.
      - a. *Coffee.*
      - b. *Tea.*
      - c. *Chocolate.*
   4. Cooking of Food.
   5. Rapid Eating.
   6. Quantity and Quality of Food.
   7. When Food should be taken.
   8. How Food should be taken.
   9. Need of a Variety.

9. THE WONDERS OF DIGESTION.

10. DISEASES
    1. Dyspepsia.
    2. The Mumps.

11. ALCOHOLIC DRINKS AND NARCOTICS.
    Alcohol.
    1. Is Alcohol a Food ?
    2. Effect upon the Digestion.
    3. Effect upon the Liver.
    4. Effect upon the Kidneys.
    5. Does Alcohol impart heat ?
    6. Does Alcohol impart strength ?
    7. The Effect upon the Waste of the Body.
    8. Alcohol creates a progressive appetite for itself.
    9. Law of Heredity.

DIGESTION AND FOOD.

Why We Need Food.—We have learned that our bodies are constantly giving off waste matter—the products of the fire, or oxidation, as the chemist terms the change going on within us (Note, p. 107). A man without food will starve to death in a few days, *i.e.*, the oxygen will have consumed all the available flesh of his body.* To replace the daily outgo, we need about two and a quarter pounds of food, and three pints of drink.†

* The stories current in the newspapers of persons who live for years without food, are, of course, untrue. The case of the Welsh Fasting Girl, which excited general interest throughout Great Britain, and was extensively copied in our own press, is in point. She had succeeded in deceiving not only the public, but, as some claim, her own parents. At last a strict watch was set by day and night, precluding the possibility of her receiving any food except at the hands of the committee, from whom she steadily refused it. In a few days she died from actual starvation. The youth of the girl, the apparent honesty of the parents, and the tragical sequel, make it one of the most remarkable cases of the kind on record.

† Every cell in the tissues is full of matter ready to set free at call its stored-up energy—derived from the meat, bread, and vegetables we have eaten. This energy will pass off quietly when the organs are in comparative rest, but violently when the muscles contract with force. When we send an order through a nerve to any part of the body, a series of tiny explosions run the entire length of the nerve, just as fire runs through a train of gunpowder. The muscle receives the stimulus, and, contracting, liberates its energy. The cells of nerve or muscle, whose contents have thus exploded, as it were, are useless, and must be carried off by the blood, just as ashes must be swept from the hearth, and new fuel be supplied to keep up a fire.

Including the eight hundred pounds of oxygen taken from the air, a man uses in a year about a ton and a half of material.* Yet during this entire time his weight may have been nearly uniform.† Our bodies are but molds, in which a certain quantity of matter, checked for a time on its ceaseless round, receives a definite form. They may be likened, says Huxley, to an eddy in the river, which retains its shape for awhile, yet every instant each particle of water is changing.

What Food Does.—We make no force ourselves. We can only use that which nature provides for us.‡ All our strength comes from the food we eat. Food is force—that is, it contains a latent power

---

* The following is the daily ration of a United States soldier. It is said to be the most generous in the world:

Bread or flour	22 ounces.
Fresh or salt beef (or pork or bacon, 12 oz.) . .	20 "
Potatoes (three times per week)	16 "
Rice	1.6 "
Coffee (or tea, 0.24 oz.)	1.6 "
Sugar	2.4 "
Beans	0.64 gill.
Vinegar	0.32 "
Salt	0.16 "

† If, however, he were kept on the scale-pan of a sensitive balance, he would find that his weight is constantly changing, increasing with each meal, and then gradually decreasing.

‡ We draw from Nature at once our substance, and the force by which we operate upon her; being, so far, parts of her great system, immersed in it for a short time and to a small extent. Enfolding us, as it were, within her arms, Nature lends us her forces to expend; we receive them, and pass them on, giving them the impress of our will, and bending them to our designs, for a little while; and then——Yes; then it is all one. The great procession pauses not, nor flags a moment, for our fall. The powers which Nature lent to us she resumes to herself, or lends, it may be, to another; the use which we have made of them, or might have made and did not, is written in her book forever.—*Health and its Conditions.*

which it gives up when it is decomposed.* Oxygen
is the magic key which unlocks for our use this hidden store.† Putting food into our bodies is like
placing a tense spring within a watch; every motion
of the body is only a new direction given to this
food-force, as every movement of the hand on the
dial is but the manifestation of the power of the
bent spring in the watch. We use the pent-up energies of meat, bread, and vegetables which are placed
at our service, and transfer them to a higher theater
of action.‡

Kinds of Food Needed.—From what has been
said it is clear that, in order to produce heat and
force, we need something that will burn, *i. e.*, with
which oxygen can combine. Experiment has proved
that to build up every organ, and keep the body

* This force is chemical affinity. It binds together the molecules which
compose the food we eat. When oxygen tears the molecules to pieces and
makes them up into smaller ones, the force is set free. As we shall learn
in Physics, it can be turned into heat, muscular motion, electricity, etc.
The principle that the different kinds of force can be changed into one
another without loss, is called the Conservation of Energy, and is one of
the grandest discoveries of modern science.—*Popular Physics*, pages 35, 39,
278.

† We have spoken of the mystery that envelops the process of the con-
version of food-force into muscular-force (note, p. 107). All physiologists
agree that muscular power has its source in the chemical decomposition of
certain substances whereby their potential energy is released. Probably
some of the food undergoes this chemical change before it passes out of
the alimentary canal; possibly some is broken up by the oxygen while it is
being swept along by the blood; but, probably by far the largest part is
converted into the various tissues of the body, and finally becomes a waste
product only after there takes place in the tissue itself that chemical disorganization that sets free its stored-up power.—FOSTER's *Physiology*.

‡ It is a grand thought that we can thus transform what is common
and gross into the refined and spiritual; that out of waving wheat, wasting
flesh, running water, and dead minerals, we can realize the glorious possibilities of human life.

11

in the best condition, we require three kinds of food.

1. *Nitrogenous Food.*—As nitrogen is a prominent constituent of the tissues of the body, food which contains it is therefore necessary to their growth and repair.* The most common forms are whites of eggs—which are nearly pure albumen; casein—the chief constituent of cheese; lean meat; and gluten —the viscid substance which gives tenacity to dough. Bodies having a great deal of nitrogen readily oxidize. Hence the peculiar character of the quick-changing, force-exciting muscle.

2. *Carbonaceous Food—i. e.,* food containing much carbon—consists of two kinds, viz., the *sugars,* and the *fats.*

(1) *The sugars* contain hydrogen and oxygen in the proportion to form water, and about the same amount of carbon. They may, therefore, be considered as water, with carbon diffused through it. In digestion, starch and gum are changed to sugar, and so are ranked with this class.

(2) *The fats* are like the sugars in composition, but contain less oxygen, and not in the proportion to form water. They combine with more oxygen in burning, and so give off more heat.

The non-nitrogenous elements of the food have, however, other uses than to develop heat.† Fat is

---

* Since this kind of food closely resembles albumen, it is sometimes called *Albuminous.* The term Proteid is also used.

† The heat they produce in burning may be turned into motion of the muscles, according to the principle of the Conservation of Energy (p. 153, note); while all the structures of the body in their oxidation develop heat.

essential to the assimilation of the food, while sugar and starch aid in digestion and may be converted into fat.* Fat and carbonaceous material both enter into the composition of the various tissues, and when, by the breaking-up of the contractile substance of the muscle, their latent energy is set free, they become the source of muscular force, as well as heat. While the tendency of the albuminous food is to excite chemical action, and hence the release of energy, the fats and carbonaceous food may be laid up in the body to serve as a storehouse of energy to supply future needs.

3. *Mineral Matters.*—Food should contain water, and certain common minerals, such as iron,† sulphur, magnesia, phosphorus, salt, and potash. About three pints of water are needed daily to dissolve the food and carry it through the circulation, to float off waste matter, to lubricate the tissues, and by evaporation to cool the system (see p. 317). It also enters largely into the composition of the body. A man weighing one hundred and fifty-four pounds contains one hundred pounds of water, about twelve gallons—enough, if rightly arranged, to drown him.‡

Iron goes to the blood disks; lime combines with

---

* In Turkey, the ladies of the harem are fed on honey and thick gruel, to make flesh, which is considered to enhance their beauty. The negroes on the sugar plantations of the South always grow fat during the sugar-making season.

† While the body can build up a solid from liquid materials on the one hand, on the other it can pour iron through its veins and reduce the hardest textures to blood.—HINTON.

‡ It is said that Blumenbach had a perfect mummy of an adult Teneriffian, which with the viscera weighed only seven and a half pounds.

phosphoric and carbonic acids to give solidity to the bones and teeth; phosphorus is essential to the activity of the brain. Salt is necessary to the secretion of some of the digestive fluids, and also to aid in working off from the system its waste products. These various minerals, except iron — sometimes given as a medicine, and salt—universally used as a condiment,* are contained in small, but sufficient quantities in meat, bread, and vegetables.

One Kind of Food is Insufficient.—A person fed on starch alone, would die. It would be a clear case of nitrogen starvation. On the other hand, as nitrogenous food contains carbon, the elements of water, and various mineral matters, life could be supported

* Animals will travel long distances to obtain salt. Men will barter gold for it; indeed, among the Gallas and on the coast of Sierra Leone, brothers will sell their sisters, husbands their wives, and parents their children for salt. In the district of Accra, on the gold coast of Africa, a handful of salt is the most valuable thing upon earth after gold, and will purchase a slave. Mungo Park tells us that with the Mandingoes and Bambaras the use of salt is such a luxury that to say of a man "he flavors his food with salt," it is to imply that he is rich; and children will suck a piece of rock-salt as if it were sugar. No stronger mark of respect or affection can be shown in Muscovy, than the sending of salt from the tables of the rich to their poorer friends. In the book of Leviticus it is expressly commanded as one of the ordinances of Moses, that every oblation of meat upon the altar shall be seasoned with salt, without lacking; and hence it is called the Salt of the Covenant of God. The Greeks and Romans also used salt in their sacrificial cakes; and it is still used in the services of the Latin church—the "*parva mica*," or pinch of salt, being in the ceremony of baptism, put into the child's mouth, while the priest says, "Receive the salt of wisdom, and may it be a propitiation to thee for eternal life." Every-where and almost always, indeed, it has been regarded as emblematical of wisdom, wit, and immortality. To taste a man's salt, was to be bound by the rites of hospitality; and no oath was more solemn than that which was sworn upon bread and salt. To sprinkle the meat with salt was to drive away the devil, and to this day, nothing is more unlucky than to spill the salt.—LETHEBY, *On Food.*

on that alone.   But such a prodigious quantity of lean meat, for example, would be required to furnish the other elements, that not only would it be very expensive, but it is likely that after a time the labor of digestion would be too onerous, and the system would give up the task in despair. The need of a diet containing both nitrogenous and carbonaceous elements is shown in the fact that even in the tropical regions oil is relished as a dressing upon salad. Instinct every-where suggests the blending. Butter is used with bread ;   rice is boiled with milk ; cheese is eaten with maccaroni, and beans are baked with pork.

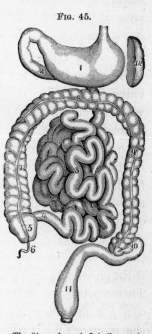

Fig. 45.

The Stomach and Intestines. **1,** *stomach ; 2, duodenum ; 3, small intestine ; 4, termination of the ileum; 5, cæcum ; 6, vermiform appendix ; 7, ascending colon ; 8, transverse colon ; 9, descending colon ; 10, sigmoid flexure of the colon ; 11, rectum; 12, spleen—a gland whose action is not understood.*—LEIDY'S *Anatomy.*

The Object of Digestion. —If our food were cast directly into the blood, it could not be used. For example, although the chemist can not see wherein the albumen of the egg differs from the albumen of the blood, yet if it be injected into the veins it is unavailable for the purposes required, and is thrown out again. In the course of digestion the food is modified in various ways whereby it is fitted for the use of the body, into which it is finally incorporated. We call this change of food into flesh *assimilation*, a name for a work done solely by the vital organs, and so mysterious in its nature that the wisest physiologist gets only glimpses here and there of its operations.

The General Plan of Digestion.—Nature has provided for this purpose an entire laboratory, furnished with a chemist's outfit of knives, mortars, baths, chemicals, filters, etc. The food is (1) chewed, mixed with the saliva in the mouth, and swallowed; (2) it is acted upon by the gastric juice in the stomach; (3) it is passed into the intestines, where it receives the bile, pancreatic juice, and other liquids which completely dissolve it;* (4) the nourishing part is absorbed in the stomach and intestines, and thence thrown into the blood-vessels, whence it is whirled through the body by the torrent of the circulation. These processes take place within the *alimentary canal*, a narrow tortuous tube which commences at the mouth, and is about thirty feet long.†

---

* Digestion, says Berzelius, is a process of rinsing. The digestive apparatus secretes, and again absorbs with the food which it has dissolved, not less than three gallons of liquid per day.—BARNARD, BIDDER, SCHMIDT, and others.

† The digestive apparatus is lined with mucous membrane that possesses functions similar to those of the outer skin. It absorbs certain substances and rejects waste matter. On account of this close connection between the inner and the outer skin, it is not surprising to find that in the lowest animals digestion is performed by means of the external skin. The amœba, which is merely a gelatinous mass, when it takes its food, extemporizes a stomach for the occasion. It simply wraps itself around the morsel, and, like an animated apple-dumpling with the apple for food and the crust for animal, goes on with the process until the operation is completed, when it unrolls itself again and lets the indigestible residue escape.

I. Mastication and Insalivation.—1. *The Saliva.*—
The food while being cut and ground by the teeth
is mixed with the saliva. This is a thin, colorless,
frothy, slightly alkaline liquid, secreted * by the mucous membrane lining
the mouth, and by
three pairs of salivary
glands (parotid, sub-
maxillary, and sublin-
gual) opening into the
mouth through ducts,
or tubes. The amount
varies, but on the av-
erage is about three
pounds per day, and
in health is always

Fig. 46.

The Parotid—one of the salivary glands.

sufficient to keep the mouth moist.† It softens and
dissolves the food, and thus enables us to get the
flavor or taste of what we eat. It contains a peculiar organic principle called *ptyaline,*‡ which, acting

The common hydra of our brooks can live when turned inside out, like a
glove; either side serving for skin or stomach, as necessity requires.

  * By secretion is meant merely a separation or picking out from the
blood.

  † The presence and often the thought of food will "make one's mouth
water." Fear checks the flow of saliva, and hence the East Indians sometimes attempt to detect theft by making those who are suspected chew
rice. The person from whom it comes out driest is adjudged the thief.

  ‡ One part of ptyaline will convert eight thousand parts of starch into
sugar.—MIALHE.

The saliva has no chemical action on the fats or the albuminous bodies.
Its frothiness enables it to carry oxygen into the stomach, and this is
thought to be of service. The action of the ptyaline commences with great
promptness, and sugar has been detected, it is said, within half a minute
after the starch was placed in the mouth. The process, however, is not
finished there, but continues after reaching the stomach.—VALENTIN. The

upon the starch of the food, changes it into glucose or grape-sugar.

2. *The Process of Swallowing.*—The food thus finely pulverized, softened, and so lubricated by the viscid saliva as to prevent friction as it passes over the delicate membranes, is conveyed by the tongue and cheek to the back of the mouth. The soft palate lifts to close the nasal opening; the epiglottis shuts down, and along this bridge the food is borne, without danger of falling into the windpipe or escaping into the nose. The muscular bands of the throat now seize it and take it beyond our control. The fibers of the œsophagus contract above, while they are lax below, and convey the food by a worm-like motion into the stomach.*

II. Gastric Digestion.—1. *The Stomach* is an irregular expansion of the digestive tube. Its shape has been compared to that of a bagpipe. It holds about three pints, though it is susceptible of some distension. It is composed of an inner, mucous membrane, which secretes the digestive fluids; an outer, smooth, well-lubricated serous one, which prevents friction, and between them a stout, muscular coat. The last consists of two principal layers of longitudinal and circular fibers. When these contract, they produce a peculiar churning motion, called the *peristaltic* (*peri*, round; *stallein*, to ar-

saliva thus prepares a small portion of food for absorption at once, and so insures at the very beginning of the operation of digestion a supply of force-producing material for the immediate use of the system.

　* We can observe the peculiar motion of the œsophagus by watching a horse's neck when he is drinking.

Fig. 47.

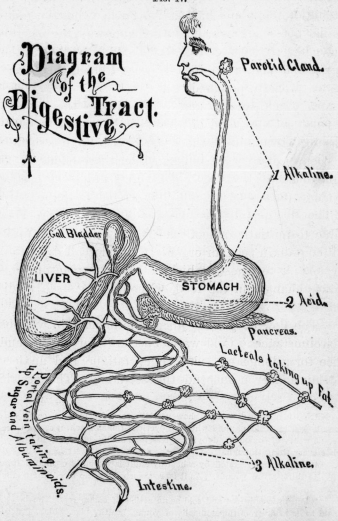

Diagram of the Digestion of the Food.   Notice how the food is submitted to the action of alkaline, acid, and then alkaline fluids.   (See note, p. 165.)

range) movement, which thoroughly mixes the contents of the stomach. At the farther end, the muscular fibers contract and form a gate-way, the *pylorus* (a gate), as it is called, which carefully guards the exit, and allows no food to pass from the stomach until properly prepared.*

2. *The Gastric Juice.*—The lining of the stomach is soft, velvety, and of a pinkish hue; but, as soon as food is admitted, the blood-vessels fill, the surface becomes of a bright red, and soon there exudes from the gastric glands a thin, colorless fluid—the gastric juice. (See p. 319.) This is secreted to the amount of twelve pounds per day.† Its acidity is probably due to muriatic or lactic acid—the acid of sour milk. It contains a peculiar organic principle called *pepsin* ‡ (*peptein*, to digest), which acts as a ferment to produce changes in the food, without being itself modified.

The flow of gastric juice is influenced by various circumstances. Cold water checks it for a time, and ice for a longer period. Anger, fatigue, and anxiety delay and even suspend the secretion. The gastric

* With a wise discretion, however, it opens for buttons, coins, etc., swallowed by accident; and when we overload the stomach, it seems to become weary of constantly denying egress, and, finally, giving up in despair, lets every thing through.

† The amount secreted by a healthy adult is variously estimated from five to thirty-seven pounds. As it is re-absorbed by the blood, there is no loss.

‡ Pepsin is prepared and sold as an article of commerce. The best is said to be made from the stomachs of young, healthy pigs, which, just before being killed, are excited with savory food that they are not allowed to eat. One grain is sufficient to dissolve eight hundred grains of coagulated white of egg. A temperature of 130° renders pepsin inert.

juice has no effect on the fats or the sugars of the food; its influence being mainly confined to the albuminous bodies, which it so changes that they become soluble in water.*

The food, reduced by the action of the gastric juice to a grayish, soupy mass, called *chyme* (kīme), escapes through that jealously-guarded door, the pylorus.

III. Intestinal Digestion.—The structure of the intestines is like that of the stomach. There is the same outer, smooth, serous membrane (peritoneum) to prevent friction, the lining of mucous membrane to secrete the digestive fluids, and the muscular coating to push

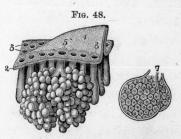

FIG. 48.

A vertical Section of the Duodenum, highly magnified. 1, a fold-like villus; 2, epithelium, or cuticle; 3, orifices of intestinal glands; 5, orifice of duodenal glands; 4, 7, more highly magnified sections of the cells of a duodenal gland.

the food forward. The intestines are divided into the *small,* and the *large.* The first part of the former opens out of the stomach, and is called the *du-o-de'-num,* as its length is equal to the breadth of twelve fingers. Here the chyme is acted upon by the *bile,* and the *pancreatic juice.*

---

* The question is often asked why the stomach itself is not digested by the gastric juice, since it belongs to the albuminous substances. Some have assigned as the probable reason that life protects that organ, and assert that living tissues can not be digested; but the fallacy of this has been clearly shown by experiments that have been made with living tissues in the course of scientific research. The latest opinion is that the blood which circulates so freely through the vessels of the lining of the stomach, being alkaline, protects the tissue against the acidity of the gastric juice.

1. *The Bile* is secreted by the liver. This gland weighs about four pounds, and is the largest in the body. It is located on the right side, below the diaphragm. The bile is of a dark, golden color, and

FIG. 49.

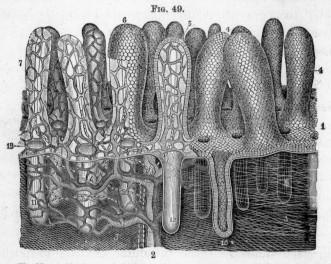

The Mucous Membrane of the Ilium, highly magnified. 1, *cellular structure of the epithelium, or outer layer ;* 2, *a vein ;* 3, *fibrous layer ;* 4, *villi covered with epithelium ;* 5, *a villus in section, showing its lining of epithelium, with its blood-vessels and lymphatics ;* 6, *a villus partially uncovered ;* 7, *a villus stripped of its epithelium ;* 8, *lymphatics or lacteals ;* 9, *orifices of the glands opening between the villi ;* 10, 11, 12, *glands ;* 13, *capillaries surrounding the orifices of the gland.*

bitter taste. About three pounds are secreted per day. When not needed for digestion, it is stored in the gall cyst.* Its action on the food, though not fully understood, is necessary to life.†

* A gall-bladder can be obtained from a butcher, and the contents kept in a bottle for examination.

† The bile is produced, unlike all the other animal secretions, from venous blood; that is, the already contaminated blood of the portal vein. Its complete suppression produces symptoms of poisoning analogous to those which follow the stoppage of respiration, and the patient dies,

2. *The Pancreatic Juice* is a secretion of the pancreas, or "sweet-bread"—a gland nearly as large as the hand, lying behind the stomach. It is alkaline, and contains a ferment called *trypsin*. This juice has the power of changing starch to sugar. Its main work, however, is in breaking up the globules of fat into myriads of minute particles, that mix freely with water, and remain suspended in it like butter in new milk. The whole mass now assumes a milky look, whence it is termed *chyle* (kīle), and passes on to the small intestine.*

3. *The Small Intestine* is an intricately-folded tube, about twenty feet long, and from an inch to an inch and one half in diameter. As the chyle passes through this tortuous channel, it receives along the entire route secretions which seem to combine the action of all the previous ones—starch, fat, and albumen being equally affected.

IV. Absorption is performed in two ways, by the *veins*, and the *lacteals*. (1.) The veins in the stom-

---

usually in a comatose condition, at the end of ten or twelve days.—DALTON. The alkaline bile neutralizes the acid contents of the stomach as they flow into the duodenum, and thus prepares the way for the pancreatic juice. It has also a slight emulsifying power (note, p. 167).

* It is curious to observe that while the gastric juice is decidedly acid, the fluids with which the food next comes into contact are alkaline. It is thus submitted to the operation alternately of alkaline, acid, and again of alkaline secretions. In the herbivora there is also a second acid juice. The reason of these alternations is not known, but it can hardly be doubted that they serve to make the digestion of the food more perfect. And although the solvent power of the gastric juice is placed in abeyance when its acidity is neutralized by the alkaline fluids, yet it appears to be the case here, as in respect to the saliva, that effects are produced by the mixture of the various secretions which are poured together into the digestive tube, that would not result from either alone.—HINTON.

ach* immediately begin to take up the water, salt, grape-sugar, and other substances that need no special preparation. The starch and the albuminous bodies are also absorbed as they are properly digested, and this process continues along the whole length of the alimentary canal. In the small intestine, there is a multitude of tiny projections (*villi*) from the folds of the mucous membrane, more than seven thousand to the square inch, giving it a soft, velvety look. These little rootlets, reaching out into the milky fluid, drink into their minute blood-vessels the nutritious part of every sort of food. (2.) The lacteals† (p. 126), a set of vessels starting in the villi side by side with the veins, absorb the principal part of the fat. They convey the chyle through the lymphatics and the thoracic duct (Fig. 43) to the veins, and so within the sweep of the circulation.

The Portal Vein‡ carries to the liver the food absorbed by the veins of the stomach and the villi of the intestines. On the way, it is greatly modified by the action of the blood itself. In the cells of the liver, it undergoes as mysterious a process as that performed by the lymphatic glands, and is then cast

---

* The veins and the lacteals are separated from the food by a thin, moist membrane, through the pores of which the fluid-food rapidly passes, in accordance with a beautiful law ("Popular Physics," p. 53) called the *Osmose* of liquids. If two liquids of different densities are separated by an animal membrane, they will mix with considerable force. There is a similar law regulating the interchange of gases through a porous partition, in obedience to which the carbonic acid of the blood, and the oxygen of the lungs, are exchanged through the thin membrane of the air-cells.

† From *lac*, milk, because of the milky look given to their contents by the chyle.

‡ So named because it enters the liver by a sort of gate-way.

into the circulation.* The food, potent with force, is now buried in that river of life from which the body springs momentarily afresh.

The Complexity of the process of digestion, as compared with the simplicity of respiration and circulation, is very marked. The mechanical operation of mastication; the lubrication of the food by mucus; the provision for the security of the respiratory organs; the grasping by the muscles of the throat; the churning movement of the stomach; the guardianship of the pylorus; the timely introduction by safe and protected channels of the saliva, the gastric juice, the bile, the pancreatic juice, and the intestinal fluids, each with its special adaptation; the curious peristaltic motion of the intestines; the twofold absorption by the veins and the lacteals; the final transformation in the lymphatics, the portal vein, and the liver,—all these present a complexity of detail, the necessity of which can be explained only when we reflect upon the variety of the substances we use for food, and the importance of its thorough preparation before it is allowed to enter the blood.

The Length of Time Required for digesting a full meal is from two to four hours. It varies with the kind of food, state of the system, perfection of mastication, etc. In the celebrated observations made

---

* In these cells, the sugar is changed into a kind of starch called *glycogen*. This is insoluble, and so is stored up in the liver, and even in the substance of the muscles, until it is needed by the body, when it is once more converted into soluble sugar and taken up by the circulation. The liver also changes the waste and surplus albuminous matter into bile, and into urea and uric acid—the forms in which nitrogenized waste is excreted by the kidneys.

upon Alexis St. Martin* by Dr. Beaumont, his stomach was found empty in two and a half hours after a meal of roast turkey, potatoes, and bread. Pigs' feet and boiled rice were disposed of in an hour. Fresh, sweet apples took one and a half hours; boiled milk, two hours; and unboiled, a quarter of an hour longer. In eggs, which occupied the same time, the case was reversed,—raw ones being digested sooner than cooked. Roast beef and mutton required three and three and a quarter hours respectively; veal, salt beef, and broiled chicken remained for four hours; and roast pork enjoyed the bad preeminence of needing five and a quarter hours.

Value of the Different Kinds of Food.—*Beef* and *Mutton* possess the greatest nutritive value of any of the meat. *Lamb* is less strengthening, but more delicate. Like the young of all animals, it should be thoroughly cooked, and at a high temperature, properly to develop its delicious flavor. *Pork* has much carbon. It sometimes contains a parasite called trichina, which may be transferred to the human system, producing disease and often death.

---

* In 1822, Alexis St. Martin, a Canadian in the employ of the American Fur Company, was accidentally shot in the left side. Two years after, the wound was entirely healed, leaving, however, an opening about two and a half inches in circumference into the stomach. Through this the mucous membrane protruded, forming a kind of valve which prevented the discharge of food, but could be readily depressed by the finger, thus exposing the interior. For several years he was under the care of Dr. Beaumont, a skillful physician, who experimented upon him by giving various kinds of food, and watching their digestion through this opening. By means of these observations, and others performed on Katherine Kutt, a woman who had a similar aperture in the stomach, we have very important information as to the digestibility of different kinds of food.

The only preventive is thorough cooking. *Fish* is more watery than flesh, and many find it difficult of digestion. Like meat, it loses its mineral constituents and natural juices when salted, and is much less nourishing. Oysters are highly nutritious, but are more easily assimilated when raw than when cooked. *Milk* is a model food, as it contains albumen, starch, fat, and mineral matter. No single substance can sustain life for so long a time. *Cheese* is very nourishing—one pound being equal in value to two of meat, but it is not adapted to a weak stomach. (See p. 322.) *Eggs* are most easily digested when the white is barely coagulated and the yolk is unchanged. *Bread** should be made of unbolted flour. The bran of wheat furnishes the mineral matter we need in our bones and teeth, gives the bulk so essential to the proper distension of the organs, and by its roughness gently stimulates them to action. *Corn* is rich in fat. It contains, however, more indigestible matter than any other grain, except oats, and is less nutritious than wheat.† The *Potato* is two thirds

---

* Very fresh bread, warm biscuit, etc., are condensed by mastication into a pasty mass that is not easily penetrated by the gastric juice, and hence they are not healthful. In Germany bread is not allowed to be sold at the baker's till it is twenty-four hours old—a wise provision for those who have not strength to resist temptation. This rule of eating may well be adopted by every one who cares more for his health than for a gratification of his appetite.

† Persons unaccustomed to the use of corn find it liable to produce derangement of the digestive organs. This was made fearfully apparent in the prisons of Andersonville during the late civil war. The vegetable food of the Federal prisoners had hitherto been chiefly wheat bread and potatoes—the corn bread so extensively used at the South being quite new to most of them as a constant article of diet. It soon became not only loathsome, but productive of serious diseases. On the other hand, it was the

water,—the rest being mainly starch. *Ripe Fruits*, and those vegetables usually eaten raw, dilute the more concentrated food, and also supply the blood with acids, which are cooling in summer, and useful, perhaps, in assimilation.

The Stimulants. — *Coffee* is about half nitrogen, and the rest fatty, saccharine, and mineral substances. It is, therefore, of much nutritive value, especially when taken with milk and sugar. Its peculiar stimulating property is due to a principle called *caffeine*. Its aroma is developed by browning, but destroyed by burning. No other substance so soon relieves the sense of fatigue.* Taken in moderation, it clears the intellect, tranquilizes the nerves, and usually leaves no unpleasant reaction. It serves also as a kind of negative food, since it retards the process of waste.

In some cases, however, it produces a rush of blood to the head, and should be at once discarded. At the close of a full meal it hinders digestion, and at night produces wakefulness. In youth, when the vital powers are strong, and the functions of nature prompt in rallying from fatigue, it is not needed, and may be injurious in stimulating a sensitive organization.

Tea possesses an active principle called *theine*.

---

principal article in the rations of the Confederate soldiers, to whom habit made it a nutritious and wholesome form of food, as was shown by their endurance.—FLINT, *Physiology of Man*, Vol. II., page 41.

* In the late civil war, the first desire of the soldiers upon halting after a wearisome march, was to make a cup of coffee. This was taken without milk, and often without sugar, yet was always welcome.

When used moderately, its effects are similar to those of coffee, except that it exerts an astringent action. It contains tannin, which, if the tea is strong, coagulates the albumen of the food—*tans* it —and thus delays digestion. In excess, tea causes nervous tremor, disturbed sleep, palpitation of the heart, and indigestion.* (See p. 322.)

Chocolate contains much fat, and also nitrogenous matter resembling albumen. Its active principle, *theobromine,*† has some of the properties of caffeine and theine.

The Cooking of Food breaks the little cells, and softens the fibers of which it is composed. In broiling or roasting meat, it should be exposed to a strong heat at once, in order to coagulate the albumen upon the outside, and thus prevent the escape of the nutritious juices. The cooking may then be finished at a lower temperature. The same principle applies to boiling meat. In making soups, on the contrary, the heat should be applied slowly, and should reach the boiling point for only a few moments at the close. This prevents the coagulation of the albumen. Frying is an unhealthful mode of cooking food, as thereby the fat becomes partially disorganized.

---

* Tea and coffee should be made with boiling water, but should not be boiled afterward. During the "steeping" process, so customary in this country, the volatile aroma is lost and a bitter principle extracted. In both England and China it is usual to infuse tea directly in the urn from which it is to be drawn. The tannin in tea is shown when a drop falls on a knife-blade. The black spot is a tannate of iron—a compound of the acid in the tea and the metal.

† It is said that Linnæus, the great botanist, was so fond of chocolate that he named the cocoa-tree "Theobroma," the food of the gods.

Rapid Eating produces many evil results. 1. There is not enough saliva mixed with the food; 2. The coarse pieces resist the action of the digestive fluids; 3. The food is washed down with drinks that dilute the gastric juice, and hinder its work; 4. We do not appreciate the quantity we eat until the stomach is overloaded; 5. Failing to get the taste of our food, we think it insipid, and hence use condiments that over-stimulate the digestive organs. In these various ways the appetite becomes depraved, the stomach vexed, the system overworked, and the foundation of dyspepsia is laid.* (See p. 324.)

The Quantity and Quality of Food required vary with the age and habits of each individual. The diet of a child† should be largely vegetable, and more abundant than that of an aged person. A sedentary occupation necessitates less food than an out-door life. One accustomed to manual labor, on entering school, should practice self-denial until his system becomes fitted to the new order of things. He should not, however, fall into the opposite error. We read of great men who have lived on bread and water, and the conscientious student sometimes thinks that, to be great, he, too, must starve himself.‡ On the contrary, many of the greatest workers

* When one is compelled to eat in a hurry, as at a railway station, he would do well to confine himself principally to meat; and to dilute this concentrated food with fruit, crackers, etc., taken afterward more leisurely.

† In youth, repair exceeds waste; hence the body grows rapidly, and the form is plump. In middle life, repair and waste equal each other, and growth ceases. In old age, waste exceeds repair; hence the powers are enfeebled and the skin lies in wrinkles on the shrunken form.

‡ As Dr. Holland well remarks, the dispensation of saw-dust has passed

are the greatest eaters. A powerful engine needs a corresponding furnace. Only, we should be careful not to use more fuel than is needed to run the machine. (See p. 325.)

The season should modify our diet. In winter, we need highly carbonaceous food, plenty of meat, fat, etc.; but in summer we should temper the heat in our corporeal stoves with fruits and vegetables.

The climate also has its necessities. The inhabitants of the frigid north have an almost insatiable longing for fat.* Thus, in 1812, when the Allies entered Paris, the Cossacks drank all the oil from the lamps, and left the streets in darkness. In tropical regions, a low, unstimulating diet of fruits forms the chief dependence.†

away. If we desire a horse to win the race, we must give him plenty of oats.

* Dr. Hayes, the arctic explorer, says, that the daily ration of the Esquimaux was from twelve to fifteen pounds of meat, one third being fat. On one occasion, he saw a man eat ten pounds of walrus flesh and blubber at a single meal. The low temperature had a remarkable effect on the members of his own party, and some of them were in the habit of drinking the contents of the oil-kettle with evident relish. Other travelers narrate the most incredible stories of the voracity of the inhabitants of arctic regions. Saritcheff, a Russian admiral, tells of a man who in his presence ate, at a meal, a mess of twenty-eight pounds of boiled rice and butter, although he had already partaken of his breakfast. Captain Cochrane further adds, in narrating this statement, that he has himself seen three of the savages consume a reindeer at a sitting.

† A natural appetite for a particular kind of food is an expression not only of desire, but of fitness. Thus the craving of childhood for sugar indicates a need of the system. It is questionable how far it is proper to force or persuade one to eat that which he disrelishes, or his stomach loathes. Life within is linked with life without. Each organ requires its peculiar nutriment, and there is often a peculiar influence demanded of which we can have no notice except by natural instinct. Yet, as we are creatures of habit and impulse, we need common sense and good judgment to correct the too often wayward promptings of an artificial craving.

When Food should be Taken.—On taking food, the blood sets at once to the alimentary canal, and the energies are fixed upon the proper performance of this work. We should not, therefore, undertake hard study, labor, or exercise directly after a hearty meal. We should give the stomach at least half an hour. He who toils with brain or muscle, and thus centers the blood in any particular organ, before eating, should allow time for the circulation to become equalized. There should be an interval of four to five hours between our regular meals, and there should be no lunching between times. With young children, where the vital processes are more rapid, less time may intervene. As a general rule, nothing should be eaten within two or three hours of retiring. (See p 336.)

How Food should be Taken.—A good laugh is the best of sauces. The meal-time should be the happiest hour of the day. Care and grief are the bitter foes of digestion. A cheerful face and a light heart are friends to long life, and nowhere do they serve us better than at the table. God designed that we should enjoy eating, and that, having stopped before satiety was reached, we should have the satisfaction always attendant on a good work well done.

Need of a Variety.—Careful investigations have shown that any one kind of food, however nutritious in itself, fails after a time to preserve the highest working power of the body. Our appetite palls when we confine our diet to a regular routine. Nature

demands variety, and she has furnished the means
of gratifying it.*

The Wonders of Digestion.—We can understand
much of the process of digestion. We can look into
the stomach and trace its various steps. Indeed, the
chemist can reproduce in his laboratory many of the
operations; "a step further," as Fontenelle has said,
"and he would surprise nature in the very act."
Just here, when he seems so successful, he is compelled to pause. At the threshold of life the wisest
physiologist reverently admires, wonders, and wor-
ships.

How strange is this transformation of food to
flesh! We make a meal of meat, vegetables, and
drink. Ground by the teeth, mixed by the stomach,
dissolved by the digestive fluids, it is swept through
the body. Each organ, as it passes, snatches its particular food. Within the cells of the tissues † it is

---

* She opens her hand, and pours forth to man the treasures of every
land and every sea, because she would give to him a wide and vigorous
life, participant of all variety. For him the corn-fields wave their golden
grain—wheat, rye, oats, maize, or rice, each different, but alike sufficing.
Freely for him the palm, the date, the banana, the bread-fruit tree, the
pine, spread out a harvest on the air; and pleasant apple, plum, or peach
solicit his ready hand. Beneath his foot lie stored the starch of the potato,
the gluten of the turnip, the sugar of the beet; while all the intermediate
space is rich with juicy herbs.

Nature bids him eat and be merry; adding to his feast the solid flesh
of bird, and beast, and fish, prepared as victims for the sacrifice: firm
muscle to make strong the arm of toil, in the industrious temperate zone;
and massive ribs of fat to kindle inward fires for the sad dwellers under
arctic skies.—*Health and its Conditions.*—HINTON.

† As the body is composed of individual organs, and each organ of separate tissues, so each tissue is made up of minute cells. Each cell is a little
world by itself, too small to be seen by the naked eye, but open to the
microscope. It has its own form and constitution as much as a special

transformed into the soft, sensitive brain, or the hard, callous bone; into briny tears, or bland saliva, or acrid perspiration; bile for digestion, oil for the hair, nails for the fingers, and flesh for the cheek.

Within us is an Almighty Architect, who superintends a thousand builders, which make in a way past all human comprehension, here a fiber of a muscle, there a filament of a nerve; here constructing a bone, there uniting a tendon,—fashioning each with scrupulous care and unerring nicety.* So, without sound of builder or stroke of hammer, goes up, day by day, the body—the glorious temple of the soul.

Diseases, etc. — 1. *Dyspepsia*, or indigestion of food, is generally caused by an over-taxing of the digestive organs. Too much food is used, and the entire system is burdened by the excess. Meals are taken at irregular hours, when the fluids are not ready. A hearty supper is eaten when the body, wearied with the day's labor, demands rest. The appetite craves no food when the digestion is enfeebled, but stimulants and condiments excite it, and the unwilling organs are oppressed by that which they can not properly manage.

Strong tea, alcoholic drinks, and tobacco derange the alimentary function.

organ in the body. It absorbs from the blood such food as suits its purposes. Moreover, the number of cells in an organ is as constant as the number of organs. As the organs expand with the growth of the body, so the cells of each tissue enlarge, but shrink again with age and the decline of life. Life begins and ends in a cell.—See *Appletons' Cyclopedia*, Art. "Absorption."

* See COOKE's *Religion and Chemistry*, page 236.

Too great variety of dishes, rich food, tempting flavors,—all lead to an overloading of the stomach. This patient, long-suffering member at last wears out. Pain, discomfort, diseases of the digestive organs, and insufficient nutrition are the penalties of violated laws. (See p. 328.)

2. *The Mumps* are an inflammation of the parotid and submaxillary glands (see p. 159). The disease is generally epidemic, and is believed to be contagious; the patient should therefore be carefully secluded for the sake of others as well as himself. The swelling may be allowed to take its course. Relief from pain is often experienced by applying flannels wrung out of hot water. Great care should be used not to check the inflammation, and, on first going out after recovery, not to take cold.

ALCOHOLIC DRINKS AND NARCOTICS.

1. ALCOHOL (Continued from p. 147).

Relation of Alcohol to the Digestive Organs.— *Is Alcohol a Food?* To answer this question, let us make a comparison. If you receive into your stomach a piece of bread or beef, Nature welcomes its presence. The juices of the system at once take hold of it, dissolve it, and transform it for the uses of the body. A million tiny fingers (lacteals and veins) reach out to grasp it, work it over, and carry it into the circulation. The blood bears it onward wherever it is needed to mend or to build "The house you live

in." Soon, it is no longer bread or beef; it is flesh
on your arm; its chemical energy is imparted to
you, and it becomes your strength.

If, on the other hand, you take into your stomach
a little alcohol, it receives no such welcome. Nature
treats it as a poison, and seeks to rid herself of the
intruder as soon as possible.* The juices of the system will flow from every pore to dilute and weaken
it, and to prevent its shriveling up the delicate
membranes with which it comes in contact. The
veins will take it up and bear it rapidly through
the system. Every organ of elimination, all the
scavengers of the body—the lungs, the kidneys, the
perspiration-glands, at once set to work to throw off
the enemy. So surely is this the case, that the
breath of a person who has drunk only a single
glass of the lightest beer will betray the fact.

The alcohol thus eliminated is entirely unchanged.
Nature apparently makes no effort to appropriate

* Food is digested, alcohol is not. Food warms the blood, directly or
indirectly; alcohol lowers the temperature. Food nourishes the body, in
the sense of assimilating itself to the tissues; alcohol does not. Food
makes blood; alcohol never does any thing more innocent than mixing with
it. Food feeds the blood-cells; alcohol destroys them. Food excites, in
health, to normal action only; alcohol tends to inflammation and disease.
Food gives force to the body; alcohol excites reaction and wastes force, in
the first place, and in the second, as a true narcotic, represses vital action
and corresponding nutrition.—If alcohol does not act like food, neither does
it behave like water. Water is the subtle but innocent vehicle of circulation, which dissolves the solid food, holds in play the chemical and vital re-
actions of the tissues, conveys the nutritive solutions from cell to cell, from
tube to tube, and carries off and expels the effete matter. Water neither
irritates tissue, wastes force, nor suppresses vital action: whereas alcohol
does all three. Alcohol hardens solid tissue, thickens the blood, narcotizes
the nerves, and in every conceivable direction antagonizes the operation
and function of water.—LEES.

it.* It courses every-where through the circulation, and into the great organs, with all its properties unmodified.

Alcohol, then, is not, like bread or beef, taken hold of, broken up by the mysterious process of digestion, and used by the body.† "It can not therefore be regarded as an aliment," or food.—FLINT. "Beer, wine, and spirits," says Liebig, "contain no element capable of entering into the composition of the blood or the muscular fiber."‡ "That alcohol is incapable of forming any part of the body," remarks Cameron, "is admitted by all physiologists. It can not be converted into brain, nerve, muscle, or blood."

* It was formerly a question considerably discussed, whether alcohol exists in the brain, or in the fluid found in the ventricles, in intoxicated persons. This was settled by Percy, who found alcohol in the brain and liver of dogs poisoned with alcohol, and of men who had died after excessive drinking. In these experiments, the presence of alcohol was determined by distillation, and the distilled substance burned with a blue flame, and dissolved camphor.—FLINT'S *Physiology of Man.*

† Because of the difficulties of such an experiment, we have not yet been able to account satisfactorily by the excretions for all the alcohol taken into the stomach. This remains as yet one of the unsolved problems of physiological chemistry. To collect the whole of the insensible perspiration, for example, is well-nigh impossible. It was supposed at one time that a part of the alcohol is oxidized—*i. e.*, burned, in the system. But such a process would impart heat, and it is now proved that alcohol cools, instead of warms, the blood. Moreover, the closest analysis fails to detect in the circulation any trace of the products of alcoholic combustion, such as aldehyde and acetic acid. "The fact," says Flint, "that alcohol is always eliminated, even when drunk in minute quantity, and that its elimination continues for a considerable time, gradually diminishing, renders it probable that all that is taken into the body is removed."

‡ The small amount of nutritive substance, chiefly sugar derived from the grain or fruit used in the manufacture of beer or wine, can not, of course, be compared with that contained in bread or beef at the same cost. Liebig says, in his Letters on Chemistry, " We can prove, with mathematical certainty, that as much flour as can lie on the point of a table-knife is more nutritious than eight quarts of the best Bavarian beer."

Effect upon the Digestion.*—Experiments tend to prove that alcohol coagulates and precipitates the pepsin from the gastric juice, and so puts a stop to its great work in the process of digestion.

The greed of alcohol for water causes it to imbibe moisture from the tissues and juices, and to inflame the delicate mucous membrane. It shows the power of Nature to adapt herself to circumstances, that the soft, velvety lining of the throat and stomach should come at length to endure the presence of a fiery liquid which, undiluted, would soon shrivel and destroy it. In self-defense, the juices pour in to weaken the alcohol, and it is soon hurried into the circulation. Before this can be done, "it must absorb about three times its bulk of water"; hence, very strong liquor may be retained in the stomach long enough to interfere seriously with the digestion, and to injure the lining coat. Habitual use of alco-

* The medical value of alcohol in its relations to digestion is not discussed in this book. The experiments of Dr. Henry Munroe, of Hull, published in the London *Medical Journal*, are here summarized as showing that the tendency to retard digestion is common to all forms of alcholic drinks.

Finely Minced Beef.	2d Hour.	4th Hour.	6th Hour.	8th Hour.	10th Hour.
I. Gastric juice and *water*.	Beef opaque.	Digesting and separating.	Beef much loosened.	Broken up into shreds.	Dissolved like soup.
II. Gastric juice with *alcohol*.	No alteration perceptible.	Slightly opaque, but beef unchanged.	Slight coating on beef.	No visible change.	Solid on cooling. *Pepsin* precipitated.
III. Gastric juice and *pale ale*.	No change.	Cloudy, with fur on beef.	Beef partly loosened.	No further change.	No digestion. *Pepsin* precipitated.

hol permanently dilates the blood-vessels; thickens and hardens the membranes; in some cases, ulcerates the surface; and, finally, "so weakens the assimilation that the proper supply of food can not be appropriated."—FLINT.*

Effect upon the Liver.—Alcohol is carried by the portal vein directly to the liver. This organ, after the brain, holds the largest share. The influence of the poison is here easily traced. "The color of the bile is soon changed from yellow to green, and even to black;" the connective tissue between the lobules becomes inflamed; and, in the case of a confirmed drunkard, hardened and shrunk, the surface often assuming a nodulated appearance known as the "hob-nailed liver." Morbid matter is sometimes deposited, causing what is called "Fatty degeneration," so that the liver is increased to twice or thrice its natural size.

Effect upon the Kidneys.—The kidneys, like the liver, are liable in time to undergo, through the influence of alcohol, a "Fatty degeneration," in which the cells become filled with particles of fat;† the

---

* The case of St. Martin (p. 168) gave an excellent opportunity to watch the action of alcohol upon the stomach. Dr. Beaumont summarized his experiments thus: "The free, ordinary use of any intoxicating liquor, when continued for some days, invariably produced inflammation, ulcerous patches, and, finally, a discharge of morbid matter tinged with blood." Yet St. Martin never complained of pain in his stomach, the narcotic influence of the alcohol preventing the signal of danger that Nature ordinarily gives.

† Disabled by the fatty deposits, the kidneys are unable to separate the waste matter coming to them for elimination from the system. The poisonous material is poured back into the circulation, and often delirium ensues. —HUBBARD. Richardson states that his experience "is to the effect that seven out of every eight instances of kidney disease are attributable to alcohol."

vessels lose their contractility; and, worst of all, the membranes may be so modified as to allow the albuminous part of the blood to filter through them, and so to rob the body of one of its most valuable constituents.*

Does Alcohol Impart Heat?—During the first flush after drinking wine, for example, a sense of warmth is felt. This is due to the tides of warm blood that are being sent to the surface of the body, owing to the vascular enlargement and to the rapid pumping of the heart. There is, however, no fresh heat developed. On the contrary, the bringing the blood to the surface causes it to cool faster, reaction sets in, a chilliness is experienced as one becomes sober, and a delicate thermometer placed under the tongue of the inebriate may show a fall of even two degrees below the standard temperature of the body. Several hours are required to restore the usual heat.

As early as 1850, Dr. N. S. Davis, of Chicago, ex-President of the American Medical Association, instituted an extensive series of experiments to determine the effect of the different articles of food and drinks on the temperature of the system. He conclusively proved that, during the digestion of all kinds of food, the temperature of the body is increased, but when alcohol is taken, either in the form of fermented or distilled beverages, the temperature begins to fall within a half-hour, and continues to decrease for two or three hours, and that the reduction of temperature, in extent as well as in duration, is in exact proportion to the amount of alcohol taken.

It naturally follows that, contrary to the accepted

* This deterioration of structure frequently gives rise to what is known as "Bright's Disease."—RICHARDSON.

opinion, liquor does not fortify against cold. The experience of travelers at the North coincides with that of Dr. Hayes, the Arctic explorer, who says: "While fat is absolutely essential to the inhabitants and travelers in arctic countries, alcohol is, in almost any shape, not only completely useless, but positively injurious. I have known strong, able-bodied men to become utterly incapable of resisting cold in consequence of the long-continued use of alcoholic drink."

Does Alcohol Impart Strength ? — Experience shows that alcohol weakens the power of undergoing severe bodily exertion.* Men who are in training for running, rowing, and other contests where great strength is required, deny themselves all liquors, even when they are ordinarily accustomed to their use.

Dr. Richardson made some interesting experiments to show the influence of alcohol upon muscular contraction. He carefully weighted the hind leg of a frog, and, by means of electricity, stimulating the muscle to its utmost power of contraction, he found out how much the frog could lift. Then administering alcohol, he discovered that the response of the muscle to the electrical current became feebler and feebler, as the narcotic began to take effect, until, at last, the animal could raise less than half the amount it lifted by the natural contraction when uninfluenced by alcohol.

* Dr. McRae, in speaking of Arctic exploration, at the meeting of the American Association for the Advancement of Science, held at Montreal in 1856, said: "The moment that a man had swallowed a drink of spirits, it was certain that his day's work was nearly at an end. It was absolutely necessary that the rule of total abstinence be rigidly enforced, if we would accomplish our day's task. The use of liquor as a beverage when we had work on hand, in that terrific cold, was out of the question."

Effect upon the Waste of the Body.—The ten-dency of alcohol is to cause a formation of an un-stable substance resembling fat,* and so the use of liquor for even a short time will increase the weight. But a more marked influence is to check the ordinary waste of the system, so that "the amount of carbonic acid exhaled from the lungs may be reduced as much as thirty to fifty per cent." —HINTON. The life-process is one of incessant change. Its rapidity is essential to vigor and strength. When the functions are in full play, each organ is being constantly torn down, and as con-stantly rebuilt with the materials furnished from our food. Any thing that checks this oxidation of the tissues, or hinders the deposition of new matter disturbs the vital functions. Both these results are the inevitable effects of alcohol; for, since the blood contains less oxygen and more carbonic acid, and the power of assimilating the food is decreased, it follows that every process of waste and repair must be correspondingly weakened. The person using liquor consequently needs less bread and beef, and so alcohol seems to him a food—a radical error, as we have shown.

Alcohol Creates a Progressive Appetite for Itself —When liquor is taken, even in the most moderate

---

* The molecular deposits equalizing the waste of the system do not go on regularly under the influence of alcohol; the tissues are not kept up to their standard; and, in time, their composition is changed by a deposit of an amorphous matter resembling fat. This is an unstable substance, and the functions of animal life all retrograde.—HUBBARD, *The Opium Habit and Alcoholism.*

quantity, it soon becomes necessary, and then arises a craving demand for an increased amount to produce the original effect. No food creates this constantly-augmenting want. A cup of milk drank at dinner does not lead one to go on, day by day, drinking more and more milk, until to get milk becomes the one great longing of the whole being. Yet this is the almost universal effect of alcohol. Hunger is satisfied by any nutritious food: the dram-drinker's thirst demands alcohol. The common experience of mankind teaches us the imminent peril that attends the formation of this progressive poison-habit. A single glass taken as a tonic may lead to the drunkard's grave.

Worse than this, the alcoholic craving may be transmitted from father to son, and young persons often find themselves cursed with a terrible disease known as alcoholism—a keen, morbid appetite for liquor that demands gratification at any cost — stamped upon their very being through the reckless indulgence of this habit on the part of some one of their ancestors.*

The Law of Heredity is, in this connection, well worth consideration. "The world is beginning to perceive," says Francis Galton, "that the life of each

---

* The American Medical Association, at their meeting in St. Paul, Minnesota (1883), re-stated in a series of resolutions their conviction, that "Alcohol should be classed with other powerful drugs; that when prescribed medically, it should be done with conscientious caution and a sense of great responsibility; that used as a beverage it is productive of a large amount of physical and mental disease; that it *entails diseased and enfeebled constitutions upon offspring*, and that it is the cause of a large percentage of the crime and pauperism of our large cities and country."

13

individual is, in some real sense, a continuation of the lives of his ancestors." "Each of us is the footing up of a double column of figures that goes back to the first pair." "We are omnibuses," remarks Holmes, "in which all our ancestors ride." We inherit from our parents our features, our physical vigor, our mental faculties, and even much of our moral character. Often, when one generation is skipped, the qualities will re-appear in the following one. The virtues, as well as the vices, of our forefathers, have added to, or subtracted from, the strength of our brain and muscle. The evil tendencies of our natures, which it is the struggle of our lives to resist, constitute a part of our heir-looms from the past. Our descendants, in turn, will have reason to bless us only if we hand down to them a pure healthy physical, mental, and moral being.

"There is a marked tendency in nature to transmit all diseased conditions. Thus, the children of consumptive parents are apt to be consumptives. But of all agents, alcohol is the most potent in establishing a heredity that exhibits itself in the destruction of mind and body.* Its malign influence was observed by the ancients long before the production of whiskey or brandy, or other distilled

* Nearly all the diseases springing from indulgence in distilled and fermented liquors are liable to become hereditary, and to descend to at least three or four generations, unless starved out by uncompromising abstinence. But the distressing aspect of the heredity of alcohol is the transmitted drink-crave. This is no dream of an enthusiast, but the result of a natural law. Men and women upon whom this dread inheritance has been forced are every-where around us, bravely struggling to lead a sober life.— DR. NORMAN KERR.

liquors, and when fermented liquors or wines only were known. Aristotle says, 'Drunken women have children like unto themselves,' and Plutarch remarks, 'One drunkard is the father of another.' The drunkard by inheritance is a more helpless slave than his progenitor, and his children are more helpless still, unless on the mother's side there is an untainted blood. For there is not only a propensity transmitted, but an actual disease of the nervous system."—DR. WILLARD PARKER.*

PRACTICAL QUESTIONS.

1. How do clothing and shelter economize food?
2. Is it well to take a long walk before breakfast?
3. Why is warm food easier to digest than cold?
4. Why is salt beef less nutritious than fresh?†
5. What should be the food of a man recovering from a fever?
6. Is a cup of black coffee a healthful close to a hearty dinner?
7. Should iced water be used at a meal?
8. Why is strong tea or coffee injurious?
9. Should food or drink be taken hot?
10. Are fruit-cakes, rich pastry, and puddings wholesome?
11. Why are warm biscuit and bread hard of digestion?
12. Should any stimulants be used in youth?
13. Why should bread be made spongy?
14. Which should remain longer in the mouth, bread or meat?
15. Why should cold water be used in making soup, and hot water in boiling meat?
16. Name the injurious effects of over-eating.
17. Why do not buckwheat cakes, with syrup and butter, taste as well in July as in January?

---

* The subject of alcohol is continued in the chapter on the Nervous System.

† The French Academicians found that flesh soaked in water so as to deprive it of its mineral matter and juices, lost its nutritive value, and that animals fed on it soon died. Indeed, for all purposes of nutrition, Liebig said it was no better than stones, and the utmost torments of hunger were hardly sufficient to induce them to continue the diet. There was plenty of nutritive food, but there was no medium for its solution and absorption, and hence it was useless.

18. Why is a late supper injurious?

19. What makes a man "bilious"?

20. What is the best remedy? *Ans.* Diet to give the organs rest, and active exercise to arouse the secretions and the circulation.

21. What is the practical use of hunger?

22. How can jugglers drink when standing on their heads?

23. Why do we relish butter on bread?

24. What would you do if you had taken arsenic by mistake? (See Appendix.)

25. Why should ham and sausage be thoroughly cooked?

26. Why do we wish butter on fish, eggs with tapioca, oil on salad, and milk with rice?

27. Explain the relation of food to exercise.

28. How do you explain the difference in the manner of eating between carnivorous and herbivorous animals?

29. Why is a child's face plump and an old man's wrinkled?

30. Show how life depends on repair and waste.

31. What is the difference between the decay of the teeth and the constant decay of the body?

32. Should biscuit and cake containing yellow spots of soda be eaten?

33. Tell how the body is composed of organs, how organs are made up of tissues, and how tissues consist of cells.

34. Why do we not need to drink three pints of water per day?

35. Why, during a pestilence, are those who use liquors as a beverage the first, and often the only victims?

36. What two secretions seem to have the same general use?

37. How may the digestive organs be strengthened?

38. Is the old rule, "after dinner sit awhile," a good one?

39. What would you do if you had taken laudanum by mistake? Paris Green? Sugar of lead? Oxalic acid? Phosphorus from matches? Ammonia? Corrosive sublimate? (See p. 265.)

40. What is the simplest way to produce vomiting, so essential in case of accidental poisoning?

41. In what way does alcohol interfere with the digestion?

42. Is alcohol assimilated?

43. What is the effect of alcohol on the albuminous substances?

44. Is there any nourishment in beer?

45. Show how the excessive use of alcohol may first increase, and, afterward, decrease, the size of the liver.

46. Will liquor help one to endure cold and exposure?

47. What is a fatty degeneration of the kidneys?

48. Contrast the action of alcohol and water in the body.

49. Is alcohol, in any proper sense of the term, a food?

50. Does liquor strengthen the muscles of a working man?

51. Is liquor a wholesome "tonic"?

52. Is it a good plan to take a glass of liquor before dinner?

VII.

THE NERVOUS SYSTEM.

> " MARK the the cloven sphere that holds
> All thoughts in its mysterious folds,
> That feels sensation's faintest thrill,
> And flashes forth the sovereign will;
> Think on the stormy world that dwells
> Lock'd in its dim and clustering cells;
> The lightning gleams of power it sheds
> Along its hollow, glassy threads!"

"As a king sits high above his subjects upon his throne, and from it speaks behests that all obey, so from the throne of the brain-cells is all the kingdom of a man directed, controlled, and influenced. For this occupant, the eyes watch, the ears hear, the tongue tastes, the nostrils smell, the skin feels. For it, language is exhausted of its treasures, and life of its experience; locomotion is accomplished, and quiet insured. When it wills, body and spirit are goaded like over-driven horses. When it allows, rest and sleep may come for recuperation. In short, the slightest penetration may not fail to perceive that all other parts obey this part, and are but ministers to its necessities."—*Odd Hours of a Physician.*

ANALYSIS OF THE NERVOUS SYSTEM.

THE NERVOUS SYSTEM.

1. THE STRUCTURE.

2. ORGANS OF THE NERVOUS SYSTEM.
- 1. The Brain
  - 1. *Description.*
  - 2. *The Cerebrum.*
  - 3. *The Cerebellum.*
- 2. The Spinal Cord
  - 1. *Its Composition.*
  - 2. *Medulla Oblongata.*
- 3. The Nerves
  - 1. *Description.*
  - 2. *Motory and Sensory.*
  - 3. *Transfer of Pain.*
  - 4. *The Spinal Nerves— 31 Pairs.*
  - 5. *The Cranial Nerves— 12 Pairs.*
  - 6. *Sympathetic System.*
  - 7. *Crossing of Cords.*
  - 8. *Reflex Action.*
  - 9. *Uses of Reflex Action.*

3. HYGIENE.
- 1. Brain Exercise.
- 2. Connection between Brain-growth and Body-growth.
- 3. Sleep.
- 4. Effect of Sleeping-draughts.
- 5. Sunlight.

4. WONDERS OF THE BRAIN.

5. ALCOHOLIC DRINKS AND NARCOTICS.
- 1. Alcohol (con'd).
  - 1. Effect of Alcohol upon the Nervous System.
    - 1. *Stage of Excitement.*
    - 2. *Stage of Muscular Weakness.*
    - 3. *Stage of Mental Weakness.*
    - 4. *Stage of Unconsciousness.*
  - 2. Effect upon the Brain.
  - 3. Effect upon the Mental and the Moral Powers.
- 2. Tobacco.
  - 1. Constituents of Tobacco.
  - 2. Physiological Effects.
  - 3. Possible Disturbances produced by Smoking.
  - 4. Influence upon the Nervous System.
  - 5. Is Tobacco a Food?
  - 6. Influence of Tobacco upon Youth.
- 3. Opium
  - 1. *Description.*
  - 2. *Physiological Effects.*
- 4. Chloral Hydrate.
- 5. Chloroform.
- 6. Cocaine.

THE NERVOUS SYSTEM.*

Structure. — The nervous system includes the *brain*, the *spinal cord*, and the *nerves*. It is composed of two kinds of matter—the *white*, and the *gray*. The former consists of minute, milk-white, glistening fibers, sometimes as small as $\frac{1}{25000}$ of an inch in diameter; the latter is made up of small, ashen-colored cells, forming a pulp-like substance of the consistency of blanc-mange.† This is often gathered in little masses, termed ganglions (*ganglion*, a knot), because, when a nerve passes through a group of the cells, they give it the appearance of a knot. The nerve-fibers are conductors, while the gray cells are generators, of nervous force.‡ The ganglia, or

* The organs of circulation, respiration, and digestion, of which we have already spoken, are often called the vegetative functions, because they belong also to the vegetable kingdom. Plants have a circulation of sap through their cells corresponding to that of the blood through the capillaries. They breathe the air through their leaves, which act the part of lungs, and they take in food which they change into their own structure by a process which answers to that of digestion. The plant, however, is a mere collection of parts incapable of any combined action. On the other hand, an animal has a nervous system which binds all the organs together.

† In addition to the cells, the gray substance contains also nerve-fibers continuous with the white-fibers, but generally much smaller. These form half the bulk of the gray substance of the spinal cord, and a large part of the deeper layer of the gray matter in the brain.—LEIDY's *Anatomy*, p. 507.

‡ What this force is we do not know. In some respects it is like electricity, but, in others, it differs materially. Its velocity is about thirty-three meters per second.—*Popular Physics*, p. 244, Note.

Fig. 50.

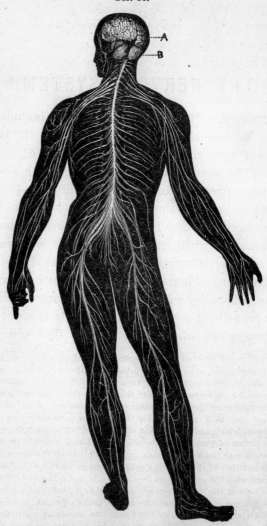

The Nervous System. A, *cerebrum;* B, *cerebellum.*

nervous centers, answer to the stations along a telegraphic line, where messages are received and transmitted, and the fibers correspond to the wires that communicate between different parts.

The Brain is the seat of the mind.* Its average weight is about fifty ounces.† It is egg shaped, and, soft and yielding, fills closely the cavity of the skull. It reposes securely on a water-bed, being surrounded by a double membrane (*arachnoid*), delicate as a spider's web, which forms a closed sac filled, like the spaces in the brain itself, with a liquid resembling water. Within this, and closely investing the brain, is a fine tissue (*pia mater*), with a mesh of blood-vessels which dips down into the hollows, and bathes them so copiously that it uses one fifth of the entire circulation of the body. Around the whole is wrapped a tough membrane (*dura mater*), which lines the bony box of the skull, and separates the various parts of the organ by strong partitions. The brain consists of two parts—the *cerebrum*, and the *cerebellum*.

The Cerebrum fills the front and upper part of

---

* In proportion to the rest of the nervous matter in the body, it is larger in man than in any of the lower animals. It is the function which the brain performs that distinguishes man from all other animals, and it is by the action of his brain that he becomes a conscious, intelligent, and responsible being. The brain is the seat of that knowledge which we express when we say I. I know it, I feel it, I saw it, are expressions of our individual consciousness, the seat of which is the brain. It is when the brain is at rest in sleep that there is least consciousness. The brain may be put under the influence of poisons, such as alcohol and chloroform, and then the body is without consciousness. From these and other facts the brain is regarded as the seat of *consciousness*.—LANKESTER.

† Cuvier's brain weighed 64½ ounces; Webster's, 53½ ounces; James Fisk's, 58 ounces; Ruloff's, 59 ounces; an idiot's, 19 ounces. See Table in FLINT'S *Nervous System*.

the skull, and comprises about seven eighths of the entire weight of the brain. As animals rise in the scale of life, this higher part makes its appearance.

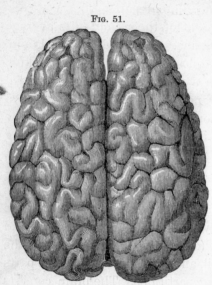

Fig. 51.

Surface of the Cerebrum.

It is a mass of white fibers, with cells of gray matter sprinkled on the outside, or lodged here and there in ganglia. It is so curiously wrinkled and folded as strikingly to resemble the meat of an English walnut. This structure gives a large surface for the gray matter,— sometimes as much as six hundred and seventy square inches. The convolutions are not noticeable in an infant, but increase with the growth of the mind, their depth and intricacy being characteristic of high mental power.

The cerebrum is divided into two hemispheres, connected beneath by fibers of white matter. Thus we have two brains,* as well as two hands and two

* This doubleness has given rise to some curious speculations. In the case of the hand, eye, etc., we know that the sensation is made more sure. Thus we can see with one eye, but not so well as with both. It is perhaps the same with the brain. We may sometimes carry on a train of thought, "build an air-castle" with one half of our brain, while the other half

eyes. This provides us with a surplus of brains, as it were, which can be drawn upon in an emergency. A large part of one hemisphere has been destroyed without particularly injuring the mental powers,*— just as a person has been blind in one eye for a long time without having discovered his loss. The cerebrum is the center of intelligence and thought.†

looks on and watches the operation; or, we may read and at the same time think of something else. So in delirium, a patient often imagines himself two persons, thus showing a want of harmony between the two halves.—DRAPER, *Human Physiology*, p. 329.

* A pointed iron bar, three and a half feet long and one inch and a quarter in diameter, was driven by the premature blasting of a rock completely through the side of the head of a man who was present. It entered below the temple, and made its exit at the top of the forehead, just about the middle line. The man was at first stunned, and lay in a delirious, semi-stupefied state for about three weeks. At the end of sixteen months, however, he was in perfect health, with wounds healed and mental and bodily functions unimpaired, except that sight was lost in the eye of the injured side.—DALTON. It is noticeable, however, that the man became changed in disposition, fickle, impatient of restraint, and profane, which he was not before. He died epileptic, nearly thirteen years after the injury. The tamping-iron and the skull are preserved in the Warren Anatomical Museum, Boston.

† In man, the cerebrum presents an immense preponderance in weight over other portions of the brain; in some of the lower animals, the cerebrum is even less in weight than the cerebellum. Another interesting point is the development of cerebral convolutions in certain animals, by which the relative amount of gray matter is increased. In fishes, reptiles, and birds, the surface of the hemispheres is smooth; but, in many mammalia, especially in those remarkable for intelligence, the cerebrum presents a greater or less number of convolutions, as it does in the human subject. —FLINT. The average weight of the human brain in proportion to the entire body is about 1 to 36. The average of mammalia is 1 to 186; of birds, 1 to 212; of reptiles, 1 to 1,321; and of fishes, 1 to 5,668. There are some animals in which the weight of the brain bears a higher proportion to the body than it does in man; thus in the blue-headed tit, the proportion is as 1 to 12; in the goldfinch, as 1 to 24; and in the field-mouse, as 1 to 31. "It does not hence follow, however, that the *cerebrum* is larger in proportion; in fact, it is probably not nearly so large; for in birds and rodent animals the sensory ganglia form a very considerable portion of the entire brain. M. Baillarger has shown that the *surface* and the *bulk* of the cerebral

Persons in whom it is seriously injured or diseased often become unable to converse intelligently, both from inability to remember words and from loss of power to articulate them.

The Cerebellum lies below the cerebrum, and in the back part of the head (Fig. 50). It is about the size of a small fist. Its structure is similar to that of the brain proper, but instead of convolutions it has parallel ridges, which, letting the gray matter down deeply into the white matter within, give it a peculiar appearance, called the *arbor-vitœ*, or tree of life (Fig. 55). This part of the brain is the center for the control of the voluntary muscles,* particu-

hemispheres are so far from bearing any constant proportion to each other in different animals that, notwithstanding the depth of the convolutions in the human cerebrum, its bulk is two and a half times as great in proportion to its surface as it is in the rabbit, the surface of whose cerebrum is smooth. The *size* of the cerebrum, considered alone, is not, however, a fair test of its intellectual power. This depends upon the quantity of *vesicular matter* which it contains, as evinced not only by superficial area, but by the number and depth of the convolutions and by the thickness of the cortical layer."—CARPENTER.

* The exact nature of the functions of the cerebellum is one of those problems concerning which there is no unanimity of opinion amongst physiologists. It may be premised, however, that the knowledge we at present possess does enable us to come to one very important conclusion with respect to the functions of the cerebellum,—it enables us to say that this organ has no independent function either in the province of mind or in the province of motility. And we may perhaps safely affirm still further, that the cerebellum is much more intimately concerned with the production of bodily movements than with the evolution of mental phenomena. The anatomical distinctness of the cerebellum from the larger brain and other parts of the nervous system is more apparent than real. . . . That there is an habitual community of action between the cerebellum and the spinal cord is, I believe, doubted by none, and the fact that an intimate functional relationship exists between the cerebrum and the cerebellum is shown by the circumstance that atrophy of one cerebral hemisphere entails a corresponding atrophy of the opposite half of the cerebellum. The subordinate or supplementary nature of the cerebellar function, however, in

larly those of locomotion.   Persons in whom it is injured or diseased walk with tottering and uncertain movements as if intoxicated, and can not perform any orderly work.

The Spinal Cord occupies the cavity of the backbone. It is protected by the same membranes as the brain, but, unlike it, the white matter is on the outside, and the gray matter is within. Deep fissures separate it into halves (Fig. 50), which are, however, joined by a bridge of the same substance. Just as it starts from the brain, there is an expansion called the *medulla oblongata* (Fig. 55).

The Nerves are glistening, silvery threads, composed, like the spinal cord, of white matter without and gray within. They ramify to all parts of the body. Often they are very near each other, yet are perfectly distinct, each conveying its own impression.* Those which carry the orders of the mind to

this latter relation seems equally well shown by the fact that atrophy of one side of the cerebellum (when it occurs as the primary event) does not entail any appreciable wasting in the opposite half of the cerebrum. What other conclusion can be drawn? If the cutting off of certain cerebral stimuli leads to a wasting of the opposite half of the cerebellum, this would seem to show that each half of the cerebellum is naturally called into activity in response to, or conjointly with, the opposite cerebral hemisphere. Whilst conversely, if atrophy of one half of the cerebellum does not entail a relative diminution in the opposite cerebral hemisphere, this would go to show that the cerebral hemispheres do not act in response to cerebellar stimuli, since their nutrition does not suffer when such stimuli are certainly absent. The action of the cerebrum is therefore shown to be primary, whilst that of the cerebellum is secondary or subordinate in the performance of those functions in which they are both concerned.—H. CHARLTON BASTIAN, *Paralysis from Brain Disease.*

* Press two fingers together, and, closing the eyes, let some one pass the point of a pin lightly from one to the other; you will be able to tell which is touched, yet if the nerves came in contact with each other anywhere in their long route to the brain, you could not thus distinguish.

the different organs are called the *motory* nerves; while those which bring back impressions which they receive are styled *sensory* nerves. If the sensory nerve leading to any part be cut, all sensation in that spot will be lost, while motion will remain; if the motory nerve be cut, all motion will be destroyed, while sensation will exist as before.

Transfer of Pain.—Strictly speaking, pain is not in any organ, but in the mind, since only that can feel. When any nerve brings news to the brain of an injury, the mind refers the pain to the end of the nerve. A familiar illustration is seen in the "funny bone" behind the elbow. Here the nerve (*ulnar*) gives sensation to the third and fourth fingers, in which, if this bone be struck, the pain will seem to be. Long after a limb has been amputated, pain will be felt in it, as if it still formed a part of the body—any injury in the stump being referred to the point to which the nerve formerly led.*

* Only about five per cent. of those who suffer amputation lose the feeling of the part taken away. There is something tragical, almost ghastly, in the idea of a spirit limb haunting a man through his life, and betraying him in unguarded moments into some effort, the failure of which suddenly reminds him of his loss. A gallant fellow, who had left an arm at Shiloh, once, when riding, attempted to use his lost hand to grasp the reins while with the other he struck his horse. A terrible fall was the result of his mistake. When the current of a battery is applied to the nerves of an arm-stump, the irritation is carried to the brain, and referred to all the regions of the lost limb. On one occasion a man's shoulder was thus electrized three inches above the point where the limb was cut off. For two years he had ceased to be conscious of his limb. As the electric current passed through, the man, who had been profoundly ignorant of its possible effects, started up, crying, "Oh, the hand! the hand!" and tried to seize it with the living grasp of the sound fingers. No resurrection of the dead could have been more startling.—DR. MITCHELL on "*Phantom Limbs*" in *Lippincott's Magazine.*

The nerves are divided into three general classes —the *spinal,* the *cranial,* and the *sympathetic.*

The Spinal Nerves, of which there are thirty-one pairs, issue from the spinal cord through apertures provided for them in the backbone. Each nerve arises by two roots; the anterior is the motory, and the posterior the sensory one. The posterior alone

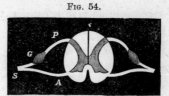

Fig. 54.

P, *posterior root of a spinal nerve;* G, *ganglion;* A, *anterior root;* S, *spinal nerve. The white portions of the figure represent the white fibers; and the dark, the gray.*

connects directly with the gray matter of the cord, and has a small ganglion of gray matter of its own at a little distance from its origin. These roots soon unite, *i. e.,* are bound up in one sheath, though they preserve their special functions. When the posterior root of a nerve is cut, the animal loses the power of feeling, and when the anterior root is cut, that of motion.

The Cranial Nerves, twelve pairs in number, spring from the lower part of the brain and the medulla oblongata.

1. The *olfactory,* or first pair of nerves, ramify through the nostrils, and are the nerves of smell.

2. The *optic,* or second pair of nerves, pass to the eyeballs, and are the nerves of vision.

3, 4, 6. The *motores oculi* (eye-movers) are three pairs of nerves used to move the eyes.

5. The *tri-facial,* or fifth pair of nerves, divide each into three branches—hence the name: the first to the upper part of the face, eyes, and nose; the second to the upper jaw and

teeth; the third to the lower jaw and the mouth, where it form: *he nerve of taste. These nerves are implicated when we hav: the toothache or neuralgia.

7. The *facial,* or seventh pair of nerves, are distributed over the face, and give it expression.*

FIG. 55.

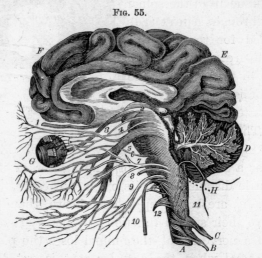

The Brain and the origin of the twelve pairs of Cranial Nerves. F, E, *the cerebrum;* D, *the cerebellum, showing the arbor-vitæ;* G, *the eye;* H, *the medulla oblongata;* A, *the spinal cord;* C *and* B, *the first two pairs of spinal nerves.*

8. The *auditory,* or eighth pair of nerves, go to the ears, and are the nerves of hearing.

9. The *glos-so-pha-ryn'-ge-al,* or ninth pair of nerves, are distributed over the mucous membrane of the pharynx, tonsils, etc.

10. The *pneu-mo-gas'-tric,* or tenth pair of nerves, preside over the larynx, lungs, liver, stomach, and one branch extends

* If it is palsied, on one side there will be a blank, while the other side will laugh or cry, and the whole face will look funny indeed. There were some cruel people in the middle ages who used to cut the nerve and deform children's faces in this way, for the purpose of making money of them at shows. When this nerve was wrongly supposed to be the seat of neuralgia, or tic-douloureux, it was often cut by surgeons. The patient suffered many dangers, and no relief of pain was gained.—MAPOTHER.

to the heart. This is the only nerve which goes so far from the head.

11. The *accessory*, or eleventh pair of nerves, rise from the spinal cord, run up to the medulla oblongata, and thence leave the skull at the same opening with the ninth and tenth pairs. They regulate the vocal movements of the larynx.

12. The *hyp-o-glos'-sal*, or twelfth pair of nerves, give motion to the tongue.

FIG. 56.

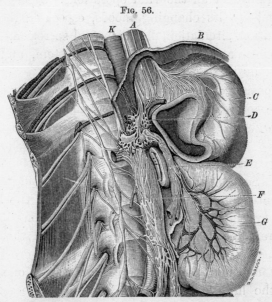

Spinal Nerves, Sympathetic Cord, and the Net-work of Sympathetic Nerves around the Internal Organs. K, *aorta;* A, *œsophagus;* B, *diaphragm;* C, *stomach.*

The Sympathetic System contains the nerves of organic life. It consists of a double chain of ganglia on either side of the backbone, extending into the chest and abdomen. From these, delicate nerves generally soft and of a grayish color, run to the organs on which life depends — the heart, lungs,

14

stomach, etc.—to the blood-vessels, and to the spinal and cranial nerves over the body. Thus the entire system is bound together with cords of sympathy, so that, "if one member suffers, all the members suffer with it."

Here lies the secret of the control exercised by the brain over all the vital operations. Every organ responds to its changing moods, especially those of respiration, circulation, digestion, and secretion,—processes intimately linked with this system, and controlled by it. (See p. 330.)

Crossing of Cords.—Each half of the body is presided over, not by its own half of the brain, but that of the opposite side. The motory nerves, as they descend from the brain, in the medulla oblongata, cross each other to the opposite side of the spinal cord. So the motor-nerves of the right side of the body are connected with the left side of the brain, and *vice versa*. Thus a derangement in one half of the brain may paralyze the opposite half of the body. The nerves going to the face do not thus cross, and therefore the face may be motionless on one side, and the limbs on the other. Each of the sensory fibers of the spinal nerves crosses over to the opposite side of the spinal cord, and so ascends to the brain; an injury to the spinal cord may, therefore, cause a loss of motion in one leg and of feeling in the other.

Reflex Action.—Since the gray matter generates the nervous force, a ganglion is capable of receiving an impression, and of sending back or *reflecting* it

so as to excite the muscles to action.   This is done
without the consciousness of the mind.* • Thus we
wink involuntarily at a flash of light or a threatened
blow.† We start at a sudden sound. We jump back
from a precipice before the mind has time to reason
upon the danger.   The spinal cord conducts certain

---

* Instances of an unconscious working of the mind are abundant.
An illustration, often quoted, is given, as follows, by Dr. Abercrombie, in
his *Intellectual Powers:*

"A lawyer had been excessively perplexed about a very complicated
question. An opinion was required from him, but the question was one of
such difficulty that he felt very uncertain how he should render it.   The
decision had to be given at a certain time, and he awoke in the morning
of that day with a feeling of great distress. He said to his wife, 'I had a
dream, and the whole thing was clearly arranged before my mind, and I
would give any thing to recover the train of thought.' His wife said to
him, 'Go and look on your table.' She had seen him get up in the night
and go to his table and sit down and write. He did so, and found there
the opinion which he had been most earnestly endeavoring to recover, lying
in his own hand-writing. There was no doubt about it whatever."

In this case the action of the brain was clearly automatic, *i. e.*, reflex.
The lawyer had worried his brain by his anxiety, and thus prevented his
mind from doing its best. But it had received an impulse in a certain
direction, and when left to itself, worked out the result. (See Appendix
for other illustrations.)

† A very eminent chemist a few years ago was making an experiment
upon some extremely explosive compound which he had discovered. He
had a small quantity of this compound in a bottle, and was holding it up
to the light, looking at it intently; and whether it was a shake of the
bottle or the warmth of his hand, I do not know, but it exploded in his
hand, and the bottle was shivered into a million of minute fragments,
which were driven in every direction. His first impression was, that they
had penetrated his eyes, but to his intense relief he found presently that
they had only struck the outside of his eyelids. You may conceive how
infinitesimally short the interval was between the explosion of the bottle
and the particles reaching his eyes; and yet in that interval the impression
had been made upon his sight, the mandate of the reflex action, so to
speak, had gone forth, the muscles of his eyelids had been called into
action, and he had closed his eyelids before the particles had reached
them, and in this manner his eyes were saved. You see what a wonderful
proof this is of the way in which the automatic action of our nervous apparatus enters into the sustenance of our lives, and the protection of our
most important organs from injury.—Dr. Carpenter.

impressions to the brain, but responds to others without troubling that organ.*   The medulla oblongata carries on the process of respiration.   The great sympathetic system binds together all the organs of the body.

Uses of Reflex Action.—We breathe eighteen times every minute ; we stand erect without a consciousness of effort ; † we walk, eat, digest, and at the same time carry on a train of thought.   Our brain is thus emancipated from the petty detail of life.   If we were obliged to attend to every breath, every pulsation of the heart, every wink of the eye, our time would be wasted in keeping alive.   Mere standing would require our entire attention.   Besides, an act which at first demands all our thought soon requires less, and at last becomes mechanical, ‡ as

* There is a story told of a man, who, having injured his spinal cord, had lost feeling and motion in his lower extremities. Dr. John Hunter experimented upon him. Tickling his feet, he asked him if he felt it ; the man, pointing to his limbs, which were kicking vigorously about, answered, "No, but you see my legs do." Illustrations of this independent action of the spinal cord are common in animals. A headless wasp will ply its sting energetically. A fowl, after its head is cut off, will flap its wings and jump about as if in pain, although, of course, all sensation has ceased. "A water-beetle, having had its head removed, remained motionless as long as it rested on a dry surface, but when cast into water, it executed the usual swimming motions with great energy and rapidity, striking all its comrades to one side by its violence, and persisting in these for more than half an hour."

† In this way we account for the perilous feats performed by the somnambulist. He is not conscious, as his operations are not directed by the cerebrum, but by the other nervous centers. Were he to attempt their repetition when awake, the emotion of fear might render it impossible.

‡ "As every one knows," says Huxley, "it takes a soldier a long time to learn his drill—for instance, to put himself into the attitude of 'attention' at the instant the word of command is heard. But, after a time, the sound of the word gives rise to the act, whether the soldier be thinking of it or not. There is a story, which is credible enough, though it may not

we say, *i. e.*, reflex.   Thus we play a familiar tune upon an instrument and carry on a conversation at the same time.   All the possibilities of an education and the power of forming habits are based upon this principle.   No act we perform ends with itself. It leaves behind it in the nervous centers a tendency to do the same thing again.   Our physical being thus conspires to fix upon us the habits of a good or an evil life.   Our very thoughts are written in our muscles, so that the expression of our face and even our features grow into harmony with the life we live.

Brain Exercise.—The nervous system demands its life and activity.   The mind grows by what it feeds on.   One who reads mainly light literature, who lolls on the sofa or worries through the platitudes of an idle or fashionable life, decays mentally ; his system loses tone, and physical weakness follows mental poverty.   On the other hand, an excessive use of the mind withdraws force from the body, whose weakness, reacting on the brain, produces gradual decay and serious diseases.   (See p. 331.)

The brain grows by the growth of the body.   The body grows through good food, fresh air, and work and rest in suitable proportion.   For the full development and perfect use of a strong mind, a strong body is essential.   Hence, in seeking to expand and

be true, of a practical joker, who, seeing a discharged veteran carrying home his dinner, suddenly called out ' Attention !' whereupon the man instantly brought his hands down and lost his mutton and potatoes in the gutter.   The drill had been thorough, and its effects had become embodied in the man's nervous structure."

store the intellect, we should be equally thoughtful of the growth and health of the body.

Sleep* is as essential as food. During the day, the process of tearing down goes on; during the night, the work of building up should make good the loss. In youth more sleep is needed than in old age, when nature makes few permanent repairs, and is content with temporary expedients. The number of hours required for sleep must be decided by each person. Napoleon took only five hours, but most people need from six to eight hours,—brain-workers even more. In general, one should sleep until he naturally wakes. If one's rest be broken, it should be made up as soon as possible. (See p. 334.)

Sunlight.—The influence of the sun's rays upon the nervous system is very marked.† It is said also

---

* Sleep procured by medicine is rarely as beneficial as that secured naturally. The disturbance to the nervous system is often sufficient to counterbalance all the good results. The habit of seeking sleep in this way, without the advice of a physician, is to be most earnestly deprecated. The dose must be constantly increased to produce the effect, and thus great injury may be caused. Often, too, where laudanum or morphine is used, the person unconsciously comes into a terrible and fatal bondage. (See p. 342.) Especially should infants never be dosed with cordials, as is a common family practice. The damage done to helpless childhood by the ignorant and reckless use of soothing syrups is frightful to contemplate. All the ordinary sleeping-draughts have life-destroying properties, as is proved by the fatal effects of an overdose. At the best, they paralyze the nerve centers, disorder the digestion, and poison the blood. Their promiscuous use is therefore full of danger.

† The necessity of light for young children is not half appreciated. Many of their diseases, and nearly all the cadaverous looks of those brought up in great cities, are ascribable to the deficiency of light and air. When we see the glass-room of the photographers in every street, in the topmost story, we grudge them their application to what is often a mere personal vanity. Why should not a nursery be constructed in the same manner? If parents knew the value of light to the skin, especially to children of a

to have the effect of developing red disks in the
blood. All vigor and activity come from the sun.
Vegetables grown in subdued light have a bleached
and faded look. An infant kept in absolute darkness
would grow into a shapeless idiot. That room is the
healthiest to which the sun has the freest access.
Epidemics frequently attack the inhabitants of the
shady side of a street, and exempt those on the
sunny side. If, on a slight indisposition, we should
go out into the open air and bright sunlight, instead
of shutting ourselves up in a close, dark chamber,
we might often avoid a serious illness. The sun-
bath is doubtless a most efficient remedy for many
diseases. Our window blinds and curtains should
be thrown back and open, and we should let the
blessed air and sun stream in to invigorate and
cheer. No house buried in shade, and no room with
darkened windows, is fit for human habitation. In
damp and darkness, lies in wait almost every disease to which flesh is heir. The sun is their only
successful foe. (See p. 336.)

Wonders of the Brain.—After having seen the
beautiful contrivances and the exquisite delicacy of
the lower organs, it is natural to suppose that when
we come to the brain we should find the most elaborate machinery. How surprising, then, it is to have

scrofulous tendency, we should have plenty of these glass-house nurseries,
where children might run about in a proper temperature, free from much
of that clothing which at present seals up the skin—that great supplementary lung—against sunlight and oxygen. They would save many a weakly
child who now perishes from lack of these necessaries of infant life.—DR.
WINTER.

revealed to us only cells and fibers! The brain is the least solid and most unsubstantial looking organ in the body. Eighty per cent. of water, seven of albumen, some fat, and a few minor substances constitute the instrument which rules the world. Strangest of all, the brain, which is the seat of sensation, is itself without sensation. Every nerve, every part of the spinal cord, is keenly alive to the slightest touch, yet "the brain may be cut, burned, or electrified without producing pain."

ALCOHOLIC DRINKS AND NARCOTICS.

ALCOHOL (Continued from p. 187).

Effect upon the Nervous System. — In the progressive influence of alcohol upon the nervous system, there are, according to the researches of Dr. Richardson, four successive stages.

1. **The Stage of Excitement.*** — The first effect of alcohol, as we have already described on page 144, is to paralyze the nerves that lead to the extreme and minute blood-vessels, and so regulate the passage of the blood through the capillary system. The

---

* The pupil should be careful to note here that alcohol does not act upon the heart directly, and cause it to contract with more force. The idea that alcohol gives energy and activity to the muscles is entirely false. It really, as we have seen (p. 183), weakens muscular contraction. The enfeeblement begins in the first stage, and continues in the other stages with increased effect. The heart beats quickly merely because the resistance of the minute controlling vessels is taken off, and it works without being under proper regulation. *What is called a stimulation or excitement is, in absolute fact, a relaxation, a partial paralysis* of one of the most important mechanisms in the animal body. Alcohol should be ranked among the narcotics.—RICHARDSON.

vital force, thus drawn into the nervous centers, drives the machinery of life with tremendous energy. The heart jumps like the main-spring of a watch when the resistance of the wheels is removed. The blood surges through the body with increased force. Every capillary tube in the system is swollen and flushed, like the reddened nose and cheek.

In all this there is exhilaration, but no nourishment; there is animation, but no permanent power conferred on brain or muscle. Alcohol may cheer for the moment. It may set the sluggish blood in motion, start the flow of thought, and excite a temporary gayety. "It may enable a wearied or feeble organism to do brisk work for a short time. It may make the brain briefly brilliant. It may excite muscle to quick action, but it does nothing at its own cost, fills up nothing it has destroyed, and itself leads to destruction." Even the mental activity it has excited is an unsafe state of mind, for that just poise of the faculties so essential to good judgment is disturbed by the presence of the intruder. Johnson well remarked, "Wine improves conversation by taking the edge off the understanding."

2. **The Stage of Muscular Weakness.**—If the action of the alcohol be still continued, the spinal cord is next affected by this powerful narcotic. The control of some of the muscles is lost. Those of the lower lip usually fail first, then those of the lower limbs, and the staggering, uncertain steps betray the result. The muscles themselves, also, become feebler as the power of contraction diminishes. The temperature, which, for a time, was slightly increased, soon begins to fall as the heat is radiated; the body is cooled, and the well-known "alcoholic chill" is felt.

3. **The Stage of Mental Weakness.**—The cerebrum is now implicated. The ideal and emotional faculties are quickened, while the will is weakened. The center of thought being overpowered, the mind is a chaos. Ideas flock in thick and fast. The tongue is loosened. The judgment loses its hold on the acts. The reason giving way, the animal instincts generally assume the mastery of the man. The hidden nature comes to the surface. All the gloss of education and social restraint falls off, and the lower nature stands revealed. The coward shows himself more craven, the braggart more boastful, the bold more

daring, and the cruel more brutal. The inebriate is liable to become the perpetrator of any outrage that the slightest provocation may suggest.

4. The Stage of Unconsciousness. — At last, prostration ensues, and the wild, mad revel of the drunkard ends with utter senselessness. In common speech, the man is "dead drunk." Brain and spinal cord are both benumbed. Fortunately, the two nervous centers which supply the heart and the diaphragm are the slowest to be influenced. So, even in this final stage, the breathing and the circulation still go on, though the other organs have stopped. Were it not for this, every person thoroughly intoxicated would die.*

Effect upon the Brain.—Alcohol seems to have a special affinity for the brain. This organ absorbs more than any other, and its delicate structure is correspondingly affected. The "Vascular enlargement" here reaches its height. The tiny vessels become clogged with blood that is unfitted to nourish, because loaded with carbonic acid, and deprived of the usual quantity of the life-giving oxygen.— HINTON. The brain is, in the language of the physiologist, malfunctioned. The mind but slowly rallies from the stupor of the fourth stage, and a sense of dullness and depression remains to show with what

* Cold has a wonderful influence in hastening this stage, so that a person, previously only in the first stage of excitement, on going out-doors on a winter night, may rapidly sink into a lethargy (become *comatose*), fall, and die. He is then commonly said to have perished with cold. The signs of this coma are of great practical importance, since so many persons die in police stations and elsewhere who are really comatose, when they are supposed to be only sound asleep. The pulse is slow, and almost imperceptible. The face is pale, and the skin cold. "If the arm be pinched, it is not moved; if the eyeballs are touched, the lids will not sink." The respiration becomes slower and slower, and, if the person dies, it is because liquid collects in the bronchial tubes, and stops the passage of the air. The man then actually drowns in his own secretions.

difficulty the fatigued organ recovers its normal condition. So marked is the effect of the narcotic poison, that some authorities hold that "a once thoroughly-intoxicated brain never fully becomes what it was before."

In time, the free use of liquor hardens and thickens the membrane enveloping the nervous matter; the nerve-corpuscles undergo a "Fatty degeneration"; the blood-vessels lose their elasticity; and the vital fluid, flowing less freely through the obstructed channels, fails to afford the old-time nourishment. The consequent deterioration of the nervous substance — the organ of thought — shows itself in the weakened mind * that we so often notice in a person accustomed to drink, and at last lays the foundation of various nervous disorders — epilepsy, paralysis, and insanity.† The law of heredity here again asserts itself, and the inebriate's children often inherit the disease which he has escaped.

Chief among the consequences of this perverted and imperfect nutrition of the brain is that intermediate state between intoxication and insanity, well known as Delirium Tremens. "It is characterized by a low, restless activity of the cerebrum, manifesting itself in muttering delirium, with occasional paroxysms of greater violence. The victim almost

---

* The habitual use of fermented liquors, even to an extent far short of what is necessary to produce intoxication, injures the body, and diminishes the mental power.—SIR HENRY THOMPSON.

† Casper, the great statistician of Berlin, says: "So far as that city is concerned, one third of the insane coming from the poorer classes, were made so by spirit-drinking."

always apprehends some direful calamity; he imagines his bed to be covered with loathsome reptiles; he sees the walls of his apartment crowded with foul specters; and he imagines his friends and attendants to be fiends come to drag him down to a fiery abyss beneath."—CARPENTER.   (See p. 287.)

Influence upon the Mental and Moral Powers.— So intimate is the relation between the body and the mind, that an injury to one harms the other. The effect of alcoholized blood is to weaken the will. The one habitually under its influence often shocks us by his indecision and his readiness to break a promise to reform.   The truth is, he has lost, in a measure, his power of self-control.   At last, he becomes physically unable to resist the craving demand of his morbid appetite.

Other faculties share in this mental wreck. The intellectual vision becomes less penetrating, the decisions of the mind less reliable, and the grasp of thought less vigorous. The logic grows muddy. A thriftless, reckless feeling is developed. Ere long, self-respect is lost, and then ambition ceases to allure, and the high spirit sinks.

Along with this mental deterioration comes also a failure of the moral sense.   The fine fiber of character undergoes a "degeneration" as certain as that of the muscles themselves. Broken promises tell of a lowered standard of veracity, and a dulled sense of honor, quite as much as of an impaired will. Under the subtle influence of the ever-present poison, signs of spiritual weakness multiply fast.   Conscience is lulled to rest. Reason is enfeebled. Customary restraints are easily thrown off. The sensibilities are blunted. There is less ability to appreciate nice shades of right and wrong. Great moral principles and motives lose their power to influence. The judgment fools with duty. The future no longer reaches back its hand to guide the present. The better nature has lost its supremacy.

The wretched victim of appetite will now gratify his tyrannical passion for drink at any expense of deceit or crime. He becomes the blind instrument of his insane impulses, and commits acts from which he would once have shrunk with horror.* Sometimes he even takes a malignant pleasure in injuring those whom Nature has ordained he should protect.†

* Richardson sums up the various diseases caused by alcohol, as follows: "(a). Diseases of the brain and nervous system, indicated by such names as apoplexy, epilepsy, paralysis, vertigo, softening of the brain, delirium tremens, dipsomania or inordinate craving for drink, loss of memory, and that general failure of the mental power, called dementia. (b). Diseases of the lungs: one form of consumption, congestion, and subsequent bronchitis. (c). Diseases of the heart: irregular beat, feebleness of the muscular walls, dilatation, disease of the valves. (d). Diseases of the blood: scurvy, excess of water or dropsy, separation of fibrin. (e). Diseases of the stomach: feebleness of the stomach, indigestion, flatulency, irritation, and sometimes inflammation. (f). Diseases of the bowels: relaxation or purging, irritation. (g). Diseases of the liver: congestion, hardening and shrinking, cirrhosis. (h). Diseases of the kidneys: change of structure into fatty or waxy-like condition and other results leading to dropsy, or sometimes to fatal sleep. (i). Diseases of the muscles: fatty change in the muscles, by which they lose their power for proper active contraction. (j). Diseases of the membranes of the body: thickening and loss of elasticity, by which the parts wrapped up in the membrane are impaired for use, and premature decay is induced."

† It has been argued that a man should not be punished for any crime he may commit during intoxication, but rather for knowingly giving up the reins of reason and conscience, and thus subjecting himself to the rule of his evil passions. Voluntarily to stimulate the mind and put it into a con-

2. TOBACCO.

The Constituents of Tobacco Smoke are numerous, but the prominent ones are carbonic acid, carbonic oxide, and ammonia gases; carbon, or soot; and nicotine. The proportion of these substances varies with different kinds of tobacco, the pipe used, and the rapidity of the combustion. Carbonic acid tends to produce sleepiness and headache. Carbonic oxide, in addition, causes a tremulous movement of the muscles, and so of the heart. Ammonia bites the tongue of the smoker, excites the salivary glands, and causes dryness of the mouth and throat. Nicotine is a powerful poison. The amount contained in one or two strong cigars, if thrown directly into the blood, would cause death. Nicotine itself is complex, yielding a volatile substance that gives the odor to the breath and clothing; and also a bitter extract which produces the sickening taste of an old pipe. In smoking, some of the nicotine is decomposed, forming pyridine, picoline, and other poisonous alkaloids.*

dition where it may drive one to ruin, is very like the act of an engineer who should get up steam in his engine, and then, having opened the valves, desert his post, and let the monster go thundering down the track to sure destruction. Certain persons are thrown into the stage of mental weakness by a single glass of liquor. How can they be excused when the fact of their peculiar liability lends additional force to the argument of abstemiousness, and they know that their only safety lies in total abstinence?—CARPENTER'S *Physiology.*

* The analysis of tobacco as given by different authorities varies greatly. The one stated in the text suffices for the purposes of this chapter. Von Eulenberg names several other products of the combustion. One hundred pounds of the dry leaf may yield as high as seven pounds of nicotine. Havana

Physiological Effects.—The poison of tobacco, set free by the process either of chewing or smoking, when for the first time it is swept through the system by the blood, powerfully affects the body. Nausea is felt, and the stomach seeks to throw off the offending substance. The brain is inflamed, and headache follows. The motor-nerves becoming irritated, giddiness ensues. Thus Nature earnestly protests against the formation of this habit. But, after repeated trials, the system adjusts itself to the new conditions. A "tolerance" of the poison is finally established, and smoking causes none of the former symptoms. Such powerful substances can not, however, be constantly inhaled without producing marked changes. The three great eliminating organs—the lungs, the skin, and the kidneys—throw off a large part of the products, but much remains in the system. When the presence of the poison is constant, and especially when the smoking or chewing is excessive, the disturbance that at first is merely functional, must necessarily, in many cases at least, lead to a chronic derangement.

Probably in this, as in the case of other deleterious articles of diet, the strong and healthy will seem to escape entirely, while the weak and those predisposed to disease will be injured in direct proportion to the extent of the indulgence. Those whose employment leads to active, out-door work, will show no sign of nicotine poisoning, while the man of

tobacco contains about two per cent., and Virginia about six per cent.—See JOHNSTON & CHURCH'S *Chemistry of Common Life*, and MILLER'S *Organic Chemistry*.

sedentary habits will sooner or later be the victim of
dyspepsia, sleeplessness, nervousness, paralysis, or
other organic difficulties. Even where the user of
tobacco himself escapes harm, the law of heredity
asserts itself, and the innocent offspring only too
often inherit an impaired constitution, and a tendency to nervous complaints.

The Various Disturbances produced in different individuals
and constitutions by smoking have been summed up by Dr.
Richardson as follows: "(a) In the blood, it causes undue fluid-
ity, and change in the red corpuscles; (b) in the stomach, it
gives rise to debility, nausea, and vomiting; (c) in the mucous
membrane of the mouth, it produces enlargement and soreness
of the tonsils—smoker's sore throat—redness, dryness, and occasional peeling of the membrane, and either unnatural firmness
and contraction, or sponginess of the gums; and, where the
pipe rests on the lips, oftentimes 'epithelial cancer'; (d) in the
heart, it causes debility of the organ, and irregular action; (e)
in the bronchial surface of the lungs, when that is already irritable, it sustains irritation, and increases the cough; (f) in the
organs of sense, it produces dilation of the pupils of the eye,
confusion of vision, bright lines, luminous or cobweb specks,
and long retention of images on the retina, with analogous
symptoms affecting the ear, viz., inability to define sounds
clearly, and the occurrence of a sharp, ringing noise like a
whistle; (g) in the brain, it impairs the activity of the organ,
oppressing it if it be nourished, but soothing it if it be exhausted; (h) it leads to paralysis in the motor and sympathetic
nerves, and to over-secretion from the glands which the sympathetic nerves control."

Is Tobacco a Food?—Here, as in the case of alcohol, the reply is a negative one. Tobacco manifests
no characteristic of a food. It can not impart to the
blood an atom of nutritive matter for building up

the body. It does not add to, but rather subtracts from, the total vital force. It confers no potential power upon muscle or brain. It stimulates by cutting off the nervous supply from the extremities and concentrating it upon the centers. But stimulation is not nourishment; it is only a rapid spending of the capital stock. There is no greater error than to mistake the exciting of an organ for its strengthening.

The Influence upon Youth.—Here, too, science utters no doubtful voice. Experience asserts only one conviction. *Tobacco retards the development of mind and body.* The law of nature is that of steady growth. It can not admit of a daily, even though it be merely a functional, disturbance that weakens the digestion, that causes the heart to labor excessively, that prevents the perfect oxidation of the blood, that interferes with the assimilation, and that deranges the nervous system.† No one has a right

* Cigarettes are especially injurious from the irritating smoke of the paper covering, taken into the lungs, and also because the poison-fumes of the tobacco are more directly inhaled. In case of the cheap cigarettes often smoked by boys, the ingredients used are harmful, while one revolts at the thought of the filthy materials, refuse cigar-stumps, etc., employed in their manufacture.

† There is one influence of tobacco that every young man should understand. In many cases, like alcohol, it seems to blunt the sensibilities, and to make its user careless of the rights and feelings of others. This is often noticed in common life. We meet every-where "devotees of the weed," who, ignoring the fact that tobacco is disagreeable to many persons, think only of the gratification of their selfish appetite. They smoke or chew in any place or company. They permit the cigar fumes to blow into the faces of passers-by. They sit where the wind carries the smoke of their pipes so that others must inhale it. They expectorate upon the floor of cars, hotels, and even private homes. They take no pains to remove the odor that lingers about their person and clothing. They force all who happen to be near, their companions, their fellow-travelers, to inhale the nauseating odor of tobacco. Every thing must be sacrificed to the one

thus to check and disturb continually the regular processes of his physical and mental progress. Hence, the young man (especially if he be of a nervous, sensitive organization) who uses tobacco deliberately diminishes the possible energy with which he might commence the work of life;* while he comes under the bondage of a habit that may become stronger than his will, and under the influence of a narcotic that may beguile his faculties and palsy his strength at the very moment when every power should be awake.

Another peril still lies in the wake of this masterful poison-habit. Tobacco causes thirst and depression that only too often and naturally lead to the use of liquor. (See p. 338.)

3. OPIUM.

Opium is the dried juice of the poppy. In Eastern countries, this flower is cultivated in immense fields

---

primal necessity of such persons—a smoke. Now, a young man just beginning life, with his fortune to make, and his success to achieve, can not afford to burden himself with a habit that is costly, that will make his presence offensive to many persons, and that may perhaps render him less sensitive to the best influences and perceptions of manhood.

* In the Polytechnic School at Paris, the pupils were divided into two classes—the smokers, and the non-smokers. The latter not only excelled on the entrance examinations, but during the entire course of study. Dr. Decaisne examined thirty-eight boys who smoked, and found twenty-seven of them diseased from nicotine poisoning. So long ago as 1868, in consequence of these results, the Minister of Public Instruction forbade the use of tobacco by the pupils.

Dr. Gihon, medical director of the Naval Academy at Annapolis, in his report for 1881, says: "The most important matter in the health-history of the students is that relating to tobacco, and its interdiction is absolutely essential to their future health and usefulness. In this view I have been sustained by my colleagues, and by all sanitarians in civil and military life whose views I have been able to obtain."

for the sake of this product. When a cut is made in the poppy-head, a tiny tear of milky juice exudes, and hardens. These little drops are gathered and prepared for the market, an acre yielding, it is said, about twenty-five pounds. Throughout the East, opium is generally smoked; but in Western countries laudanum and paregoric (tinctures of opium), and morphine—a powerful alkaloid contained in opium, are generally used. The drug itself is also eaten.

Physiological Effect.—Opium, in its various forms, acts directly upon the nerves, a small dose quieting pain, and a larger one soothing to sleep. It arouses the brain, and fires the imagination to a wonderful pitch.* The reaction from this unnatural excitant is correspondingly depressing; and the melancholy, the "overwhelming horror" that ensues, calls for a renewal of the stimulus. The dose must be gradually increased to produce the original exhilaration.† The

* So far as its effects are concerned, it matters little in what form opium is taken, whether solid as in pills, liquid as in laudanum, or vaporized, as when inhaled from a pipe. The opium slave is characterized by trembling steps, a curved spine, sunken glassy eyes, sallow withered features, and often by contraction of the muscles of the neck and fingers. In the East, when the drug ceases its influence, the opium-eater renews it with corrosive sublimate till, finally, this also fails of effect, and he gradually sinks into the grave.

† The victim of opium is bound to a drug from which he derives no benefits, but which slowly deprives him of health and happiness, finally to end in idiocy or premature death. Whatever the victim's condition or surroundings may be, the opium must be taken at certain times with inexorable regularity. The liquor or tobacco user can, for a time, go without the use of these agents, and no regular hours are necessary. During sickness, and more especially during the eruptive fevers, he does not desire tobacco or liquor. The opium-eater has no such reprieves; his dose must be taken, and, in painful complications affecting the stomach, a large increase is demanded to sustain the system. If, in forming the habit, two doses are taken each day, the victim is obliged to maintain that number.

seductive nature of the drug leads the unfortunate victim on step by step until he finds himself fast bound in the fetters of one of the most tyrannical habits known to man.

To go on is to wreck all one's powers—physical and mental. To throw off the habit, requires a determination that but few possess. Yet even when the custom is broken, the system is long in recovering from the shock. There seems to be a failure of every organ. The digestion is weakened, food is no longer relished, the muscles waste, the skin shrivels, the nervous centers are paralyzed, and a premature old age comes on apace. De Quincey, four months after he had cast away the opium-bonds, wrote, "Think of me as one still agitated, writhing, throbbing, palpitating, shattered."

No person can be too careful in the use of laudanum, paregoric, and morphine. They may be taken on a physician's prescription as a sedative from racking pain,* but if followed up for any

It is the unceasing, everlasting slavery of regularity that humiliates opium-eaters by a sense of their own weakness.—HUBBARD *on The Opium Habit and Alcoholism.*

* Many persons learn to inject morphine beneath the skin by means of a "hypodermic syringe." The operation is painless, and seems an innocent one. It throws the narcotic directly into the circulation, and relief from pain is often almost instantaneous. But the danger of forming the opium habit is not lessened, and the effect of using the drug in this form for a long time is just as injurious as opium-smoking itself. "Opium in one of its forms enters largely into the composition of many of the pain-killers and patent medicines so freely advertised for domestic use in the present day, and for this reason the greatest care is needed in having recourse to any of them. Taken, perhaps, in the first instance, to alleviate the torments of neuralgia or toothache, what proves to be a remedy soon becomes a source of gratification, which the wretchedness that follows on abstinence renders increasingly difficult to lay aside. The same must be

length of time, the powerful habit may be formed
ere one is aware.   Then comes the opium-eater's
grave, or the opium-eater's struggle for life !

4. CHLORAL HYDRATE.

Chloral Hydrate is a drug frequently used to
cause sleep.   It leaves behind no headache or lassi-
tude, as is often the case with morphine.   It is, however, a treacherous remedy.   It is cumulative in its
effects, *i. e.*, even a small and harmless dose, per-
sisted in for a long period, may produce a gradual
accumulation of evil results that in the end will
prove fatal.

The Physiological Effect of its prolonged use is
very marked.   The appetite becomes capricious.   The
secretions are unnatural.   Nausea and flatulency
often ensue.   Then the nervous system is involved.
The heart is affected.   Sleep, instead of responding
to the drug, as at first, is broken and disturbed.   The
eyesight fails.   The circulation is enfeebled, and the
pulse becomes weak, rapid, and irregular.   There is
a tendency to fainting and to difficult respiration.
Sometimes the impoverished blood induces a disease

said of bromide of potassium and hydrate of chloral, frequently resorted to
as a remedy for sleeplessness : the system quickly becomes habituated to
their use, and they can then be relinquished only at the cost of much suffering.   Indeed, the last mentioned of these two drugs obtains over the
mind a power which may be compared to that of opium, and is, moreover,
liable to occasion the disease known as chloralism, by which the system
ultimately becomes a complete wreck.   Looking at the whole question of
the medicinal use of narcotics, it is perhaps not too much to say that they
should never be employed except with the authority of a competent medical
adviser.—*Chambers' Journal.*

resembling scurvy, the ends of the fingers ulcerate, and the face is disfigured by blotches. An excessive dose may result in death.

Prolonged habitual use of chloral hydrate tends to debase the mind and morals of the subject in the same manner as indulgence in alcohol, ether, or chloroform.

5. CHLOROFORM.

Chloroform is an artificial product generally obtained, by distillation, from a mixture of chloride of lime, water, and alcohol. It was discovered in 1831 by Samuel Guthrie, of Sackett's Harbor, New York. It is a colorless, transparent volatile liquid, with a strong ethereal odor.

Physiological Effect.— Chloroform is a powerful anæsthetic, which, when inhaled, causes a temporary paralysis of the nervous system, and thus a complete insensibility to pain. There is great peril attending its use, even in the hands of the most skillful and experienced practitioners. It is sometimes prescribed by a physician, and afterward (as in the case of laudanum, morphine, and chloral) the sufferer, charmed with the release from pain and the peaceful slumber secured, buys the Lethean liquid for himself. Its use soon becomes an apparent necessity. The craving for the narcotic at a stated time is almost irresistible. The patient, compelled to give up the use of chloroform, will demand, entreat, pray for another dose, in a heart-rending manner, never to be forgotten. Paleness and debility, the earliest symptoms, are followed by mental prostration. Familiarity with this dangerous drug begets carelessness, and its victims are frequently found dead in their beds, with the handkerchief from which they inhaled the volatile poison clutched in their lifeless hands.

6. COCAINE.

Cocaine is an alkaloid prepared from the erythroxylon coca, a shrub, five or six feet high, found wild in the mountainous regions of Ecuador and Peru, where it is also cultivated by the natives. The South American Indians, for centuries, have chewed coca leaves as a stimulant, but the highly poisonous principle, now called cocaine, to which the plant owes its peculiar effects, was not discovered till 1859. Within a few years this drug has come into favor as an agent to produce local anæsthesia, and has proved exceedingly valuable in surgical operations upon the eye and other sensitive organs. It has already, however, been diverted from its legitimate use as a benefaction, and to the other evils of the day is now added the "cocaine habit," which is, perhaps, even more dangerous and difficult to abandon than either the alcohol or the opium habit.

Physiological Effect. — Applied locally, cocaine greatly lessens and even annihilates pain. Taken internally, it acts as a powerful stimulant to the nervous system, its physiological action being similar to that of theine (p. 170), caffeine, and theobromine. Used hypodermically, its immediate effect, says one to whom it was thus administered, is to cause "great pallor of countenance, profuse frontal perspiration, sunken eyes, enlarged pupils, lessened sensitiveness of the cornea and conjunctiva, lowered arterial tension, and a feeble pulse and heartbeat. Under its influence I could not reason. Every thing seemed to run through my brain, and in vain I summoned all my will-power to overcome an overwhelming sleepiness." A few doses of this drug will in some persons produce temporary insanity. Used to excess, it leads to permanent madness or idiocy. "Cocaine," says a writer in the *Medical Review*, "is a dangerous therapeutic toy not to be used as a sensational plaything. If it should come into as general use as the other intoxicants of its class, it will help to fill the asylums, inebriate and insane."

PRACTICAL QUESTIONS.

1. Why is the pain of incipient hip-disease frequently felt in the knee?

2. Why does a child require more sleep than an aged person?

3. When you put your finger in the palm of a sleeping child, why will he grasp it?

4. How may we strengthen the brain?

5. What is the object of pain?

6. Why will a blow on the stomach sometimes stop the heart?

7. How long will it take for the brain of a man six feet high to receive news of an injury to his foot, and to reply?

8. How can we grow beautiful?

9. Why do intestinal worms sometimes affect a child's sight?

10. Is there any indication of character in physiognomy?

11. When one's finger is burned, where is the ache?

12. Is a generally-closed parlor a healthful room?

13. Why can an idle scholar read his lesson and at the same time count the marbles in his pocket?

14. In amputating a limb, what part, when divided, will cause the keenest pain?

15. What is the effect of bad air on nervous people?

16. Is there any truth in the proverb that "he who sleeps dines"?

17. What does a high, wide forehead indicate?

18. How does indigestion frequently cause a headache?

19. What is the cause of one's foot being "asleep"?*

20. When an injury to the nose has been remedied by transplanting skin from the forehead, why is a touch to the former felt in the latter?

21. Are closely-curtained windows healthful?

22. Why, in falling from a height, do the limbs instinctively take a position to defend the important organs?

23. What causes the pylorus to open and close at the right time?

24. Why is pleasant exercise most beneficial?

25. Why does grief cause one to lose his appetite?

26. Why should we never study directly after dinner?

27. What produces the peristaltic movement of the stomach?

28. Why is a healthy child so restless and full of mischief?

29. Why is a slight blow on the back of a rabbit's neck fatal?

30. Why can one walk and carry on a conversation at the same time?

31. What are the dangers of over-study?

32. What is the influence of idleness upon the brain?

33. State the close relation which exists between physical and mental health and disease.

34. In what consists the value of the power of habit?

35. How many pairs of nerves supply the eye?

36. Describe the reflex actions in reading aloud.

37. Under what circumstances does paralysis occur?

38. If the eyelids of a profound sleeper were raised, and a candle brought near, would the iris contract?

39. How does one cough in his sleep?

40. Give illustrations of the unconscious action of the brain.

41. Is chewing tobacco more injurious than smoking?

42. Ought a man to retire from business while his faculties are still unimpaired?

43. Which is the more exhaustive to the brain, worry or severe mental application?

44. Is it a blessing to be placed beyond the necessity for work?

45. Show how anger, hate, and the other degrading passions are destructive to the brain. †

---

* Here the nervous force is prevented from passing by compression. Just how this is done, or what is kept from passing, we can not tell. If a current of electricity were moving through a rubber tube full of mercury, a slight squeeze would interrupt it. These cases may depend on the same general principle, but we can not assert it.—HUXLEY. The tingling sensation caused by the compression is transferred to the foot, whence the nerve starts.

† "One of the surest means for keeping the body and mind in perfect health consists in learning to hold the passions in subservience to the reasoning faculties. This rule applies to every passion. Man, distinguished from all other animals by the peculiarity

46. Are not amusements, to repair the waste of the nervous energy, especially needed by persons whose life is one of care and toil?

47. Is not severe mental labor incompatible with a rapidly-growing body?

48. How shall we induce the system to perform all its functions regularly?

49. How does alcohol interfere with the action of the nerves?

50. What is the general effect of alcohol upon the character?

51. Does alcohol tend to produce clearness and vigor of thought?

52. What is the general effect of alcohol on the muscles?

53. Does alcohol have any effect on the bones? The skin?

54. What is the cause of the "alcoholic chill"?

55. Show how alcohol tends to develop man's lower, rather than his higher, nature.

56. When we wish really to strengthen the brain, should we use alcohol?

57. Why is alcohol used to preserve anatomical specimens?

58. What is meant by an inherited taste for liquor?

59. Ought a person to be punished for a crime committed during intoxication?

60. Should a boy ever smoke?

61. To what extent are we responsible for the health of our body?

62. Why does alcohol tend to collect in the brain?

63. Does the use of alcohol tend to increase crime and poverty?

---

that his reason is placed above his passions to be the director of his will, can protect himself from every mere animal degradation resulting from passionate excitement. The education of the man should be directed not to suppress such passions as are ennobling, but to bring all under governance, and specially to subdue those most destructive passions, anger, hate, and fear."

VIII.

THE SPECIAL SENSES.

" SEE how yon beam of seeming white
    Is braided out of seven-hued light;
    Yet in those lucid globes no ray
    By any chance shall break astray.
    Hark, how the rolling surge of sound,
    Arches and spirals circling round,
    Wakes the hush'd spirit through thine ear
    With music it is heaven to hear."

                               HOLMES.

"Let us remember that if we get a glimpse of the details of natural phenomena, and of those movements which constitute life, it is not in considering them as a whole, but in analyzing them as far as our limited means will permit. In the vibrations of the globe of air which surrounds our planet, as in the undulations of the ether which fills the immensity of space, it is always by molecules which are intangible for us, put in motion by nature, always by the infinitely little, that she acts in exciting the organs of sense, and she has modeled these organs in a proportion which enables them to partake in the movement which she impresses upon the universe. She can paint with equal facility on a fraction of a line of space on the retina, the grandest landscape or the nervelets of a rose-leaf; the celestial vault on which Sirius is but a luminous point, or the sparkling dust of a butterfly's wing: the roar of the tempest, the roll of thunder, the echo of an avalanche, find equal place in the labyrinth whose almost imperceptible cavities seem destined to receive only the most delicate sounds."

ANALYSIS OF THE SPECIAL SENSES.

THE SPECIAL SENSES.

1. THE TOUCH...
   1. Description of the Organ.
   2. Its Uses.

2. THE TASTE...
   1. Description of the Organ.
   2. Its Uses.

3. THE SMELL...
   1. Description of the Organ.
   2. Its Uses.

4. THE HEARING
   1. Description of the Organ...........
      a. *External Ear.*
      b. *Middle Ear.*
      c. *Internal Ear.*
   2. How we hear.
   3. Hygiene of the Ear.

5. THE SIGHT....
   1. Description of the Organ.
   2. Eyelids, and Tears.
   3. Structure of the Retina.
   4. How we see.
   5. The Use of the Crystalline Lens.
   6. Near and Far Sight.
   7. Color-blindness.
   8. Hygiene of the Eyes.

THE SPECIAL SENSES.

1. TOUCH.

Description. — Touch is sometimes called the "common sense," since its nerves are spread over the whole body. It is most delicate, however, in the point of the tongue and the tips of the fingers. The surface of the cutis is covered with minute, conical projections called *papillæ* (Fig. 24).* Each one of these papillæ contains its tiny nerve-twigs, which receive the impression and transmit it to the brain, where the perception is produced.

Uses. — Touch is the first of the senses used by a child. By it we obtain our idea of solidity, and throughout life rectify all other sensations. Thus, when we see any thing curious, our first desire is to handle it.

The sensation of touch is generally relied upon, yet, if we hold a marble in the manner shown in Fig. 57, it will seem like two marbles; and if we touch the fingers thus crossed to our tongue, we shall seem to feel two tongues. Again, if we close our eyes and let another person move one of our fingers over a plane surface, first lightly, then with

---

* In the palm of the hand, where there are at least twelve thousand in a square inch, we can see the fine ridges along which they are arranged.

greater pressure, and then lightly again, we shall think the surface concave.

FIG. 57.

This organ is capable of wonderful cultivation. The physician acquires by practice the *tactus eruditus*, or learned touch, which is often of great service, while the delicacy of touch possessed by the blind almost compensates the loss of the absent sense.* (See p. 346.)

2. TASTE.

Description.—This sense is located in the papillæ of the tongue and palate. These papillæ start up when tasting, as you can see by placing a drop of vinegar on another person's tongue, or your own before a mirror. The velvety look of this organ is given by hair-like projections of the cuticle upon

---

* The sympathy between the different organs shows how they all combine to make a home for the mind. When one sense fails, the others endeavor to remedy the defect. It is touching to see how the blind man gets along without eyes, and the deaf without ears. Cuthbert, though blind, was the most efficient polisher of telescopic mirrors in London. Saunderson, the successor of Newton as professor of mathematics at Cambridge, could distinguish between real and spurious medals. There is an instance recorded of a blind man who could recognize colors. The author knew one who could tell when he was approaching a tree, by what he described as the "different feeling of the air."

some of the papillæ. They absorb the liquid to be tasted, and convey it to the nerves.* The back of

FIG. 58.

The Tongue, showing the three kinds of Papillæ—the conical (D),the whip-like (K,I) the circumvallate or entrenched (H, L) ; E, F, G, nerves ; C, glottis.—LANKESTER.

the tongue is most sensitive to salt and bitter sub- stances, and, as this part is supplied by the ninth pair of nerves (Fig. 56), in sympathy with the stom- ach, such flavors, by sympathy, often produce vom- iting. The edges of the tongue are most sensitive to sweet and sour substances, and as this part is sup-

---

* An insoluble substance is therefore tasteless.

plied by the fifth pair of nerves, which also goes to the face, an acid, by sympathy, distorts the countenance.

The Use of the Taste was originally to guide in the selection of food; but this sense has become so depraved by condiments and the force of habit that it would be a difficult task to tell what are one's natural tastes.

3. SMELL.*

Description.—The nose, the seat of the sense of smell, is composed of cartilage covered with muscles and skin, and joined to the skull by small bones. The nostrils open at the back into the pharynx, and are lined by a continuation of the mucous membrane of the throat. The olfactory nerves (first pair, Fig. 55) enter through a sieve-like, bony plate at the roof of the nose, and are distributed over the inner surface of the two olfactory chambers. (See p. 346.) The object to be smelled need not touch the nose, but tiny particles borne on the air enter the nasal passages.†

* The sense of smell is so intimately connected with that of taste that we often fail to distinguish between them. Garlic, vanilla, coffee and various spices, which seem to have such distinct taste, have really a powerful odor, but a feeble flavor.

† Three quarters of a grain of musk placed in a room will cause a powerful smell for a considerable length of time without any sensible diminution in weight, and the box in which musk has been placed retains the perfume for almost an indefinite period. Haller relates that some papers which had been perfumed by a grain of ambergris, were still very odoriferous after a lapse of forty years. Odors are transported by the air to a considerable distance. A dog recognizes his master's approach by smell even when he is far away; and we are assured by navigators that the winds bring the delicious odors of the balmy forests of Ceylon to a distance of ten leagues from the coast. Even after making due allowance for the effects of the imagination, it is certain that odors act as an excitant on the

Fig. 59.

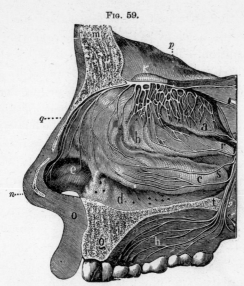

A, b, c, d, *interior of the nose, which is lined by a mucous membrane ;* n, *the nose ;* e, *the wing of the nose ;* q, *the nose bones ;* o, *the upper lip ;* g, *section of the upper jaw-bone ;* h, *the upper part of the mouth, or hard palate ;* m, *frontal bone of the skull ;* k, *the ganglion or bulb of the olfactory nerve in the skull, from which are seen the branches of the nerve passing in all directions.*

The Uses of the sense of smell are to guide us in the choice of our food, and to warn us against bad air, and unhealthy localities. (See p. 348.)

brain, which may be dangerous when long continued. They are especially dreaded by the Roman women. It is well known that in ancient times the women of Rome indulged in a most immoderate use of baths and perfumes; but those of our times have nothing in common with them in this respect; and the words of a lady are quoted, who said on admiring an artificial rose, "It is all the more beautiful that it has no smell." We are warned by the proverb not to discuss colors or tastes, and we may add odors also. Men and nations differ singularly in this respect. The Laplander and the Es-quimaux find the smell of fish-oil delicious. Wrangel says his compatriots, the Russians, are very fond of the odor of pickled cabbage, which forms an important part of their food; and asafœtida, it is said, is used as a condi-ment in Persia, and, in spite of its name, there are persons who do not find its odor disagreeable any more than that of valerian.— *Wonders of the Human body.*

16

4. HEARING.

Description.—The ear is divided into the *external, middle,* and *internal* ear.

1. *The External Ear* is a sheet of cartilage curiously folded for catching sound. The auditory canal, *B,* or tube of this ear-trumpet, is about an inch long. Across the lower end is stretched *the membrane of the tympanum* or drum, which is kept soft by a fluid wax.

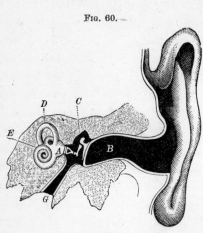

Fig. 60.

The Ear.

2. *The Middle Ear* is a cavity, at the bottom of which is the Eustachian tube, *G,* leading to the mouth. Across this chamber hangs a chain of three singular little bones, *C,* named from their shape the *hammer,* the *anvil,* and the *stirrup.* All together these tiny bones weigh only a few grains, yet they are covered by a periosteum, are supplied with blood-vessels, and they articulate with perfect joints (one a ball-and-socket, the other a hinge), having synovial membranes, cartilages, ligaments, and muscles.

3. *The Internal Ear,* or labyrinth, as it is sometimes called from its complex character, is hollowed

out of the solid bone. In front, is the vestibule or ante-chamber, *A*, about as large as a grain of wheat; from it open three *semicircular canals*, *D*, and the winding stair of the *cochlea*, or snail shell, *E*. Here expand the delicate fibrils of the auditory nerve. Floating in the liquid which fills the labyrinth is a little bag containing hair-like bristles, fine sand, and two ear-stones (*otoliths*). All these knocking against the ends of the nerves, serve to increase any impulse given to the liquid in which they lie. Finally, to complete this delicate apparatus, in the cochlea are minute tendrils, named the fibers of Corti, from their discoverer. These are regularly arranged,—the longest at the bottom, and the shortest at the top. Could this spiral plate, which coils two and a half times around, be unrolled and made to stand upright, it would form a beautiful microscopic harp of three thousand strings. If it were possible to strike these cords as one can the keyboard of a piano, he could produce in the mind of the person experimented upon every variety of tone which the ear can distinguish.

How We Hear.—Whenever one body strikes another in the air, waves are produced, just as when we throw a stone into the water a series of concentric circles surrounds the spot where it sinks. These waves of air strike upon the membrane. This vibrates, and sends the motion along the chain of bones in the middle ear to the fluids of the labyrinth. Here bristles, sand, and stones pound away, and the wondrous harp of the cochlea, catching up the pulsations,* carries them to the fibers of the auditory nerve, which conveys them to the brain, and gives to the mind the idea of sound.

Care of the Ear.—The delicacy of the ear is such that it needs the greatest care. Cold water should not be allowed to enter the auditory canal. If the wax accumulate, never remove it with a hard instrument, lest the delicate membrane be injured, but with a little warm water, after which turn the head to let the water run out, and wipe the ear dry. The hair around the ears should never be left wet, as it may chill this sensitive organ. If an insect get in the external ear, pour in a little oil to kill it, and then remove with tepid water. The object of the Eustachian tube is to admit air into the ear, and thus equalize the pressure on the membrane. If it become closed by a cold, or if, from any cause, the pressure be made unequal, so as to produce an unpleasant feeling in the ear, relief may often be obtained by grasping the nose and forcibly swallowing. (See p. 350.)

5. SIGHT.

Description.—The eye is lodged in a bony cavity, protected by the overhanging brow. It is a globe, about an inch in diameter. The ball is covered by

---

* The original motion is constantly modified by the medium through which it passes. The bristles, otoliths, and Cortian fibers of the ear, and the rods and cones of the eye (p. 239) serve to convert the vibrations into pulsations which act as *stimuli* of the appropriate nerve. The molecular change thus produced in the nerve-fibers is propagated to the brain.— See *Popular Physics*, p. 182.

three coats—(1) the *sclerotic, d,* a tough, horny casing, which gives shape to the eye, the convex, transparent part in front forming a window, the *cornea, c;*

FIG. 61.

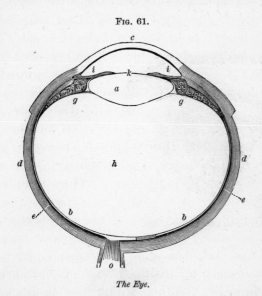

The Eye.

(2) the *choroid, e,* a black lining, to absorb the superfluous light;* and (3) the *retina, b,* a membrane in which expand fibers of the *optic nerve, o.* The *crystalline lens, a,* brings the rays of light to a focus on the retina. The lens is kept in place by the ciliary processes, *g,* arranged like the rays in the disk of a passion-flower. Between the cornea and the crystalline lens is a limpid fluid termed the *aqueous humor;* while the *vitreous humor*—a transparent,

---

* Neither white rabbits nor albinos have this black lining, and hence their sight is confused.

jelly-like liquid—fills the space (*h*) back of the crystalline lens. The pupil, *k*, is a hole in the colored, muscular curtain, *i*, the *iris* (rainbow). (See p. 352.)

Eyelids and Tears.—The eyelids are close-fitting shutters to screen the eye. The inner side is lined with a mucous membrane that is exceedingly sensitive, and thus aids in protecting the eye from any irritating substance. The looseness of the skin favors swelling from inflammation or the effusion of blood, as in a "black eye." The eyelashes serve as a kind of sieve to exclude the dust, and, with the lids, to shield against a blinding light. Just within the lashes are oil glands, which lubricate the edges of the lids, and prevent them from adhering to each other. The tear or *lachrymal* gland, *G*, is an oblong body lodged in the bony wall of the orbit. It empties by several ducts upon the inner surface, at the outer edge of the upper eyelid. Thence the tears, washing the eye, run into the *lachrymal lake*, *D*, a little basin with a rounded border fitted for their reception. On each side of this lake two canals, *C*, *C*, drain off the overplus through the duct, *B*, into the nose. In old age and in disease, these canals fail to conduct

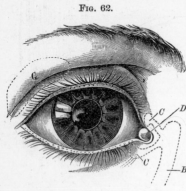

Fig. 62.

The Eyelashes and the Tear-glands.

the tears away, and hence the lachrymal lake over-flows upon the face.

Structure of the Retina.—In Fig. 63 is shown a section of the retina, greatly mag-nified, since this membrane never exceeds $\frac{1}{80}$ of an inch in thickness. On the inner surface next to the vitreous humor, is a lining mem-brane not shown in the cut. Next to the choroid and comprising about $\frac{1}{4}$ the entire thickness of the retina, is a multitude of transparent, color-less, microscopic rods, a, evenly ar-ranged and packed side by side, like the seeds on the disk of a sunflower. Among them, at regular intervals, are interspersed the cones, b. Delicate nerve fibers pass from the ends of the rods and cones, each expanding into a granular body, c, thence weaving a mesh, d, and again expanding into the gran-ules, f. Last is a layer of fine

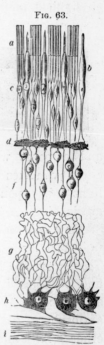

FIG. 63.

Structure of the Retina.

nerve-fibers, g, and gray, ganglionic cells, h, like the gray matter of the brain, whence filaments extend into i, the fibers of the optic nerve. (See p. 354.)

The layer of rods and cones is to the eye what the bristles, otoliths, and Cortian fibers are to the ear. Indeed, the nerve itself is insensible to light. At the point where it enters the eye, there are no rods and cones, and this is called the *blind spot*. A simple experiment will illustrate the fact. Hold this book directly before the face, and, closing the left eye, look steadily with the right at the left-hand circle in Fig. 64. Move the book back and forth,

FIG. 64.

and a point will be found where the right-hand circle vanishes from sight. At that moment its light falls upon the spot where the rods and cones are lacking.

How We See.—There is believed to be a kind of universal atmosphere, termed *ether*, filling all space. This substance is infinitely more subtle than the air, and occupies its pores, as well as those of all other substances. As sound is caused by waves in the atmosphere, so light is produced by waves in the ether. A lamp-light, for example, sets in motion waves of ether, which pass in through the pupil of the eye, to the retina, where the rods and cones transmit the vibration through the optic nerve to the brain, and then the mind perceives the light. (Note, p. 236.)

The Use of the Crystalline Lens.*—A convex lens, as a common burning-glass, bends the rays of

---

* The uses of the eye and ear are dependent upon the principles of Optics and Acoustics. They are therefore best treated in Physics.

light which pass through it, so that they meet at a
point called the *focus.* The crystalline lens con-
verges the rays of light which enter the eye, and

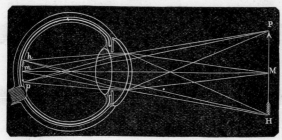

*Diagram showing how an image of an object is formed upon the Retina by the
Crystalline Lens.*

brings them to a focus on the retina.* The healthy
lens has a power of changing its convexity so as
to adapt † itself to near and to distant objects. (See
Fig. 66.)

Near and Far Sight.—If the lens be too convex,
it will bring the rays to a focus before they reach
the retina; if too flat, they will reach the retina be-

---

* The cornea and the humors of the eye act in the same manner as
the crystalline lens, but not so powerfully.

† The simplest way of experimenting on the "adjustment of the eye"
is to stick two stout needles upright into a straight piece of wood,—not
exactly, but nearly in the same straight line, so that, on applying the eye
to one end of the piece of wood, one needle (*A*) shall be seen about six
inches off, and the other (*B*) just on one side of it, at twelve inches distance. If the observer looks at the needle *B* he will find that he sees it
very distinctly, and without the least sense of effort; but the image of *A*
is blurred, and more or less double. Now, let him try to make this blurred
image of the needle *A* distinct. He will find he can do so readily enough,
but that the act is accompanied by a sense of fatigue. And in proportion
as *A* becomes distinct, *B* will become blurred. Nor will any effort enable
him to see *A* and *B* distinctly at the same time.—HUXLEY.

fore coming to a focus. In either case, the sight will be indistinct. A more common defect, however, is in the shape of the globe of the eye, which is either flattened or elongated. In the former case (see *G*, Fig. 67), objects at a distance can be seen most distinctly —hence that is called far-sightedness.* In

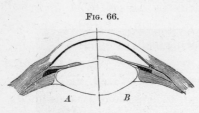

FIG. 66.

Adjustment of the Crystalline Lens.—A, *for far objects, and* B, *for near.*

the latter, objects near by are clearer, and hence this is termed near-sightedness. Far-sightedness is remedied by convex glasses; near-sightedness, by con-

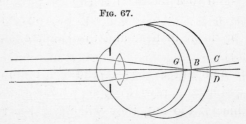

FIG. 67.

Diagram illustrating the position of the Retina.—B, *in natural sight;* G, *in far sight; and* C, *in near sight.*

cave. When glasses will improve the sight they should be worn; † any delay will be liable to injure

* This should not be confounded with the long sight of old people, which is caused by the stiffness of the ciliary muscles, whereby the lens can not adapt itself to the varying distances of objects.

† Dr. Henry W. Williams, the celebrated ophthalmologist, says that, in some cases, glasses are more necessary at six or eight years of age than to the majority of healthy eyes at sixty. Sometimes children find accidentally that they can see better through grandmother's spectacles. They should then be supplied with their own.

the eyes, by straining their already impaired power. Cataract is a disease in which there is an opacity of the crystalline lens or its capsules, which obscures the vision. The lens may be caused to be absorbed, or may be removed by a skillful surgeon and the defect remedied by wearing convex glasses.

Color-blind Persons receive only two of the three elementary color-sensations (green, red, violet). The spectrum appears to them to consist of two decidedly different colors, with a band of neutral tint between. The extreme red end is invisible, and a bright scarlet and a deep green appear alike. They are unable to distinguish between the leaves of a cherry-tree and its fruit by the color of the two, and see no difference between blue and yellow cloth. Whittier, the poet, it is said, can not tell red from green unless in direct sunlight. Once he patched some damaged wall-paper in his library by matching a green vine in the pattern with one of a bright autumnal crimson. This defect in the eye is often unnoticed, and many railway accidents have doubtless happened through an inability to detect the color of signal lights.

Care of the Eyes.—The shape of the eye can not be changed by rubbing and pressing it, as many suppose, but the sight may thus be fatally injured. Children troubled by near-sightedness should not lean forward at their work, as thereby the vessels of the eye become overcharged with blood. They should avoid fine print, and try, in every possible way, to spare their eyes. If middle age be reached without especial difficulty of sight, the person is comparatively safe. Most cases of squinting are caused by long-sightedness, the muscles being strained in the effort to obtain distinct vision. In childhood, it may be cured by a competent surgeon, who will generally cut the muscle that draws the eye out of place.

After any severe illness, especially after measles, scarlatina, or typhoid fever, the eyes should be used with extreme caution, since they share in the general debility of the body, and recover their strength slowly. Healthy eyes even should never be used to read fine print or by a dim light. Serious injury may be caused by an imprudence of this kind. Reading upon the cars is also a fruitful source of harm. The lens, striving to adapt itself to the incessantly-varying distance of the page, soon becomes wearied. Whenever the eyes begin to ache, it is a warning that they are being overtaxed and need rest.

Objects that get into the eye should be removed before they cause inflammation; rubbing in the meantime only irritates and increases the sensitiveness. If the eye be shut for a few moments, so as to let the tears accumulate, and the upper lid be then lifted by taking hold of it at the center, the cinder or dust is often washed away at once. Trifling objects can be removed by simply drawing the upper lid as far as possible over the lower one; when the lid flies back to its place, the friction will detach any light substance. If it becomes necessary, turn the upper lid over a pencil, and the intruder may then be wiped off with a handkerchief. "Eye-stones" are a popular delusion. When they seem to take out a cinder, it is only because they raise the eyelid, and allow the tears to wash it out. No one should ever use an eye-wash, except by medical advice. The eye is too delicate an organ to be trifled with, and when any disease is suspected, a reliable physician should be consulted. This is especially necessary, since, when one eye is injured, the other, by sympathy, is liable to become inflamed, and perhaps be destroyed.

When reading or working, the *light should be at the left side, or at the rear; never in front.*

The constant increase of defective eyesight among the pupils in our schools is an alarming fact. Dr. Agnew considers that our school-rooms are fast making us a spectacle-using people. Near-sightedness seems to increase from class to class, until in the upper departments, there are sometimes as high as fifty per cent. of the pupils thus afflicted. The causes are (1), desks so placed as to make the light from the windows shine directly into the eyes of the scholars; (2), cross-lights from opposite windows; (3), insufficient light; (4), small type that strains the eyes; and (5), the position of the pupil as he bends over his desk or slate, causing the blood to settle in his eyes. All these causes can be remedied; the position of the desks can be changed; windows can be shaded, or new ones inserted; books and newspapers that try the eyes can be rejected; and every pupil can be taught how to sit at study.

PRACTICAL QUESTIONS.

1. Why does a laundress test the temperature of her flat-iron by holding it near her cheek?

2. When we are cold, why do we spread the palms of our hands before the fire?

3. What is meant by a "furred tongue"?

4. Why has sand or sulphur no taste?

5. What was the origin of the word palatable?

6. Why does a cold in the head injure the flavor of our coffee?

7. Name some so-called flavors that are really sensations of touch.

8. What is the object of the hairs in the nostrils?

9. What use does the nose subserve in the process of respiration?

10. Why do we sometimes hold the nose when we take unpleasant medicine?

11. Why was the nose placed over the mouth?

12. Describe how the hand is adapted to be the instrument of touch.

13. Besides being the organ of taste, what use does the tongue subserve?

14. Why is not the act of tasting complete until we swallow?

15. Why do all things have the same flavor when one's tongue is "furred" by fever?

16. Which sense is the more useful—hearing or sight?

17. Which coat is the white of the eye?

18. What makes the difference in the color of eyes?

19. Why do we snuff the air when we wish to obtain a distinct smell?

20. Why do red-hot iron and frozen mercury (−40°) produce the same sensation?

21. Why can an elderly person drink tea which to a child would be unbearably hot?

22. Why does an old man hold his paper so far from his eyes?

23. Would you rather be punished on the tips of your fingers than on the palm of your hand?

24. What is the object of the eyelashes? Are the hairs straight?

25. What is the use of winking?

26. When you wink, do the eyelids touch at once along their whole length? Why?

27. How many rows of hairs are there in the eyelashes?

28. Do all nations have eyes of the same shape?

29. Why does snuff-taking cause a flow of tears?

30. Why does a fall cause one to "see stars"?

31. Why can we not see with the nose, or smell with the eyes?

32. What causes the roughness of a cat's tongue?

33. Is the cuticle essential to touch?

34. Can one tickle himself?

35. Why does a bitter taste often produce vomiting?

36. Is there any danger in looking "cross-eyed" for fun?

37. Should school-room desks face a window?

38. Why do we look at a person to whom we are listening attentively?

39. Do we really feel with our fingers?

40. Is the eye a perfect sphere? (See Fig. 61.)

41. How often do we wink?

42. Why is the interior of a telescope or microscope often painted black?

43. What is "the apple of the eye"?

44. What form of glasses do old people require?

45. Should we ever wash our ears with cold water?

46. What is the object of the winding passages in the nose?

47. Can a smoker tell in the dark, whether or not his cigar is lighted?

48. Will a nerve re-unite after it has been cut?

49. Will the sight give us an idea of solidity?*

---

* A case occurred a few years ago, in London, where a friend of my own performed an operation upon a young woman who had been born blind, and, though an attempt had been made in early years to cure her, it had failed. She was able just to distinguish large objects, the general shadow, as it were, without any distinct perception of form, and to distinguish light from darkness. She could work well with her needle by the touch, and could use her scissors and bodkin and other implements by the training of her hand, so to speak, alone. Well, my friend happened to see her, and he examined her eyes, and told her that he thought he could get her sight restored; at any rate, it was worth a trial. The operation succeeded; and, being a man of intelligence and quite aware of the interest of such a case, he carefully studied and observed it; and he completely confirmed all that had been previously laid down by the experience of similar cases. There was one little incident which will give you an idea of the education which is required for what you would suppose is a thing perfectly simple and obvious. She could not distinguish by sight the things that she was perfectly familiar with by the touch, at least when they were first presented to her eyes. She could not recognize even a pair of scissors. Now, you would have supposed that a pair of scissors, of all things in the world, having been continually used by her, and their form having become perfectly familiar to her hands, would have been most readily recognized by her sight; and yet she did not know what they were; she had not an idea until she was told, and then she laughed, as she said, at her own stupidity. No stupidity at all; she had never learned it, and it was one of those things which she could not know without learning. One of the earliest cases of this kind was related by the celebrated Cheselden, a surgeon of the early part of last century. Cheselden relates how a youth just in this condition had been accustomed to play with a cat and a dog; but for some time after he attained his sight he never could tell which was which, and used to be continually making mistakes. One day, being rather ashamed of himself for having called the cat the dog, he took up the cat in his arms and looked at her very attentively for some time, stroking her all the while; and in this way he associated the impression derived from the touch, and made himself master (so to speak) of the whole idea of the animal. He then put the cat down, saying: "Now, puss, I shall know you another time."—CARPENTER.

50. Why can a skillful surgeon determinate the condition of the brain and other internal organs by examining the interior of the eye?*

51. Is there any truth in the idea that the image of the murderer can be seen in the eye of the dead victim?

52. What is the length of the optic nerve? *Ans.* About three fourths of an inch.

53. Why does an injury to one eye generally affect the other eye?

Ans. The optic nerves give off no branches in passing from their origin in two ganglia situated between the cerebrum and the cerebellum, and their termination in the eyeballs; but, in the middle of their course, they *decussate*, or unite in one mass. The fibers of the two nerves here pass from side to side, and intermingle. The two ganglia are also united directly by fibers. Thus the eyes are not really separate organs of sight, but a kind of double organ to perform a single function.

---

* This is done by means of an instrument called the ophthalmoscope. Light is thrown into the eye with a concave mirror, and the interior of the organ examined with a lens.

IX.

HEALTH AND DISEASE.—DEATH AND DECAY.

"HEALTH is the vital principle of bliss."

THOMSON.

"There are three wicks to the lamp of a man's life: brain, blood, and breath. Press the brain a little, its light goes out, followed by both the others. Stop the heart a minute, and out go all three of the wicks. Choke the air out of the lungs, and presently the fluid ceases to supply the other centers of flame, and all is soon stagnation, cold, and darkness."

O. W. HOLMES.

"Calmly he looked on either Life, and here
Saw nothing to regret, or there to fear;
From Nature's temp'rate feast rose satisfy'd,
Thank'd Heaven that he had lived, and that he died."

POPE.

HEALTH AND DISEASE.—DEATH AND DECAY.

Value of Health. — The body is the instrument which the mind uses. If it be dulled or nicked, the effect of the best labor will be impaired. The grandest gifts of mind or fortune are comparatively valueless unless there be a healthy body to use and enjoy them. The beggar, sturdy and brave with his out-door life, is really happier than the rich man in his palace with the gout to twinge him amid his pleasures. The day has gone by when delicacy is considered an element of beauty. Weakness is timid and irresolute; strength is full of force and energy. Weakness walks or creeps; strength speeds the race, wins the goal, and rejoices in the victory.

False Ideas of Disease. — It was formerly supposed that diseases were caused by evil spirits, who entered the body and deranged its action. Incantations, spells, etc., were resorted to in order to drive them out. By others, disease was thought to come arbitrarily, or as a special visitation of an overruling power. Hence, it was to be removed by fasting and prayer. Modern science teaches us that disease is not a thing, but a state. When our food is properly assimilated, the waste matter promptly excreted, and all the organs work in harmony, we are well; when any derangement of these functions occurs, we are sick. Sickness is discord, as health is concord. If we abuse or misuse any instrument, we impair its ability to produce a perfect harmony. A suffering body is simply the penalty of violated law.

Prevention of Disease.—Doubtless a large proportion of the ills which now afflict and rob us of so much time and pleasure might easily be avoided. A proper knowledge and observance of hygienic laws would greatly lessen the number of such diseases as consumption, catarrh, gout, rheumatism, dyspepsia, etc. There are parts of England where one half the children die before they are five years old. Every physiologist knows that at least nine tenths of these lives could be saved by an observance of the simple laws of health. Professor Bennet, in a lecture at Edinburgh, estimated that one hundred thousand persons die annually in Great Britain from causes easily preventable.

With the advance of science, the causes of many diseases have been determined. Vaccination has been found to prevent or mitigate the ravages of small-pox. Scurvy, formerly so fatal among sailors that it was deemed "a mysterious infliction of Divine Justice against which man strives in vain," is now entirely avoided by the use of vegetables or lime-juice. Cholera, whose approach still strikes dread, and for which there is no known specific, is but the penalty for filthy streets, bad drainage, and over-crowded tenements, and may be controlled, if not prevented, by suitable sanitary measures. It was, no doubt, the intention that we should wear out by the general decay of all the organs,* rather than by the giving out of any single part, and that all should work together harmoniously until the vital force is exhausted.

Cure of Disease.—The first step in the cure of any disease is to obey the law of health which has been violated. If medicine be taken, it is not to destroy the disease, since that is not a thing to be destroyed, but to hold the deranged action in check while nature repairs the injury, and again brings the system into harmonious movement. This tendency of nature is our chief reliance. The best physicians are coming to have diminished confidence in medicine itself, and to place greater dependence upon sanitary and hygienic measures, and upon the efforts which nature always makes to repair injuries and soothe disordered action. They endeavor only to give to nature a fair chance, and sometimes to

---

* So long as the phenomena of waste and repair are in harmony—so long, in other words, as the builder follows the scavenger—so long man exists in integrity and repair—just, indeed, as houses exist. Derange nutrition, and at once degeneration, or rather let us say, alteration begins. Alas! that we are so ignorant that there are many things about our house, which, seeing them weaken, we know not how to strengthen. About the brick and the mortar, the frame and the rafters, we are not unlearned; but within are many complexities, many chinks and crannies, full in themselves of secondary chinks and crannies, and these so small, so deep, so recessed, that it happens every day that the destroyer settles himself in some place so obscure, that, while he kills, he laughs at defiance. You or I meet with an accident in our watch. We consult the watchmaker, and he repairs the injury. If we were all that watchmakers, like ourselves, should be, a man could be made to keep time until he died from old age or annihilating accident. This I firmly and fully believe.—*Odd Hours of a Physician.*

assist her by the intelligent employment of proper medicines. The indiscriminate use of patent nostrums and sovereign remedies of whose constituents we know nothing, and by which powerful drugs are imbibed at hap-hazard, can not be too greatly deprecated. When one needs medicine, he needs also a competent physician to advise its use.

Death and Decay.—By a mystery we can not understand, life is linked with death, and out of the decay of our bodies they, day by day, spring afresh. At last the vital force which has held death and decay in bondage, and compelled them to minister to our growth, and to serve the needs of our life, faints and yields the struggle. These powers which have so long time been our servants, gather about our dying couch, and their last offices usher us into the new life and the grander possibilities of the world to come. This last birth, we who see the fading, not the dawning, life, call death.

> " O Father! grant Thy love divine,
>   To make these mystic temples Thine,
>   When wasting age and wearying strife
>   Have sapp'd the leaning walls of life;
>   When darkness gathers over all,
>   And the last tottering pillars fall,
>   Take the poor dust Thy mercy warms,
>   And mold it into heavenly forms."
>   HOLMES.

HINTS ABOUT THE SICK-ROOM.

A Sick-room should be the lightest and cheeriest in the house. A small, close, dark bedroom or a recess is bad enough for one in health, but unendurable for a sick person. In a case of fever, and in many acute diseases, it should be remote from the noise of the family; but when one is recovering from an accident, and in all attacks where quiet is not needed, the patient may be where he can amuse himself by watching the movements of the household, or looking out upon the street.

The ventilation must be thorough. Bad air will poison both the sick and the well. A fire-place is, therefore, desirable. Windows should open easily. By carefully protecting the patient with extra blankets, the room may be frequently aired. If there be no direct draught, much may be done to change the air, by simply swinging an outer door to and fro many times.

A bare floor, with strips of carpet here and there to deaden noise, is cleanest, and keeps the air freest from dust. Cane-bottomed chairs are preferable to upholstered ones. All unnecessary furniture should be removed out of the way. A straw bed or a mattress is better than feathers. The bed-hangings, lace curtains, etc., should be taken down. Creaking hinges should be oiled. Sperm candles are better than kerosene lamps.

Never whisper in a sick-room. All necessary conversation should be carried on in the usual tone of voice. Do not call a physician unnecessarily, but if one be employed, *obey his directions* implicitly. Never give nostrums over-officious friends may suggest. Do not allow visitors to see the patient, except it be necessary. Never bustle about the room, nor go on tiptoe, but move in a quiet, ordinary way. Do not keep the bottles in the continued sight of the sick person. Never let drinking-water stand in the room.

Do not raise the patient's head to drink, but have a cup with a long spout, or use a bent tube, or even a straw. Do not tempt the appetite when it craves no food. Bathe frequently, but let the physician prescribe the method. Give written directions to the watchers. Have all medicines carefully marked. Remove all soiled clothing, etc., at once from the room. Change the linen much oftener than in health. When you wish to change the sheets, and the patient is unable to rise, roll the under sheet tightly lengthwise to the middle of the bed; put on the clean sheet, with half its width folded up, closely to the other roll; lift the patient on to the newly-made part, remove the soiled sheet, and then spread out the clean one.

DISINFECTANTS.

Remember, first, that deodorizers and disinfectants are not the same. A bad smell, for instance, may be smothered by some more powerful odor, while its cause remains uninfluenced. Bear also in mind the fact that no deodorizer and no disinfectant can take the place of perfect cleanliness and thorough ventilation. No purifyer can rival the oxygen contained in strong and continued currents of fresh, cold air, and every disinfectant finds an indispensable ally in floods of scalding water.

An excellent disinfectant may be made by dissolving in a pail of water either of the following: (1), a quarter of a pound of sulphate of zinc and two ounces of common salt for each gallon of water; (2), a pound and a half of copperas, for each gallon of water. Towels, bed-linen, handkerchiefs, etc., should be soaked at least an hour, in a solution of the first kind, and then be boiled, before washing.* Vaults, drains, vessels used in

---

* It is *best* to burn all articles which have been in contact with persons sick with contagious or infectious diseases.

In using the zinc solution, place the articles in it as soon as they are removed from the patient, and before they are taken from the room; if practicable, have the solution boiling hot at the time. In fumigating apartments, all the openings should be made as nearly air-tight as possible. The articles to be included in the fumigation should be so exposed and spread out that the sulphurous vapor may penetrate every portion of them. For a room about ten feet square, at least two pounds of sulphur should be used; for larger rooms, proportionally increased quantities. Put the sulphur in iron pans supported upon bricks placed in wash-tubs containing a

the sick-room, etc., should be disinfected by a solution of the second kind; chloride of lime may also be used for the same purpose. Rooms, furniture, and articles that can not be treated with the solution of the first kind, should be thoroughly fumigated with burning sulphur. Where walls are unpapered, re-whitewash with pure, freshly-slacked quicklime, adding one pint of the best fluid carbolic acid to every gallon of the fluid whitewash. Powdered stone lime sprinkled on foul, wet places, or placed in pans in damp rooms, will absorb the moisture; and dry, fresh charcoal-powder may be combined with it to absorb noxious gases.

WHAT TO DO TILL THE DOCTOR COMES.

The following instructions are intended simply to aid in an emergency. When accidents or a sudden severe illness occur, there is necessarily, in most cases, a longer or shorter interval before a physician can arrive. These moments are often very precious, and life may depend upon a little knowledge and much self-possession. The instructions are therefore given as briefly as possible, that they may be easily carried in the memory. A few suggestions in regard to common ailments are included.

Burns.—When a person's clothes catch fire, quickly lay him on the ground, wrap him in a coat, mat, shawl, carpet, or in his own garments, as best you can to extinguish the flame. Pour on plenty of water till the half-burned clothing is cooled. Then carry the sufferer to a warm room, lay him on a table or a carpeted floor, and with a sharp knife or scissors remove his clothing.

The treatment of a burn consists in protecting from the air.* An excellent remedy is to apply soft cloths kept wet with sweet

---

little water, set it on fire by hot coals or with the aid of a spoonful of alcohol, or by a long fuse set on train as the last opening to the room is closed. Allow the apartment to remain sealed for twenty-four hours. Great care should be taken not to inhale the poisonous fumes in firing the sulphur. After the fumigation, allow free currents of air to pass through the apartment; expose all movable articles for as long time as may be to the sun and the wind out-of-doors; beat and shake the carpets, hangings, pillows, etc.

The disinfectants and the instructions for using them, as given above, are mainly those recommended by the National Board of Health.

* It is a great mistake to suppose that salves will "draw out the fire" of a burn, or heal a bruise or cut. The vital force must unite the divided tissue by the deposit of material and the formation of new cells.

oil, or with tepid water *which contains all the "cooking soda" that it will dissolve.* Afterward dress the wound with carbolic acid salve. Wrap a dry bandage upon the outside. Then remove the patient to a bed and cover warmly.* Apply cool water to a small burn till the smart ceases, and then cover with ointment. Do not remove the dressings until they become stiff and irritating; then take them from a part at a time; dress and cover again quickly.

Cuts, Wounds, etc.—The method of stopping the bleeding has been described on page 128. If an artery is severed, a physician should be called at once. If the bleeding is not profuse, apply cold water until it ceases, dry the skin, draw the edges of the wound together, and secure them by strips of adhesive plaster. Protect with an outer bandage. This dressing should remain for several days. In the meantime wet it frequently with cool water to subdue inflammation. When suppuration begins, wash occasionally with tepid water and Castile soap.

Dr. Woodbridge, of New York, in a recent address, gave the following directions as to "What to do in case of a sudden wound when the surgeon is not at hand." "An experienced person would naturally close the lips of the wound as quickly as possible, and apply a bandage. If the wound is bleeding freely, but no artery is spouting blood, the first thing to be done is to wash it with water at an ordinary temperature. To every pint of water add either five grains of corrosive sublimate, or two and a half tea-spoonfuls of carbolic acid. If the acid is used, add two table-spoonfuls of glycerine, to prevent its irritating the wound. If there is neither of these articles in the house, add four table-spoonfuls of borax to the water. Wash the wound, close it, and apply a compress of a folded square of cotton or linen. Wet it in the solution used for washing the wound and

---

* In case of a large burn, lose no delay in bringing a physician. If a burn be near a joint or on the face, even if small, let a doctor see it, and do not be in any hurry about having it healed. Remember that with all the care and skill which can be used, contractions will sometimes take place. The danger to life from a burn or scald is not in proportion to its severity, but to its extent—that is, a small part, such as a hand or a foot, may be burned so deeply as to cripple it for life, and yet not much endanger the general health; but a slight amount of burning, a mere scorching, over two thirds of the body, may prove fatal.—Hope.

bandage quickly and firmly. If the bleeding is profuse, a sponge dipped in very hot water and wrung out in a dry cloth should be applied as quickly as possible. If this is not available, use ice, or cloths wrung out in ice water. If a large vein or artery is spouting, it must be stopped at once by compression. This may be done by a rubber tube wound around the arm tightly above the elbow or above the knee, where the pulse is felt to beat; or an improvised 'tourniquet' may be used. A hard apple or a stone is placed in a folded handkerchief, and rolled firmly in place. This bandage is applied so that the hard object rests on the point where the artery beats, and is then tied loosely around the arm. A stick is thrust through the loose bandage and turned till the flow of blood ceases."

Bleeding from the Nose is rarely dangerous, and often beneficial. When it becomes necessary to stop it, sit upright and compress the nostrils between the thumb and forefinger, or with the thumb press upward upon the upper lip. A piece of ice, a snow-ball, or a compress wet with cold water may be applied to the back of the neck.

A Sprain* is often more painful and dangerous than a dislocation. Wrap the injured part in flannels wrung out of hot water, and cover with a dry bandage, or, better, with oiled silk. Liniments and stimulating applications are injurious in the first stages, but useful when the inflammation is subdued. *Do not let the limb hang down; keep the joint still.* Without attention to these points, no remedies are likely to be of much service. A sprained limb must be kept quiet, even after all pain has ceased. If used too soon, dangerous consequences may ensue. Many instances have been known in which, from premature use of an injured limb, the inflammation has been renewed and made chronic, the bones at the joint have become permanently diseased, and amputation has been necessitated.

---

* "A sprain," says Dr. Hope, in that admirable little book entitled *Till the Doctor comes and How to help Him*, "is a very painful and very serious thing. When you consider that from the tips of the fingers to the wrist, or from the ends of the toes to the leg, there are not less than thirty separate bones, all tied together with straps, cords, and elastic bands, and about twenty hinges, all to be kept in good working order, you will not wonder at sprains being frequent and sometimes serious."

Diarrhea, Cholera Morbus, etc., are often caused by eating indigestible or tainted food, such as unripe or decaying fruit, or stale vegetables; or by drinking impure water or poisoned milk (see p. 321). Sometimes the disturbance may be traced to a checking of the perspiration; but more frequently to peculiar conditions of the atmosphere, especially in large cities. Such diseases are most prevalent in humid weather, when the days are hot and the nights cold and moist. Especial attention should at such times be paid to the diet. If an attack comes on, ascertain, if possible, its cause. You can thereby aid your physician, and, if the cause be removable, can protect the rest of the household. If the limbs are cold, take a hot bath, followed by a thorough rubbing. Then go to bed and lie quietly on the back. In ordinary cases, rest is better than medicine. If there be pain, have flannels wrung out of hot water applied to the abdomen.* A mustard poultice will serve the same purpose if more convenient. Eat no fruit, vegetables, pastry, or pork. Use water sparingly. If much thirst exist, give small pieces of ice, or limited quantities of cold tea or toast-water. Take particular pains with the diet for some days after the bowel-irritation has ceased.

Croup.—There are two kinds of croup—true and false. True croup comes on gradually, and is less likely to excite alarm than false croup, which comes on suddenly. True croup is attended with fever and false membrane in the throat; false croup is not attended with fever or false membrane. True croup is almost always fatal in four or five days; false croup recovers, but is liable to come on again. The great majority of cases of the so-called croup are simply cases of spasm of the glottis. "Croupy children" are those who are liable to these attacks of false croup, which are most frequent during the period of teething.—DR. GEO. M. BEARD. Croup occurs commonly in children between the ages of two and seven years. At this period, if a child has a hollow cough, with more or less fever, flushed face, red watery eyes, and especially *if it have a hoarse voice, and*

---

* If it be difficult to manage the foments, lay a hot plate over the flannels and cover with some protection. By having a change of hot plates, the foments can be kept at a uniform high temperature. This plan will be found useful in all cases where foments are needed.

show signs of uneasiness about the throat, send at once for a doctor. Induce mild vomiting by doses of syrup of ipecac. Put the feet in a hot mustard and water bath. Apply hot fomentations, rapidly renewed, to the chest and throat. A "croupy" child should be carefully shielded from all physical excitation, sudden waking from sleep, and any punishment that tends to awaken intense fear or terror. Irritation of the air-passages through faulty swallowing in drinking hastily, should be guarded against. Good pure air, warm clothing, and a nourishing diet are indispensable.

Common Sore Throat.—Wrap the neck in a wet bandage, and cover with flannel or a clean woolen stocking. Gargle the throat frequently with a solution of a tea-spoonful of salt in a pint of water, or thirty grains of chlorate of potash in a wine-glass of water.

Fits, Apoplexy, Epilepsy, etc.—These call for immediate action and prompt medical attendance. Children who are teething, or troubled with intestinal worms, or from various causes, are sometimes suddenly seized with convulsions. Apply cloths wet in cold water—or, better still, ice wrapped in oiled silk—to the head, and *especially to the back of the neck,* taking care, however, that the ice or wet cloths do not remain too long. Apply mustard plasters to the stomach and legs. A full hot bath is excellent if the cold applications fail. Endeavor to induce vomiting. Seek to determine the cause, and consult with your physician for further guidance.

Apoplexy may be distinguished from a fainting fit by the red face, hot skin, and labored breathing ; whereas, in a faint, the face and lips lose color, and the skin becomes cold. In many cases, death follows so quickly upon an apoplectic seizure, that little effectual service can be given. Call the nearest physician, loosen the clothing, and raise the head and shoulders, taking care not to bend the head forward on the neck. Keep the head cool. Do not move the patient unnecessarily.

In a common fainting fit, give the patient as much air as possible. Lay him flat upon the floor or ground, and keep the crowd away.

All that can be done in a fit of epilepsy is to prevent the patient from injuring himself ; especially put something in his mouth to keep him from biting his tongue. A cork, a piece of India rubber, or even a tightly-rolled handkerchief, placed between the teeth will answer this purpose. Give the sufferer fresh air; loosen his clothing, and place him in a comfortable position. Epilepsy may be due to various causes,—improper diet, overexcitement, etc. Consult with a physician, and study to avoid the occasion.

Concussion of the Brain generally arises from some contusion of the head, from violent blows, or from a shock received by the whole body in consequence of falling from a height. In any case of injury to the head where insensibility ensues, a doctor should be called at once. Remove the patient to a quiet room; loosen his clothing; strive to restore circulation by gentle friction, using the hand or a cloth for this purpose; apply cold water to the head, and, if the patient's body be cold and his skin clammy, put hot bottles at his feet. Ammonia may be cautiously held to the nose. Beyond this, it is not safe for a nonprofessional to go, in case of a severe injury to the head. Concussion is more or less serious, according to the injury which the brain has sustained; but even in slight cases, when a temporary dizziness appears to be the only result, careful treatment should be observed both at the time of the injury and afterward. Cases of head-injury are often more grave in their consequences than in their immediate symptoms. Sometimes the patient appears to be getting better when really he is worse. Rest and quiet should be observed for several weeks after an accident which has in any way affected the brain.

Toothache and Earache.—Insert in the hollow tooth cotton wet with laudanum, spirits of camphor, or chloroform. When the nerve is exposed, wet it with creosote or carbolic acid. Hot cloths or a hot brick wrapped in cloth and held to the face will often relieve the toothache. In a similar manner treat the ear, wetting the cloth in hot water, and letting the vapor pass into the ear.

Choking.—Ordinarily a smart blow between the shoulders, causing a compression of the chest and a sudden expulsion of the air from the lungs, will throw out the offending substance. If the person can swallow, and the object be small, give plenty of bread or potato, and water to wash it down. Press upon the tongue with a spoon, when, perhaps, you may see the object, and draw it out with your thumb and finger, or a blunt pair of scissors. If neither of these remedies avail, give an emetic of syrup of ipecac or mustard and warm water.

Frost Bites are frequently so sudden that one is not aware when they occur. In Canada it is not uncommon for persons meeting in the street to say, "Mind, sir, your nose looks whitish." The blood cools and runs slowly, and the blood-vessels become choked and swollen. *Keep from the heat.* Rub the part quickly with snow, if necessary for hours, till the natural color is restored. If one is benumbed with cold, take him into a cold room, remove the wet clothes, rub the body dry, cover with blankets, and give a little warm tea or other suitable drink. On recovering, let him be brought to a fire gradually.*

Fevers, and many acute diseases, are often preceded by a loss of appetite, headache, shivering, "pains in the bones," indisposition to work, etc. In such cases, sponge with tepid water, and rub the body till all aglow. Go to bed, place hot bricks to the feet, take nothing but a little gruel or beef tea, and drink moderately of warm, cream-of-tartar water. If you do not feel better the next morning, call a physician. If that be impossible, take a dose of castor-oil or Epsom salt.

Sun-stroke is a sudden prostration caused by intense heat. The same effect is produced by the burning rays of the sun and the fierce fire of a furnace. When a person falls under such circumstances, place your hand on his chest. If the skin be cool and moist, it is not a sun-stroke; but if it be dry and "biting hot," there can be no mistake. Time is now precious. At once carry the sufferer to the nearest pump or hydrant, and dash cold water on the head and chest until consciousness is restored.—DR. H. C. WOOD.

To prevent sun-stroke, wear a porous hat, and in the top of it place a wet handkerchief; also drink freely of water, not ice-cold, to induce abundant perspiration.

---

* If you are caught in a snow-storm, look for a snow-bank in the lee of a hill, or a wood out of the wind, or a hollow in the plain filled with snow. Scrape out a hole big enough to creep into, and the drifting snow will keep you warm. Men and animals have been preserved after days of such imprisonment. Remember that if you give way to sleep in the open field, you will never awake.

Asphyxia, or apparent death, whether produced by drowning, suffocation, bad air, or coal gas, requires very similar treatment. Send immediately for blankets, dry clothing, and a physician. Treat the sufferer upon the spot, if the weather be not too unfavorable.

1. Loosen the clothing about the neck and chest.

2. Turn the patient on his face, open the mouth, draw out the tongue, and cleanse the nostrils, so as to clear the air-passages.

3. Place the patient on his back, grasp his arms firmly above the elbows, and pull them gently upward until they meet over the head, in order to draw air into the lungs. Then bring the arms back by the side, to expel the air. Repeat the process about fifteen times per minute. Alternate pressure upon the chest, and blowing air into the mouth through a quill or with a pair of bellows, may aid your efforts. Excite the nostrils with snuff or smelling salts, or by passing hartshorn under the nose. Do not cease effort while there is hope. Life has been restored after five hours of suspended animation.*

4. When respiration is established, wrap the patient in dry, warm clothes, and rub the limbs under the blankets or over the dry clothing energetically *toward the heart.* Apply heated flannels, bottles of hot water, etc., to the limbs, and mustard plasters † to the chest.

Foreign Bodies in the Ear.—Insects may be killed by dropping a little sweet-oil into the ear. Beans, peas, etc., may generally be removed by so holding the head that the affected ear will be toward the ground, and then *cautiously* syringing tepid water into it from below. Do not use much force lest the

---

* Another simple method of artificial respiration is described in the *British Medical Journal.* The body of the patient is laid on the back, with clothes loosened, and the mouth and nose wiped; two by-standers pass their right hands under the body at the level of the waist, and grasp each other's hand, then raise the body until the tips of the fingers and the toes of the subject alone touch the ground; count fifteen rapidly; then lower the body flat to the ground, and press the elbows to the side hard; count fifteen again; then raise the body again for the same length of time; and so on, alternately raising and lowering. The head, arms, and legs are to be allowed to dangle down freely when the body is raised.

† The best mustard poultice is the paper plaster now sold by every druggist. It is always ready, and can be carried by a traveler. It has only to be dipped in water, and applied at once.

tympanum be injured. If this fail, dry the ear, stick the end of a little linen swab into thick glue, let the patient lie on one side, put this into the ear until it touches the substance, keep it there three quarters of an hour while it hardens, and then draw them all out together. Be careful that the glue does not touch the skin at any point, and that you are at work upon the right ear. Children often deceive one as to the ear which is affected.

Foreign Bodies in the Nose, such as beans, cherry-pits, etc., may frequently be removed by closing the opposite nostril, and then blowing into the child's mouth forcibly. The air, unable to escape except through the affected nostril, will sweep the obstruction before it.

ANTIDOTES TO POISONS.

Acids: *Nitric* (aqua fortis), *hydrochloric* (muriatic), *sulphuric* (oil of vitriol), *oxalic*, etc.—Drink a little water to weaken the acid, or, still better, take strong soap-suds. Stir some magnesia in water, and drink freely. If the magnesia be not at hand, use chalk, soda, lime, whiting, soap, or even knock a piece of plaster from the wall, and scraping off the white outside coat pound it fine, mix with milk or water, and drink at once. Follow with warm water, or flax-seed tea.

Alkalies: *Potash, soda, lye, ammonia* (hartshorn).—Drink weak vinegar or lemon juice. Follow with castor or linseed oil, or thick cream.

Antimony: *Antimonial Wine, tartar emetic,* etc.—Drink strong, green tea, and in the meantime chew the dry leaves. The direct antidote is a solution of nut-gall or oak-bark.

Arsenic: *Cobalt, Scheele's green, fly-powder, ratsbane,* etc.— Give *plenty of milk, whites of eggs,* or induce vomiting by mustard and warm water ; * or even soap-suds.

Bite of a Snake or a Mad Dog.—Tie a bandage above the wound, if on a limb. Wash the bite thoroughly, and, if possible, let the person suck it strongly. Rub some lunar caustic

* See that the mustard is well mixed with the water, in the proportion of about half an ounce of the former to a pint of the latter.

18

or potash in the wound, or heat the point of a small poker or a steel-sharpener white hot, and press it into the bite for a moment. It will scarcely cause pain, and will be effectual in arresting the absorption of the poison, unless a vein has been struck.

Copper: *Sulphate of copper* (blue vitriol), *acetate of copper* (verdigris).—Take whites of eggs or soda. Use milk freely.

Laudanum: *Opium, paregoric, soothing cordial, soothing syrup,* etc.—Give an emetic at once of syrup of ipecac, or mustard and warm water, etc. After vomiting, use strong coffee freely. *Keep the patient awake* by pinching, pulling the hair, walking about, dashing water in the face, and any expedient possible.

Lead: *White lead, acetate of lead* (sugar of lead), *red lead.*— Give an emetic of syrup of ipecac, or mustard and warm water, or salt and water. Follow with a dose of Epsom salt.

Matches: *Phosphorus.* — Give magnesia, chalk, whiting, or even flour in water, and follow with mucilaginous drinks.

Mercury: *Calomel, chloride of mercury* (corrosive sublimate, bug poison), *red precipitate.*—Drink milk copiously. Take the whites of eggs, or stir flour in water, and use freely.

Nitrate of Silver (lunar caustic).—Give salt and water, and follow with castor-oil.

Nitrate of Potash (salpeter, niter).—Give mustard and warm water, or syrup of ipecac. Follow with flour and water, and cream or sweet oil.

Prussic Acid (oil of bitter almonds), *cyanide of potassium.* —Take a tea-spoonful of hartshorn in a pint of water. Apply smelling salts to the nose, and dash cold water in the face.

Sting of an Insect.—Apply a little hartshorn or spirits of camphor, or soda moistened with water, or a paste of clean earth and saliva.

Sulphate of Iron (green vitriol).—Give syrup of ipecac, or mustard and warm water, or any convenient emetic; then magnesia and water.

X.

SELECTED READINGS

TO ILLUSTRATE AND SUPPLEMENT THE TEXT.

Arranged in order of the subjects to which they refer.

"READ not to contradict and confute, nor to believe and take for granted, nor to find talk and discourse, but to weigh and consider."

LORD BACON.

"He who learns the rules of wisdom without conforming to them in his life, is like a man who labored in his fields but did not sow."

SAADI.

SELECTED READINGS.

The figures indicate the pages in the text upon which the corresponding subjects will be found.

THE SKELETON.

Man, as Compared with other Vertebrate Animals (p. 3). —Man, the lord of the animal kingdom, is constructed after the same type as the cat that purrs at his feet, the ox that he eats, the horse that bears his burden, the bird that sings in his cage, the snake that crawls across his pathway, the toad that hides in his garden, and the fish that swims in his aquarium. All these are but modifications of one creative thought, showing how the Almighty Worker delights in repeating the same chord, with infinite variations. There are marked physical peculiarities, however, which distinguish man from the other mammals. Thus, the position of the spinal opening in the middle third of the base of the skull, thereby balancing the head and admitting an upright posture; the sigmoid S-curve of the vertebral column; the ability of opposing the well-developed thumb to the fingers; the shortened foot, the sole resting flat on the ground; the size and position of the great toe; the length of the arms, reaching half-way from the hip to the knees; the relatively great development of the brain; the freedom of the anterior extremities from use in locomotion, and the consequent erect and biped position. In addition, man is the only mammal that truly walks; that is endowed with the power of speech; and that is cosmopolitan, readily adapting himself to extremes of heat and cold, and making his home in all parts of the globe. —STEELE'S *Popular Zoology.*

Union of Fractures (p. 8).—In the course of a week after a fracture, there is a soft yet firm substance, something between ligament and cartilage in consistence, which surrounds the broken extremities of the bone, and adheres to it above and below. The neighboring muscles and tendons are closely at-

FIG. 68.

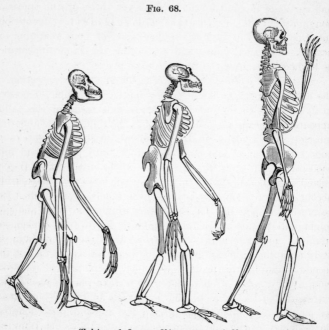

Skeleton of Orang, Chimpanzee, and Man.

tached to its surface, and the fractured extremities of the bone, lie, as it were, loose in a cavity in the center, with a small quantity of vascular albumen, resembling a semi-transparent jelly.

Here, then, is a kind of splint which nature contrives, and which is nearly completed within a week from the date of the accident. We call this new formation the *callus*. This process goes on, the surrounding substance becoming thicker and of still firmer consistence. In the course of a few days more, the thin jelly which lay in contact with the broken ends of the bone has disappeared, and its place is supplied by a callus continuous with that which formed the original capsule. This is the termination of the first stage of curative progress. The broken ends of the bones are now completely imbedded in a mass of vascular organized substance or callus, something between gristle and cartilage in consistence ; and as yet there are no traces of bony matter in it. At this time, if you remove the adventitious substance, you will find the broken ends of bone retaining exactly their original figure and presenting the same appearance as immediately after the fracture took place.

At the end of about three weeks, if you make a section of the callus, minute specks of earthy matter are visible, deposited in it here and there, and at the same time some of the callus appears to disappear on the outside, so that the neighboring muscles and tendons no longer adhere to it. The specks of bone become larger and more numerous until they extend into each other ; and thus by degrees the whole of the callus is converted into bone. Even at this period, however, there is not absolute bony union, for although the whole of the callus has become bone, it is not yet identified with the old bone, and you might still pick it off with a penknife, leaving the broken extremities not materially altered from what they were immediately after the injury. This may be regarded as the end of the second stage of the process by which a fracture is repaired. Now a third series of changes begins to take place. The broken extremities of the bones become intimately united by bony matter passing from one to the other. The mass of new bone on the outside, formed by the ossification of the callus, being no longer wanted, is absorbed ; by degrees the whole of it disappears, and the bone is left having the same dimensions which it had before the occurrence of the accident.

The process of union is completed in young persons sooner than in those advanced in life ; in the upper extremities sooner than in the lower ; and in smaller animals more speedily than in man. In human subjects a broken arm or fore-arm will be healed in from six to eight weeks, while a leg or thigh will occupy nine or ten weeks.—Sir B. C. Brodie.

The Hand and the Foot (p. 21).—*Man Compared with the*

Ape.—The peculiar prehensible power possessed by the hand of man is chiefly dependent upon the size and power of the thumb, which is more developed in him than it is in the highest apes. The thumb of the human hand can be brought into exact oppo-

FIG. 69.

a *b*

a. *Monkey's Hand and Foot.*
b. *Human Hand and Foot.*

sition to the extremities of all the fingers, whether singly or in combination; while in those quadrumana which most nearly approach man, the thumb is so short, and the fingers so much elongated, that their tips can scarcely be brought into opposition; and the thumb and the fingers are so weak that they can never be opposed to each other with any degree of force. Hence, though well suited to cling round bodies of a certain size, such as the small branches of trees, the

anterior extremities of the quadrumana can neither seize very minute objects with such precision nor support large ones with such firmness as are essential to the dexterous performance of a variety of operations for which the hand of man is admirably adapted.

The human foot is, in proportion to the size of the whole body, larger, broader, and stronger than that of any other mammal, save the kangaroo. The surface of the astragalus (ankle-bone) which articulates with the tibia, looks almost vertically upward, and hardly at all inward, when the sole is flat upon the ground; and the lateral facets are more nearly at right angles to this surface than in any ape. The plane of the foot is directed at right angles to that of the leg; and its sole is concave, so that the weight of the body falls on the summit of an arch, of which the os calcis (heel-bone) and the metatarsal bones form the two points of support. This arched form of the foot, and the contact of the whole plantar surface with the ground, are particularly noticeable in man, most of the apes having the os calcis small, straight, and more or less raised from the ground, while they touch, when standing erect, with the outer side only of the foot. The function of the *hallux*, or great toe, moreover, is strikingly contrasted in man and the ape; for, while in the latter it is nearly as opposable as the thumb, and can be used to almost the same extent as an instrument of prehension, it chiefly serves in the former to extend the basis of support, and to advance the body in progression.—DR. W. B. CARPENTER.

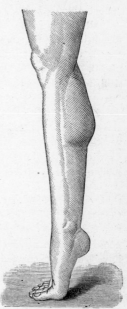

FIG. 70.

The Leg in standing.

The Natural Flexibility of the Toes, and How it is Destroyed.—We often admire the suppleness of the fingers by means of which we can perform such a variety of acts with swiftness and delicacy. Did it ever occur to you that the toes, which in most feet seem incapable of a free and graceful motion, even when they are not stiffened and absolutely deformed by the compression of the modern shoe, are also provided by Nature with a considerable degree of flexibility? The phalanges of the toes, though more feebly developed, have really the same movements among themselves as those of the fingers, and, in case of necessity, their powers can be strengthened and educated to a surprising degree. There are well-known instances of persons who, born without hands, or having lost them by accident, have successfully supplied the deficiency by a cultivated use of their feet. Some of these have distinguished themselves in the world of art. Who that has been so fortunate as to visit the Picture-Gallery in Antwerp on some fine morning when the armless artist, M. Felu, was working at his easel, can forget the wonderful dexterity with which he wielded his brushes, mixed the oils on his palette, and shaded the colors on his canvas, all with his agile feet? The writer well remembers the ease and grace with which, at the close of a pleasant interview, this cultured man put the tip of his foot into his coat-pocket, drew out a visiting card, wrote his name and address upon it, and presented it to her between his toes!

Contrast this intelligent adaptation of a delicate physical mechanism with the barbarous treatment it too commonly receives. The Chinese are at least consistent. They cripple and distort the feet of their high-born daughters until they crush out all the power and gracefulness of nature in the artificial formation of what they term a "golden lily"; but they never expect these golden-lilied women to make their withered feet useful. With us, on the contrary, every girl would like to walk well, to display in her general movements something of the "poetry of motion"; yet the absurd and arbitrary fashion of our foot-gear not only makes an elastic step one of the rarest of accomplishments, but renders oftentimes the simple act of walking a painful burden. The calluses, corns, bunions, ingrowing nails, and repulsive deformities that are caused by and hidden under the narrow-toed, high-heeled instruments of torture we often wear for fashion's sake are uncomfortable suggestions that our practices are not greatly in advance of those of our Celestial sisters. Dowie, a sensible Scotch shoemaker, satirizes the shape of a fashionable boot as suited only to "the foot of a goose with the great toe in the middle." The error which may have led to the adoption of this conventional shape appears to lie in a misconception of the natural formation of the foot, and of the relation of the two feet to each other. It is true, that when the toes are covered with their soft parts, the second toe appears a little longer than the first, and this appearance, emphasized and exaggerated, is perhaps responsible for a practical assumption that Nature intended an even-sided, tapering foot. On the contrary, the natural foot gradually expands in breadth from the instep to the toes and, in the skeleton itself, the great toe is the longest.

"There is no law of beauty," says Dr. Ellis, "which makes it necessary to reduce the foot to even-sided symmetry. An architect required to provide more space on one than on the other side of a building would not seek to conceal or even to minimize the difference; he would seek rather to accentuate it, and give the two sides of the structure distinctive features . . . . Moreover, the sense of symmetry is, or ought to be, satisfied by the exact correspondence of the two feet, which, taken jointly, may be described as the two halves of an unequally expanded dome."—E. B. S.

THE MUSCLES.

Attachment of the Muscles to the Bones (p. 30).—One of the two bones to which a muscle is attached is usually less mobile than the other, so that when the muscle shortens, the latter is drawn down against the former. In such a case, the point of attachment of the muscle to the less mobile bone is called its origin, while the point to which it is fixed on the more mobile bone is called its attachment. . . . A muscle is not always extended between two contiguous bones. Occasionally, passing over one bone it attaches itself to the next. This is the case with several muscles which, originating from the pelvic bone, pass across the upper thigh-bone, and attach themselves to the lower thigh-bone. In such cases the muscle is capable of two different movements : it can either stretch the knee, previously bent, so that the upper and the lower thigh-bones are in a straight line ; or it can raise the whole extended leg yet higher, and bring it nearer to the pelvis. But the points of origin and of attachment of muscles may exchange offices. When both legs stand firmly on the ground, the above-mentioned muscles are unable to raise the thigh ; instead, on shortening, they draw down the pelvis, which now presents the more mobile point, and thus bend forward the whole upper part of the body.

One important consequence of the attachment of the muscles to the bones is the extension thus effected. If the limb of a dead body is placed in the position which it ordinarily occupied during life, and if one end of a muscle is then separated from its point of attachment, it draws itself back, and becomes shorter. The same thing happens during life, as is observable in the operation of cutting the tendons, as practiced by surgeons to cure curvatures. The result being the same during life and after death, this phenomenon is evidently due to the action of elasticity. It thus appears that the muscles are stretched by reason of their attachment to the skeleton, and that, on account

of their elasticity, they are continually striving to shorten
Now, when several muscles are attached to one bone in such a
way that they pull in opposite directions, the bone must assume
a position in which the tension of all the muscles is balanced,
and all these tensions must combine to press together the
socketed parts with a certain force, thus evidently contributing
to the strength of the socket connection. . . . This balanced
position of all the limbs, which thus depends on the elasticity
of the muscles, may be observed during sleep, for then all
active muscular action ceases. It will be observed that the
limbs are then generally slightly bent, so that they form very
obtuse angles to each other.

Not all muscles are, however, extended between bones. The
tendons of some pass into soft structures, such as the muscles
of the face. In this case, also, the different muscles exercise a
mutual power of extension, though it is but slight, and they
thus effect a definite balanced position of the soft parts, as may
be observed in the position of the mouth-opening in the face.—
ROSENTHAL, *Muscles and Nerves*.

Muscular Fibers (p. 31).—The anatomical composition of
flesh is very similar in every kind of creature, whether it be the
muscle of the ox or of the fly; that is to say, there are certain
tubes which are filled with minute parts or elements, and the
adhesion of the tubes together makes up the substance of the
flesh. These tubes may be represented grossly by imagining the
finger of a glove, to be called the sarcolemma, or muscle-fiber
pouch, and this to be so small as not to be apparent to the
naked eye, but filled with nuclei and the juices peculiar to
each animal. Hundreds of such fingers attached together
would represent a bundle of muscular fibers. The tubes are
of fine tissue, but are tolerably permanent; whilst the contents are in direct communication with the circulating blood
and pursue an incessant course of chemical change and physical
renewal.—EDWARD SMITH, *Foods*.

The Smooth Muscle-fibers consist of long spindle-shaped
cells, the ends of which are frequently spirally twisted, and
in the center of which exists a long rod-shaped kernel or
nucleus. Unlike striated muscle, they do not form separate
muscular masses, but occur scattered, or arranged in more or

less dense layers or strata, in almost all organs.* Arranged in regular order, they very frequently form widely extending membranes, especially in such tube-shaped structures as the blood-vessels, the intestine, etc., the walls of which are composed of these smooth muscle-fibers. In such cases they are usually arranged in two layers, one of which consists of ring-shaped

FIG. 71.

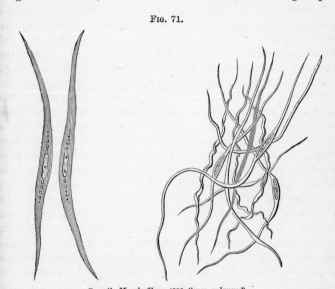

Smooth Muscle-fibers (300 times enlarged).

fibers surrounding the tube, while the other consists of fibers arranged parallel to the tube. When, therefore, these muscle-fibers contract, they are able both to reduce the circumference and to shorten the length of the walls of the tube in which they occur. This is of great importance in the case of the smaller arteries, in which the smooth muscle-fibers, arranged in the form of a ring, are able greatly to contract, or even entirely to close the vessels, thus regulating the current of blood through

* An instance of a considerable accumulation of smooth muscle-fibers is afforded by the muscle-pouch of birds, which, with the exception of the outer and inner skin coverings, consists solely of these fibers collected in extensive layers.

the capillaries. In other cases, as in the intestine, they serve to set the contents of the tubes in motion. In the latter cases the contraction does not take place simultaneously throughout the length of the tube; but, commencing at one point, it continually propagates itself along fresh lengths of the tube, so that the contents are slowly driven forward.

As a rule, such parts as are provided only with smooth muscle-fibers are not voluntarily movable, while striated muscle-fibers are subject to the will. The latter have, therefore, been also distinguished as voluntary, the former as involuntary muscles. The heart, however, exhibits an exception, for, though it is provided with striated muscle-fibers, the will has no direct influence upon it, its motions being exerted and regulated independently of the will. Moreover, the muscle-fibers of the heart are peculiar in that they are destitute of sarcolemma, the naked muscle-fibers directly touching each other. This is so far interesting that direct irritations, if applied to some point of the heart, are transferred to all the other muscle-fibers. In addition to this, the muscle-fibers of the heart are branched, but such branched fibers occur also in other places; for example, in the tongue of the frog, where they are branched like a tree. Smooth muscle-fibers being, therefore, not subject to the will are caused to contract, either by local irritation, such as the pressure of the matter contained within the tubes, or by the nervous system. The contractions of striated muscle-fibers are effected, in the natural course of organic life, only by the influence of the nerves.—ROSENTHAL.

Over-exertion and Personal Imprudence (p. 40).—Among children there is little danger of over-exertion. When a little child reaches the point of healthy fatigue, he usually collapses into rest and sleep. But with youth comes the spirit of ambition and emulation. A lad, for instance, is determined to win a race, to throw his opponent in a football scramble, to lift a heavier weight than his strength will warrant; or a girl is stimulated by the passion she may possess for piano-playing, painting dancing, or tennis. The moment of exhaustion comes, but the end is not accomplished, and the will goads on the weary muscles, perhaps to one supreme effort which terminates in a sharp and sudden illness, perhaps to days and weeks of con tinued and incessant application, during which the whole system is undermined. Thus is laid the foundation for a feeble and suffering maturity.

To elderly people, over-exertion has peculiar dangers, dependent largely upon the changes which gradually take place in the tissues of the body. The walls of the blood-vessels become less and less elastic, and more and more brittle, as life advances, until at last they are ready to give way from any severe or unusual pressure. We constantly see old people hastening their death by personal imprudence. An old gentleman running to catch the morning train; an old farmer hastening to turn the strayed sheep out of a cornfield; the old sportsman having a last run with the hounds; the last pull at the oars; the last attempt of old age to play at vigorous manhood.

A prominent American physician has said that between the ages of forty and fifty every wise man will have ceased to run to "catch" trains or street cars; and that between fifty and sixty he will have permanently discarded haste of all kinds. Equal precautions should be observed by both young and old, but especially by those advanced in life, in regard to extremes of heat, cold, or storm. William Cullen Bryant, by exposing himself to a scorching sun and refusing to permit a friend to protect him with an umbrella while delivering an address in Central Park, received injuries to his system that carried him to his grave. Ralph Waldo Emerson, by standing in a chilling wind, contracted a cold and died. George Dawson, by going thoughtlessly into a freezing atmosphere from the sweltering rooms of a crowded reception, took cold which resulted in pneumonia and death. Matthew Arnold, for years a sufferer from heart difficulty, in a single instance neglected the advice of his physician not to indulge in any violent exercise, made repeated attempts and finally succeeded in jumping a fence, and in a few hours was a dead man. Roscoe Conkling braved the most terrible blizzard ever known in the east and sacrificed his life. And yet, these were all men of exceptional prudence. Probably no other five persons in the world of like surroundings and vocations were more careful of their health. In an unguarded moment their prudence left them, and they paid the terrible penalty.—*Compiled.*

Effects of Insufficient Out-door Exercise upon the Young (p. 41).—Children deprived of adequate out-door exercise are always delicate, pale, and tender; or, in a figurative sense, they are like the sprig of vegetation in a dark, dank hole,— bleached and spindling. . . . An inactive in-door life is one of the most effectual ways of weakening the young body. It renders the growth unnaturally soft and tender, and thus susceptible to harm from the slightest causes. It hinders the garnering of strength necessary for a long life, and gives to the germs of disease a resistless power over an organization so weak and deficient. . . . Measles, scarlet fever, and diphtheria find among such a congenial soil, and run riot among the elements of the body held together by so frail a thread. . . . Such children are always at the mercy of the weather. Colds and coughs are standard disorders in winter, headaches and habitual languor in summer. . . . The scape-goat for this result is the climate: if that was only better, mothers are sure their children's health would also be better. No, it would not be better: no earthly climate is good enough to preserve health and strength under such unnatural training. . . . Children of the laboring classes, often dirty and imperfectly clad, seldom have colds, simply for the reason that, for the greater part of the day, they have the freedom of the streets. It is not the dirt, it is not the rags, *but the life-giving force of an active out-door life* that renders such children so strong and healthy.—BLACK, *Ten Laws of Health.*

Popular Modes of Out-door Exercise (p. 42).—*Walking.*— Every person has his own particular step, caused by the conformity, shape, and length of his bones, and the height of his body. Such a thing, then, as a regulation step is unnatural and any attempt at equalizing the step of individuals of different heights must result in a loss of power.

The moment, also, that walking comes to be *up-hill,* fatigue is sensibly increased. The center of gravity of the body is changed, and the muscular force necessary to provide for the change causes the fixing of the diaphragm, and a rigid condition of many muscles. Respiration is interfered with, owing to the fixing of the diaphragm, and the heart becomes affected thereby. A person with a sensitive or diseased heart can during a walk, tell when the slightest rise in the ground occurs

We make climbing more exhausting from the habit we have of suspending the breath. Let the reader *hold his breath* and run up twenty-four steps of a stair, and then perform the same act *breathing freely* and deeply. It will be found that by the first act marked breathlessness will be induced, whereas by the latter the effect is much less. This management of the breath constitutes the difference between the beginner and the experienced athlete. The enormous increase of the quantity of air consumed during exercise will at once bring home a number of lessons. One is, that exercise is best taken in the open air, and not in gymnasia; another, that free play to act for the regions of the chest and abdomen must be given. On no account must a tight belt be worn around the soft-walled abdomen. If a belt is preferred to braces, let it be applied below the top of the haunch bone, where the bones can resist the pressure.

Whatever may be the pastimes indulged in by young men, walking should never be neglected. The oarsman will become "stale" unless the method of exercise is varied; the gymnast will develop the upper part of his body, while his lower extremities will remain spindle-shanks. So with all other forms of exercise; success, in any form of game, sport, or gymnastic training, can not be attained unless walking be freely taken.

Skating is simply an exaggerated swinging walk, with this difference, that the foot on which one rests is not stationary, but moves along at a rapid rate. The benefit to the circulation, respiration, and digestion is even greater in skating than in walking. The dangers from skating are:

1. The giving away of the ice. Great caution should be used in regard to the safety of a frozen pond or river.

2. Taking cold from becoming overheated, and from subsequent inactive exposure. Physiological knowledge will teach people that, when they begin to skate, outer wraps should be laid aside, and again put on when skating is finished.

3. Sprains, especially of the ankle, and other minor accidents arising from falls. Ankle-boots with strong uppers should be worn during skating. Those who have weak ankles ought to wear skates with ankle-straps and buckles, acme skates being relegated to those who are not afraid of going "over their foot."

Rowing.—The muscles employed in rowing may be summed up under two heads—those that are used in the forward swing, and those used in the backward. In the *forward* swing all the joints of the lower extremity, the hip, knee, and ankle, are flexed; the shoulder is brought forward; the elbow is straightened; and the wrist is first extended and then flexed, in feathering the oar. The body is bent forward by the muscles in front of the abdomen and spinal column. In the *backward* movement the reverse takes place; the lower extremity, the hip, knee, and ankle are straightened; the shoulder is pulled back; the elbow is flexed; and the wrist is held straight. The body is bent backward by the muscles at the lower part of the back, and by those of the spine in general. It will be seen that the enormous number of joints put into use, and the varying positions employed, call into play nearly every muscle of the limbs and trunk. Rowing gives more work to the muscles of the back than any other kind of exercise. This is of the first importance to both men and women, but especially to women. The chief work of the muscles of the back is to support the body in the erect position, and the better they are developed the better will the carriage be, and the less likelihood of stooping shoulders, contracted chests, and the like. Now, the work of the muscles in supporting the body is largely relegated in women to the stays, and, in consequence, the muscles undergo wasting and fatty degeneration, in fact, atrophy; so that when the stays are left off, the muscles are unfit to support the body. Rowing exercises these muscles condemned to waste, and imparts a natural carriage to the girl's frame. In rowing, as in horseback riding, the clothing should be loose, stays left off, and flannels worn next the skin. The dress itself should be of woolen, and there should always be in the boat a large wrap to use when one stops rowing. The following practical rules should be observed by rowers:

1. Never row after a full meal.
2. Stop when fatigue comes on.
3. *Allow the breath to escape while the oar is in the water.* A novice usually holds his breath at each stroke, and pulls so rapidly that in a few minutes he becomes breathless, and is forced to stop. Not only is this uncomfortable, but it is dan-

gerous. In the case of both young and old, it may give rise to an abdominal rupture (hernia), dilation of the cavities of the heart, rupture of a heart-valve, varicose veins, etc. Instead of fixing the diaphragm and holding the breath during the time of pulling, as novices are apt to do, *do exactly the opposite.* Let the diaphragm go loose, and allow the breath to escape.

4. Change the clothing from the skin outward as soon as the day's rowing is finished.

5. Before retiring for the night, have a warm bath, temperature 92° Fahr. This is a specific against the aches and muscular stiffness which often follow a long pull on the water.

Swimming.—A word of warning is necessary in regard to those learning to swim in rivers. Boys at school, when they take to river bathing, often carry it to a dangerous extent. They get into the water, and now in, now out on the bank, sometimes remain for hours. This may take place day after day, and if the weather continues warm and the holidays last long enough, the boy may reduce himself to the lowest ebb of feebleness, and possibly develop the seeds of latent disease. He may even die from the effects of this prolonged immersion and mad-cap exposure.

The muscular exertion undergone during swimming, especially by those who swim only occasionally, is very great. The experienced swimmer conserves his strength, as do proficients at all feats, but the occasional swimmer, like the occasional rower, puts forth treble the energy required, and soon becomes exhausted. In the first place, it is a new act for the muscles to perform ; they are taken off from the beaten tracks, and are grouped together in new associations ; hence they lack adjustment and adaptation. Again, as in other feats for which one is untrained, the heart and lungs do not work in time. Ease and speed in swimming depend upon the attainment of harmony in the working of the muscles, heart, and lungs.

Diving is an accomplishment attached to swimming, which involves many dangers, and is well-nigh useless. The customary dive off a spring-board into the shallow water of a swimming-bath is dangerous in the extreme. The only place where diving should be attempted is into deep water, at least fifteen or twenty feet, where there is no danger of striking the bottom.

Lawn-Tennis.—Of all modern inventions in the way of games, lawn-tennis is the best.

The dangers attendant on lawn-tennis are:—

1. Over-exertion, causing rupture and deranged circulation, especially in the case of those with weak hearts, or those who, being out of condition, or too fat, suddenly engage in the game too long or too violently.

2. Rupture of the *tendon of Achilles*, from taking a sudden bound. In such an accident the subject falls down, with a sensation as if struck with a club on the leg.

3. Rupture of one of the heads of the biceps in the arm. Here the arm drops helplessly, and a muscular knob rises up on the inner and upper part of the arm.

4. The tennis arm. This trouble arises from the method of manipulating the bat. The pain is felt over the upper end of the radius.

Many of the strains, ruptured tendons, and torn muscles in tennis-players are caused by the want of heels to tennis shoes. As, ordinarily, we walk on heels which vary from half an inch to an inch, there must be a considerable extra strain thrown on the muscles of the calf of the leg, when the heels are left off. Especially during a sudden spring is this apparent, when to rise from off the heels on to the toes requires a greatly increased force. Tennis shoes should therefore have fairly-deep, broad heels.

Horseback Riding is a mixed exercise, partly active and partly passive, the lower parts of the body being in some measure employed, while the upper parts in easy cantering are almost wholly relaxed. It is peculiarly suited to dyspeptics, from its direct action upon the abdominal viscera, the contents of which are stimulated by the continued agitation and succussion, consequent on the motion in riding.

Bicycling and Tricycling.—While strongly recommending bicycling to men, and tricycling to both men and women in health, those suffering from heart or lung affections, ruptures, scrofula, joint disease, or like maladies, should not indulge in them without medical sanction. For abdominal complaints, such as dyspepsia, congestion of the liver, constipation, and the like, the exercise is excellent.

Base-Ball is an essentially American game, which brings into play nearly all the muscles of the body. Its chief danger lies in being hit by the hard, forcibly pitched ball, and, for weak persons, in the violence of the exercise.

Foot-Ball is a rough-and-tumble game, suited only to that class of boys and men, who, brimming over with animal life, take small heed of the accidents liable to occur.

Light and Heavy Gymnastics. — For wet weather, and when out-door exercise is not practicable, gymnastics are most advisable. Boys and girls, at the age of fifteen or sixteen, often shoot up and become tall and lanky; they want filling out, and are troubled with growing pains. Even men, when tall and thin, are seldom very erect, their muscles are too weak; and there is only one way of overcoming this weakness—by exercising them. Nothing more is wanted than a pair of very light Indian clubs, a pair of light wooden dumb-bells, a long wooden rod, and a pair of wooden rings,—the last for combined exercises. Indeed, a systematic motion of the body itself, without any extra artificial resistance, is quite sufficient for the purposes of physical education. In nearly all our large cities are found gymnasia, provided with competent instructors, and every facility for both light and heavy gymnastics. Exercise in a gymnasium is open to the objection of being too brief and too severe, and of simply causing an increase of muscular development. Besides, it is generally unequal in its results, being better adapted to the cultivation of strength in the upper extremities and portion of the body than in the lower. Nevertheless, during inclement weather, or with persons in whom the muscles of the arms and chest are defective, moderate gymnastic exercise is far better than no exercise.—*Compiled.* (*Mostly from "The Influence of Exercise" in The Book of Health.*)

THE SKIN.

The Hair (p. 52).—*Baldness, and its Causes.*—Various reasons are assigned for the baldness which is so prevalent among comparatively young men in our country. One writer says: "The premature baldness and grayness of the Americans as a people

is in great measure owing to the non-observance of hygienic
rules, and to excess of mental and physical labor in a climate
foreign to the race." Others attribute it to the close unventilated hats commonly worn by men. Dr. Nichols, in the *Popular
Science News*, gives his opinion thus:

"In our view, it is largely due to modern methods of treatment of the hair and scalp. The erroneous idea prevails, that
the skin which holds the hair-follicles and the delicate secretory
organs of the scalp must be kept as 'clean,' so to speak, as the
face or hands; consequently young men patronize barbers or
hair-dressers, and once or twice a week they have what is called
a 'shampoo' operation performed. This consists in a thorough
scouring of the hair and scalp with dilute ammonia, water, and
soap, so that a heavy 'lather' is produced, and the glandular
secretions, which are the natural protection of the hair, and
promotive of its growth, are saponified and removed. No act
could be more directly destructive of a healthy growth of hair
than this. . . . Women do not shampoo or wash the hair as
often as the other sex, and consequently they are in a large
degree exempt from baldness in middle life. It is true, however, that many women in cities make frequent visits to the
hair-dressers, and subject their tresses to the 'scouring' process.
If this becomes common, it will not be long before baldness will
overtake the young mothers as well as the fathers, and the time
will be hastened when even children will have no hair to destroy
with ammonia or other caustic cosmetics.

"The advice we have to offer to young men and maidens
is,—let your hair alone; keep at a safe distance from hair-dressing rooms and drug-shops, where are sold oils, alkaline substances, alcoholic mixtures, etc., for use upon the hair. They are
all pernicious, and will do you harm. The head and hair may
be washed occasionally with soft, tepid water, without soap of
any kind. As a rule, the only appliances needed in the care of
the hair are good combs and brushes; and they should not be
used harshly, so as to wound the scalp. Avoid all 'electric' and
wire-made brushes. No electricity can be stored in a hair-brush:
if it could be, it is not needed."

Sudden Blanching of the Hair from Violent Emotions.—The
color of the hair depends mainly upon the presence of pigment

granules, which range in tint from a light yellow to an intense black. A recent investigator has succeeded in extracting the coloring matter of the hair, and has found that all the different shades are produced by the mixture of three primary colors— red, yellow, and black. "In the pure golden yellow hair there is only the yellow pigment; in red hair the red pigment is mixed with more or less yellow, producing the various shades of red and orange; in dark hair the black is always mixed with yellow and red, but the latter are overpowered by the black; and it seems that even the blackest hair, such as that of the negro, contains as much red pigment as the very reddest hair." Hence, "if in the negro the black pigment had not been developed, the hair of all negroes would be a fiery red."—DR. C. H. LEONARD. *The Hair: Its Diseases and Treatment.*

The gradual disappearance of this pigment causes the gray or white hair of old age. This natural change in color does not necessarily denote loss of vitality in the hair, as it often continues to grow as vigorously as before it began to whiten. Cases of sudden blanching of the hair from extreme grief or terror are often quoted, — those of Sir Thomas More and of Marie Antoinette being well-known instances in point. An interesting circumstance has been discovered with regard to such cases, namely, that the change of color is not dependent upon the disappearance of the pigment of the hair, which always takes place slowly, but upon the sudden development in its interior of a number of air-bubbles, that hide and destroy the effect of the pigment, which itself remains unaltered. Dr. Landois mentions the case of a German printer whom he attended, at a hospital, in the summer of 1865.

This man had long been intemperate in his habits, in consequence of which he was seized with delirium tremens. The delirium, as is usual in such cases, was of an extremely terrifying nature, and lasted four days. On the evening of the fourth day the hair was unaltered, but on the morning of the fifth the delirium had disappeared, and his hair, which previously was fair, had become gray. It was examined with the microscope, when it was found that the pigment was still present, but that the central streak of each was filled with air-bubbles.

How this superabundance of air finds its way into the hair

in these cases of sudden blanching, physiologists have not yet been able satisfactorily to explain.—In this connection, however, it may be observed that air-bubbles exist, more or less, in all hair, mingled with the pigment granules.

The feathers of birds owe their bright colors to an oily secretion corresponding to the pigment in hair, and microscopical observation has revealed the fact that when these colors fade the oily secretion disappears, and is replaced by air. That extreme terror may blanch feathers as well as hair is shown in the case of a poor little starling, which upon being rescued from the claws of a cat became suddenly white.

The Nails (p. 54).—The nails are mere modifications of the scarfskin, their horny appearance and feeling being due to the fact that the scales or plates of which they are composed are much harder and more closely packed. The root of the nail lies embedded, to the extent of about the twelfth part of an inch, in a fold of the sensitive skin, and, as may be observed from an inspection of the part, the scarfskin is not exactly continuous with the nail, but projects a little above it, forming a narrow margin.

The nail, like the scarfskin, rests upon, and is intimately connected with, a structure almost identical with the sensitive skin ; this is, however, thrown into ridges, which run parallel to one another, except at the back part, where they radiate from the center of the root. On examining the surface of the nail, a semicircular whitish portion is detected near its root; its color is dependent upon the fact that the ridges there contain fewer blood-vessels, and therefore less blood, and on account of its half-moon shape it is called the *lunula.*

The nail is constantly increasing in length, owing to the formation of new cells at the root, which push it forward, while the increase in its thickness is due to the secretion of new cells from the sensitive layer beneath, so that the farther the nail grows from the root, the thicker it becomes. Its nutrition, and consequently its growth, suffers in disease, the portion growing during disease being thinner than that growing in health ; and accordingly a transverse groove is seen upon the nail, corresponding to the time of an illness. It will thus be seen that by a mere examination of the nail we can astonish our friends by telling them when they have been ill; and it has been estimated that the nail of the thumb grows from its root to its free extremity in five months, that of the great toe in twenty months, so that a transverse groove in the middle of the former indicates an illness about two and a half months before, and in the middle of the latter, about ten months.

The culture of the nails, which when perfect constitute so great a beauty, is of much importance; but the tendency is to injure them by too much attention. The scissors should never be used except to pare the free edges when they have become ragged or too long, and the folds of scarfskin which overlap the roots should not, as a rule, be touched, unless they be frayed, when the torn edges may be snipped off, so as to prevent their being torn further, which may cause much pain, and even inflammation. The upper surfaces of the nails should on no account be touched with the knife, as is so often done, the nail-brush being amply sufficient to keep them clean, without impairing their smooth and polished surfaces.—HINTON.

Baths and Bathing (p. 65).—*Physical Cleanliness Promotes Moral Purity.*—The old adage that cleanliness is next to godliness, must have had its origin in the feeling of moral elevation which generally accompanies scrupulous bodily purity. Frequent bathing promotes purity of mind and morals. The man who is accustomed to be physically clean shrinks instinctively from contact with all uncleanliness. Personal neatness, when grown into a habit, draws after it so many excellences, that it may well be called a social virtue. Without it, refined intercourse would be impossible; for its neglect not only indicates a want of proper self-respect, but a disrespect of the feelings of others which argues a low tone of the moral sense. All nations, as they advance in civilization and refinement of manners, pay increased attention to the purity of the person.

What, then, shall we say of people who, after all that has been said and written upon the subject, seldom or never bathe, who allow the pores of the skin to get blocked up with a combination of dust and perspired matter, which is as effectual in its way as plaster to the walls of a building? Could they but once be tempted to taste the delights which arise from a perfectly clean and well-acting skin; the cheerfulness, nay, the feeling of moral as well as physical elevation, which accompanies the sense of that cleanliness, they would soon esteem the little time and trouble spent in the bath, and in the proper care of the surface of the body, as time and labor very well spent.— DR. STRANGE.

The feet, particularly, should receive daily attention, if it be no more than a vigorous rubbing with a wet cloth, followed by a dry one. After a long walk, also, nothing is more refreshing, especially in summer, than a generous foot-bath in cool or tepid water, followed by an entire change in shoes and stockings. This is really a necessary precaution, if the feet have become wet from the dampness of the ground; and if the walk has heated the body so that the stockings are moist with perspiration, it is not only an act of prudence, but an instinct of personal neatness.

Ancient Greek and Roman Baths.—From the earliest historic times the necessity for frequent and thorough ablution has been recognized by artificial provisions for this purpose. The Greeks had "steaming baths" and "fragrant anointing oils," as far back as Homer's time, a thousand years before Christ, but the Romans surpassed all preceding and subsequent nations by their magnificent and luxuriously equipped Thermæ, in which a bath cost less than a cent, and was often free. A full Roman bath included hot air, dry rubbing, hot, tepid, and cold water immersions, scraping with bronze instruments, and anointing with precious perfumes.

The Modern Russian and *Turkish baths* are the nearest approaches we have to the Roman bath. These are found in nearly all our larger cities.

The Turkish Bath is conducted in a modified form in this country, generally with hot air instead of steam. Its frequent use not only tends to keep the body in a state of perfect cleanliness, but it imparts a clear, fresh color to the complexion which is hardly attained by other means.

"Its most important effect," says a writer in the *Popular Science Monthly*, "is the stimulation of the emunctory action of the skin. By this means we are enabled to wash as it were the solid and fluid tissues, and especially the blood and skin, by passing water through them from within outward to the surface of the body. Hence, in practice, one of the most essential requisites is copious draughts of water during the sweating."

During the operation of a Turkish bath, the novice is often astonished at the amount of effete matter eliminated from the pores of the skin. "A surprising quantity of scarfskin, which no washing could remove, peels off, especially if a glove of camel's-hair or goat's-hair be used, as they are in the East, where also the soles of the feet are scraped with pumice. The deposit of this skin of only a week's date, when collected, is often as large as one's fist. Much more solid matter is contained in the perspiration of those who take the bath for the first time, or after a long interval. Nothing escapes through the skin, save what is noxious if retained. This bath should never be used in case of advanced lung diseases, great debility, acute inflammations, or persons who labor under any form of heart disease; but I think its influence is directly curative in rheumatic, gouty, and scrofulous affections, some skin diseases, and the earlier stages of feverish colds and ague. It is said to have calming effects in the treatment of insanity, and the use of it was suggested from the heavy smell the skin of persons thus afflicted often has."—MAPOTHER'S *Lectures on Public Health.*

A somewhat heroic bath, used in Siberia to drive away a threatened fever, consists of a thorough parboiling, within an inch or two of a steaming furnace, after which the subject is "drubbed and flogged for about half an hour with a bundle of birch twigs, leaf and all." A douche of cold water is then dashed over the exhausted bather, when he is ready to be put into bed.

Sea-bathing.—Before the age of seven years, and after fifty-five, sea-baths should be used with the greatest caution. All persons unaccustomed to sea-bathing should begin with a warm or tepid bath, in-doors, proceeding by degrees to the cold in-door bath, and then to the open sea.

The sea-bath should be taken, if possible, when the sun is shining, when the water has been warmed by contact with the heated sands, and never during the digestion of the principal meal, or late in the evening. Immediately on plunging into the water, which need not, except in persons of full habit, cover the head, brisk motion of some kind should be used. Those who can swim should do so; those who can not, should make as much exertion of the limbs as possible, or rub the body with their hands. The delicate, and particularly those who are recovering from illness, should remove from the bath *as soon as the glow arrives;* or, if that be not felt at all, then after *one* plunge.

Danger in Bathing when Overheated.—It is unwise to bathe when copious perspiration has continued for an hour or more, unless the heat of the weather be excessive, or the sweating has been induced by loading with clothes, rather than by exertion. When much perspiration has been produced by muscular exercise, it is unsafe to bathe, because the body is so fatigued and exhausted, that the reaction can not be insured, and the effect may be to congest the internal organs, and notably the nerve-centers. The last gives cramp. If the weather be chilly, or there be a cold wind, so that the body may be rapidly cooled at the surface while undressing, it is not safe to bathe. Under such conditions, the further chill of immersion in cold water will take place at the precise moment at which the reaction consequent upon the chill of exposure by undressing ought to take place, and this second chill will not only delay or altogether prevent the reaction, but will convert the bath from a mere stimulant to a depressant, ending in the abstraction of a large amount of animal heat and congestion of the internal organs and nerve-centers. The aim must be to avoid two chills, and to make sure that the body is in such a condition as to secure a quick reaction on emerging from the water, without relying too much on the possible effect of friction by rubbing. The actual temperature of the water does not affect the question so much as its relative temperature in comparison with that of the surrounding air. It ought to be much lower than that of the air. These maxims receive a striking re-enforcement from the case of a young soldier who a few days ago plunged into the river near Manchester, England, after having heated himself by rowing. He was immediately taken with cramps, and was drowned. When taken out, his body was found "twisted," and the vessels of his head showed every evidence of congestion.—*Popular Science Monthly, September, 1883.*

Bather's Cramp.—Cramp is a painful and tonic muscular spasm. It may occur in any part of the body, but it is especially apt to take place in the lower extremities, and in its milder forms it is limited to a single muscle. The pain is severe, and the contracted muscles are hard and exquisitely tender. In a few minutes the spasm and pain cease, leaving a local sensation of fatigue and soreness. When cramp affects only one extremity, no swimmer or bather endowed with average presence of mind need drown; but when cramp seizes the whole of the voluntary muscular system, as it probably does in the worst cases, nothing in the absence of prompt and efficient extraneous assistance can save the individual from drowning.* Prolongation of muscular exertion, as in continued swimming, and forcible and sudden muscular exertion, as in swimming with very vigorous and rapid strokes, are efficient and frequent causes of cramp. These muscular conditions, however, usually give rise only to the slighter and more localized forms. Serious cramp is a peril which menaces most persons with highly developed muscles. Its most powerful and most avoidable cause is the sudden immersion of the body, when its surface is highly heated, in water of a relatively low temperature. —*Popular Science News.*

Protection of the Ear in Sea-bathing.—Special attention should be paid by bathers to the exclusion of salt water from the mouth and ears. Many cases of inflammation of the ear, followed by severe and lasting trouble, even to deafness, are chargeable to the neglect of this precaution. In-coming waves should never be received in the face or the ears, and the sea-water which enters the ears when floating or diving should be wiped out by soft cotton ; indeed, the best plan is to plug the openings of the ears with cotton, which is to be kept there during the bath.— *Science.*

How one who Knows not how to Swim can Escape Drowning.— It is well for every one to learn the art of swimming, yet it is

* Even this is often unavailable, as in the case of the Cornell University post-graduate drowned in Hall Creek, Ithaca, June 10, 1888. In this instance the day was hot and oppressive, and the victim sank soon after entering the water. "His companions at once hastened to his relief, and recovered his body in a few minutes. Professor Wilder, of the University, was hurriedly summoned, and every possible method was resorted to in order to induce respiration, but the vital spark had fled. An attack of cramps is supposed to have been the cause of drowning."

a knowledge possessed by comparatively few people. Mr. Henry MacCormac, a writer in *Nature*, gives some common sense instructions that, if heeded, may be of great service to those persons who, not knowing how to swim, may find themselves accidentally precipitated into the water. We condense from his article, adding some directions, as follows:

In order to escape drowning, it is necessary only to do as the brute does, namely, to walk or tread the water. The brute has no advantage over man in regard to his relative weight, and yet the man perishes while the brute survives. The ignorance of so simple a possibility as that of treading water strikes me as one of the most singular things in the history of man. Perhaps something is to be ascribed to the vague meaning which is attached to the word *Swim*. The dog is wholly incapable of *swimming* as a man swims, but nothing is more certain than that a man, without previous training or instruction, can swim just as a dog swims, and that by so doing without fear or hesitancy, he will be just as safe as is the dog. The brute thus circumstanced continues to go on all fours, as if he were on land, *keeping his head well out of the water*. So with the man who wishes to save his life and can not otherwise swim. He must strike alternately, with hand and foot,—*one, two, one, two*, —without hurry or precipitation, exactly as the brute does. Whether he be provided with paw or hoof, the beast swims with perfect ease and buoyancy. So, too, can the human being, if he will, with the further immense advantage of having a paddle-formed hand, and of being able, when tired, to rest himself by floating, an act of which the animal has no conception. The printed direction should be pasted up in all boat-houses, on every boat, at every bathing-place, and in every school: *Tread water when you find yourself out of your depth*. This is all that need be said, unless, indeed, we add: *Float when you are tired*. To float, one needs only to turn upon his back, keeping—as always when in the water—the mouth and chin well up and the lungs full of air.— Every one of us, of whatever age and however encumbered with clothing, may tread water, even in a breaking sea, with as much facility as a four-footed animal. The position of the water-treader is, really, very much safer and better than the sprawling attitude of the ordinary swimmer. But the chief advantage lies in the fact that we can tread water without preliminary teaching, whereas, though we recommend all to learn how to swim, it involves time and pains, entails considerable fatigue, and is, after all, very seldom adequately acquired.

Hints on Clothing (p. 67).—*Advantages of Woolen Fabrics.*—Wool is more irritating than cotton, on account of the stiffness of the hairs with which it bristles; but the excitation it produces becomes a therapeutic means whenever the skin needs a stimulant.

The use of wool is particularly desirable in some countries and under some conditions of life. Professor Brocchi, a writer well known for his investigations in malaria, attributes the good health and vigor of the ancient Romans to their habit of wearing coarse woolen clothes; when they began to disuse them, and to wear lighter goods and silks, they became less vigorous and less able to resist the morbid influence of bad air. It was at about the time the women began to dress in notably fine tissues that the insalubrity of the Roman air began first to be complained of. "In the English army and navy," says Dr. Balestra, "the soldiers of garrisons in unhealthy places are obliged constantly to wear wool next to the skin, and to cover themselves with sufficient clothing, for protection against paludine fevers, dysentery, cholera, and other diseases." According to Pâtissier, similar measures have been found effectual in preserving the health of workmen employed on dikes, canals, and ditches, in marshy lands; while, previous to the employment of these precautions, mortality from fevers was considerable among them.

Dr. Balestra has proved by direct experiments in marshy regions that thick and hairy woolen garments arrest in their down a portion of the germs borne in by the air, which thus reaches the skin filtered and purified. The ancient Romans wore ample over-garments over their tunics, and never put them away. It is no less important to be well covered during the night; and precautions of this kind should be recommended to all who live in a swampy country. We are sometimes astonished when we see the natives of particularly warm countries enveloped in woolen, as the Arab in his burnoose, or the Spanish peasant in his tobacco-colored cloak. Such materials protect both against the rays of the sun and against the coolness of the night, and are excellent regulators of heat. It is dangerously imprudent to travel in southern countries without provision of warm clothing.—*Revue des Deux Mondes.*

Weight is not Warmth.—While speaking of the warmth of clothing for inclement weather, it would be incorrect not to speak of weight in relation to warmth. Many persons mistake weight for warmth, and thus feeble people are actually borne down and weakened by the excess of heavy clothing which is piled on them. Good woolen or fur fabrics retain the heat, and yet are light. When fabrics intended for sustaining warmth are made up of cotton, the mistake of accepting weight for warmth is made. The same errors are often made in respect to bed coverings, and with the same results.

Poisonously Dyed Clothing.—The introduction of wearing apparel, socks, stockings, and flannels which have been made, by new processes of dyeing, to assume a rich red or yellow color, has led to a local disease of the skin, attended, in rare cases with slight constitutional symptoms. This disease is due to the dye-stuffs. The chief poisonous dyes are the red and yellow coralline, substances derived from that series of chemical bodies which have been obtained of late years from coal tar, and commonly known as the aniline series.

The coloring principle is extremely active as a local poison It induces on the skin a reddish, slightly raised eruption of minute round pimples which stud the reddened surface, and which if the irritation be severe and long-continued, pass into vesicles discharging a thin watery ichor and producing a superficial sore. The disease is readily curable if the cause of it be removed, and, as a general rule, it is purely local in character. I have, however, once seen it pass beyond the local stage. A young gentleman consulted me for what he considered was a rapidly developed attack of erysipelas on the chest and back. He was indeed, covered with an intensely red rash, and he was affected with nervous symptoms, with faintness and depression of pulse of a singular and severe kind. I traced both the local eruption and the general malady to the effect of the organic dye in a red woolen chest and back "comforter." On removing the "comforter" all the symptoms ceased. Similar and even fatal cases have been known from the wearing of highly colored hose.

Uncleanliness of Dress.—Uncleanly attire creates conditions favorable to disease. Clothing worn too long at a time becomes saturated with the excretions and exhalations of the body, and, by preventing the free transpiration from the surface of the skin, induces oppression of the physical powers and mental inactivity. This observation will be accepted by most persons as true in respect to under-clothing; it is equally true in regard to those outer garments which are often worn, unremittingly, until the linings, torn and soiled, are unfit altogether for contact with the cleaner garments beneath them. Health will not be clothed in dirty raiment. They who wear such raiment suffer from trains of minor complaints; from oppression, dullness, headache, nausea, which, though trifling in themselves, taken one by one, when put together greatly reduce that standard of perfect health by which the value of life is correctly and effectively maintained.—RICHARDSON.

RESPIRATION.

The Vocal Organs.—*Musical Tones in Speaking* (p. 76).— Voice is divided into singing and speaking voice. One differs from the other almost as much as noises do from musical sounds. In speaking, the sounds are too short to be easily appreciable, and are not separated by fixed and regular intervals, like those of singing; they are linked together, generally by insensible transitions; they are not united by the fixed relations of the gamut, and can only be noted with difficulty. That it is the short duration of speaking sounds which distinguishes them from those of singing, is proved by this, that if we prolong the intonation of a syllable, or utter it like a note, the musical sound becomes evident. So, if we pronounce all the syllables of a phrase in the same tone, the speaking voice closely resembles psalm-singing. Every one must have noticed this in hearing school-boys recite or read in a monotone, and the analogy is complete when the last two or three syllables are pronounced in a different tone. Spoken voice is, moreover, always a chant more or less marked, according to the individual and the sentiment which the words express. . . . It is related of Grétry, that he amused himself by noting as exactly as possible the

2C

"Bonjour, monsieur!" (Good-day, sir!) of the persons who visited him; and these words expressed by their intonation, in fact, the most opposite sentiments, in spite of the constant identity of the literal sense.

Speech without a Tongue.—De Jussieu relates that he saw a girl fifteen years old, in Lisbon, who was born without a tongue, and yet who spoke so distinctly as not to excite in the minds of those who listened to her the least suspicion of the absence of that organ.

The Transactions of the Royal Society of London (1742) contain an account of a woman who had not the slightest vestige of a tongue, but who could, notwithstanding, drink, eat, and speak as well and as distinctly as any one, and even articulate the words in singing. Other instances have been known where individuals, after losing a portion of the tongue by accident or disease, have again been able to speak after a longer or shorter period.—Le Pileur.

Stimulants and the Voice.—"The Drinker's Throat" is a recognized pathological condition, and the Germans have a popular phrase, "He drinks his throat away." Isambert has pointed out the directly local irritant effect of both alcohol and tobacco on the throat, and also the mode by which these agents, on absorption into the system, re-manifest their presence by predisposing to local pharyngeal inflammations. Dr. Krishaber affirms: "It is generally admitted that alcoholic beverages and tobacco irritate the mucous membrane of the throat, directly affect the voice, and leave on it ineffaceable traces. We hold with equal certainty that tea and coffee, although not directly affecting the voice, do so indirectly by acting on the nervous system, and through it the vocal organs, as well as by some general nervous derangement not very pronounced, but great enough to deprive the singer of the full powers and capabilities of his voice."

Dr. Mackenzie says: "The influence of the general health upon the voice is very marked. Alcohol and tobacco should never be used. The hoarse tones of the confirmed votary of Bacchus are due to chronic inflammation of the lining membrane of the larynx; the originally smooth surface being roughened and thickened by the irritation of alcohol, the vocal cords have less freedom of movement, and their vibrations are blurred, or rather muffled, by the unevenness of their contiguous edges."

A young American lady of marked musical gifts once asked Adelina Patti's advice upon preparing for the stage. She found the great singer wrapped in furs, although the weather was not severe. After hearing her visitor, Patti replied: "Are you willing to give up *every thing* for your art? If you wish to succeed, you must learn to eat moderately, take no stimulants —not even tea or coffee—keep as regular hours as possible consistent with your public appearance, and even deny yourself the luxury of friends. When you hear of a great vocalist giving extravagant wine-suppers, you may be sure that the singer herself takes nothing. To be a successful *artiste* you must be married, soul and body, to your art." Like the young man to whom Christ spake, the young woman "went away sorrowful," and, balancing the terms, concluded to forego the contest.

Abdominal Respiration (p. 81).—It has often been stated that the respiration of woman differs from that of man, in being limited almost entirely to the chest. In order to investigate this subject scientifically, Dr. Mays, of Philadelphia, devised an ingenious instrument for examining the respiration of the native Indian girls in the Lincoln Institution. The girls had not yet been subjected to the restrictions of civilized dress. He says:

"In all, I examined the movements of eighty-two chests, and in each case took an abdominal and a costal tracing. The girls were partly pure and partly mixed with white blood, and their ages ranged from between ten and twenty years. Thus there were thirty-three full-blooded Indians, five one fourth, thirty-five one half, and two three fourths white. *Seventy-five* showed a *decided abdominal* type of breathing, three a costal type, and three in which both were about even. *Those who showed the costal type, or a divergence from the abdominal type, came from the more civilized tribes,* like the Mohawks and Chippewas, and were either *one half or three fourths white;* while in *no single instance* did a full-blooded Indian girl possess this type of breathing.

"From these observations it obviously follows that, so far

as the Indian is concerned, the abdominal is the original type of respiration in both male and female, and that the costal type in the civilized female is developed through the constricting influence of dress around the abdomen. While these tracings were taken an incident occurred which demonstrated that abdominal constriction could modify the movements of the thorax during respiration. At my first visit to the institution I obtained an exceptional costal type of respiration from a full-blooded Indian girl. At my next visit I concluded to repeat this observation, and found that, contrary to my instructions concerning loose clothing, etc., this girl at my first visit had worn three tight belts around her abdomen. After these were removed she gave the abdominal type of breathing, which is characteristic of nearly all the Indian girls."

To us these facts are invaluable. It shows the faulty construction of modern female dress, which restricts the motion of abdominal respiration. It explains why, as experience has taught us, it is necessary to restore this abdominal rhythm, by proper movements, in order permanently to cure the affections of the lower portion of the trunk. It demonstrates conclusively that woman's dress, to be injurious, needs only to interfere with the proper motion of respiration, even though it exercises not the slightest compression.—*Health Record.*

The Germ Theory of Disease (p. 86).—*What are Disease Germs?*—Microscopical investigation has revealed throughout Nature, in the air, in water—especially when it contains organic matter, and even within the bodies of persons and animals, myriads of infinitesimal active organisms which live, multiply, and die in endless succession. These have been named *bacteria* (bacterium, a rod, so called from the general rod-shape first observed), and also *microbes* (microbe, a small living object). Some investigators apply the latter term as a general one, limiting the former to such microbes as are believed to be special disease-producers. The "Germ Theory" teaches that the seeds or *spores* of bacteria, floating in the air we breathe or in the water we drink, are taken into our bodies where, under conditions favorable to their growth, they develop, multiply, and, each after its own species, produce distinctive evil results.— Thus, according to this theory, there are special varieties of microbes that cause, respectively, diphtheria, erysipelas, scarlatina, cholera, etc.—One of the most common microbes in nature is the bacterium of putrefaction, found every-where in decaying organic matter.*

By the species of microbes called ferments all fermented liquors are artificially produced (see p. 132); these also cause the "rising" of bread.—These wonderful little existences are thus made to perform an important part in the economy of Nature. "Nourished at the expense of putrefying organic matter, they reduce its complex constituents into soluble mineral substances, which they return to the soil to serve afresh for the nourishment of similar plants. Thus they clear the surface of the earth from dead bodies and fœcal matter, and from all the useless substances which are the refuse of life; and thus they unite animals and plants in an endless chain."—TROUESSART.

How Disease Germs Grow.—Experiments having shown that no life is known to spring from inanimate matter, we may reasonably suppose that just as wheat does not grow except from seed, so no disease occurs without some disease germ to produce it. Then, again, we may logically assume that each disease is due to the development of a particular kind of germ. If we plant small-pox germs, we do not reap a crop of scarlatina or measles; but, just as wheat springs from wheat, each disease has its own distinctive germs. Each comes from a parent stock, and has existed somewhere previously. . . . Under ordinary circumstances, these germs, though nearly always present, are comparatively few in number, and in an extremely dry and indurated state. Hence, they may frequently enter our bodies without meeting with the conditions essential to their growth; for

---

* This is the microbe found in impure water. If we take half a glass of spring or river water, and leave it uncovered for a few days, we shall observe upon it a thin coating of what appears to be a fine dust. Place, now, a drop of this dusty water under a cover-glass, and examine it under a microscope with a magnifying power of about five hundred diameters. The revelation is astonishing. "The whole field of the microscope is in motion; hundreds of bacteria, resembling minute transparent worms, are swimming in every direction with an undulatory motion like that of an eel or snake. Some are detached, others united in pairs, others in chains or chaplets or cylindrical rods. . . . All these forms represent the different transformations of *Bacterium terno*, or the microbe of putrefaction. Those which are dead appear as small, rigid, and immovable rods."—TROUESSART.

experiments have shown that it is very difficult to moisten them, and till they are moistened, they do not begin to develop. In a healthy system they remain inactive. But any thing tending to weaken or impair the bodily organs, furnishes favorable conditions, and thus epidemics almost always originate and are most fatal in those quarters of our great cities where dirt, squalor, and foul air render sound health almost an impossibility. . . . Having once got a beginning, epidemics rapidly spread. The germs are then sent into the air in great numbers, and in a moist state; and the probabilities of their entering, and of their establishing themselves even in healthy bodies, are vastly increased. . . . Climate and the weather have also much influence on the vitality of these germs. Cold is a preventive against some diseases, heat against others. Tyndall found that sunlight greatly retarded and sometimes entirely prevented putrefaction; while dirt is always favorable to the growth and development of germs. *Sunshine and cleanliness are undoubtedly the best and cheapest preventives against disease.—"Disease Germs," Chambers' Journal.*

You know the exquisitely truthful figures employed in the New Testament regarding leaven. A particle hid in three measures of meal leavens it all. A little leaven leaveneth the whole lump. In a similar manner a particle of contagium spreads through the human body, and may be so multiplied as to strike down whole populations. Consider the effect produced upon the system by a microscopic quantity of the virus of small-pox. That virus is to all intents and purposes a seed. It is sown as leaven is sown, it grows and multiplies as leaven grows and multiplies, and it always reproduces itself. . . . Contagia are living things, which demand certain elements of life, just as inexorably as trees, or wheat, or barley; and it is not difficult to see that a crop of a given parasite may so far use up a constituent existing in small quantities in the body, but essential in the growth of the parasite, as to render the body unfit for the production of a second crop. The soil is exhausted; and until the lost constituent is restored, the body is protected from any further attack from the same disorder. To exhaust a soil, however, a parasite less vigorous and destructive than the really virulent one may suffice; and if, after having, by means of a feebler organism, exhausted the soil without fatal result, the most highly virulent parasite be introduced into the system, it will prove powerless. This, in the language of the germ theory, is the whole secret of vaccination.—TYNDALL.

Disease Germs Contained in Atmospheric Dust.—Take the extracted juice of beef or mutton, so prepared as to be perfectly transparent, and entirely free from the living germs of bacteria. Into the clear liquid let fall the tiniest drop of an infusion charged with the bacteria of putrefaction. Twenty-four hours subsequently, the clear extract will be found muddy throughout, the turbidity being due to swarms of bacteria generated by the drop with which the infusion was inoculated. At the same time the infusion will have passed from a state of sweetness to a state of putridity. Let a drop similar to that which has produced this effect fall into an open wound: the juices of the living body nourish the bacteria as the beef or mutton juice nourished them, and you have putrefaction produced within the system. The air, as I have said, is laden with floating matter which, when it falls upon the wound, acts substantially like the drop. . . . A few years ago I was bathing in an Alpine stream, and, returning to my clothes from the cascade which had been my shower-bath, I slipped upon a block of granite, the sharp crystals of which stamped themselves into my naked shin. The wound was an awkward one, but, being in vigorous health at the time, I hoped for a speedy recovery. Dipping a clean pocket-handkerchief into the stream, I wrapped it round the wound, limped home, and remained for four or five days quietly in bed. There was no pain, and at the end of this time I thought myself quite fit to quit my room. The wound, when uncovered, was found perfectly clean, uninflamed, and entirely free from pus. Placing over it a bit of gold-beater's-skin, I walked about all day. Toward evening, itching and heat were felt; a large accumulation of pus followed, and I was forced to go to bed again. The water-bandage was restored, but it was powerless to check the action now set up; arnica was applied, but it made matters worse. The inflammation increased alarmingly, until finally I was ignobly carried on men's shoulders down the mountain, and transported to Geneva, where, thanks to the kindness of friends, I was immediately placed in the best medical hands. On the morning after my arrival in Geneva, Dr. Gautier discovered an abscess in my instep, at a distance of five inches from the wound. The two were connected by a channel, or *sinus*, as it is technically called, through which he was able to empty the abscess without the application of the lance.

By what agency was that channel formed—what was it that thus tore asunder the sound tissue of my instep, and kept me for six weeks a prisoner in bed? In the very room where the water-dressing had been removed from my wound and the gold-oeater's-skin applied to it, I opened this year a number of tubes, containing perfectly clear and sweet infusions of fish, flesh, and vegetable. These hermetically-sealed infusions had been exposed for weeks, both to the sun of the Alps and to the warmth of a kitchen, without showing the slightest turbidity or signs of life. But two days after they were opened, the greater number of them swarmed with the bacteria of putrefaction, the germs of which had been contracted from the dust-laden air of the room. And, had the pus from my abscess been examined, my memory of its appearance leads me to infer that it would have been found equally swarming with these bacteria—that it was their germs which got into my incautiously-opened wound. They were the subtile workers that burrowed down my shin, dug the abscess in my instep, and produced effects which might well have proved fatal to me.—TYNDALL.

Disease Germs Carried in Soiled Clothing (p. 89).—The conveyance of cholera germs by bodies of men moving along the lines of human communication, without necessarily affecting the individuals who transport them, is now easy to understand ; for it is well established that clothes or linen soiled by cholera patients may not only impart the germs with which they are contaminated to those who handle them when fresh, but that, after having been dried and packed, they may infect persons at any distance who incautiously unfold them. Thus, while the nurses of cholera patients may, with proper precautions, enjoy an absolute immunity from attack, the disease germs may be introduced into new localities without any ostensible indication of their presence. It is obvious that the only security against such introduction consists in the destruction or thorough disinfection of every scrap of clothing or linen which has been about the person of a cholera patient.—DR. CARPENTER.

I have known scarlet fever to be carried by the clothing of a nurse into a healthy family, and communicate the disease to every member of the family. I have known cholera to be communicated by the clothes of the affected person to the women engaged in washing the clothes. I have known small-pox conveyed by clothes that had been made in a room where the tailor had by his side sufferers from the terrible malady. I have seen the new cloth, out of which was to come the riding-habit for some innocent child to rejoice in as she first wore it, undergo the preliminary duty of forming part of the bed-clothing of another child stricken down with fever. Lastly, I have known scarlet fever, small-pox, typhus, and cholera, communicated by clothing contaminated in the laundry.—DR. RICHARDSON.

The Sanitary Home (see p. 94).—1. *The Site.*—First and foremost of all the things you are to consider, is the healthfulness of a situation. The brightest house and cheeriest outlook in nature will be made somber by the constant presence of a doctor, and the wandering around of an unseen, but ever felt, specter in the shape of miasm. . . . Malaria—malus, bad; aria, air—means, in its common definition, simply bad air. Miasma is its synonym,—infecting effluvia floating in the air. Because, as everybody knows, certain places have always chills and fever associated with them, and other places have not, it follows that between such places there is some fact of difference; this fact is the presence of miasm, a cause of disease, having a signification associative with the locality. . . .

Vegetation, heat, and moisture: these are the three active agents in the production of miasma, to which a fourth is to be added, in the influence of non-drainage, either by the way of the atmosphere or running water. The strongest example of a malarious locality one might make would be in suggesting a marshy valley in a tropical climate, so overrun with fixed water as to destroy a prolific vegetation, yet not covering it enough to protect the garbage from the putrefying influences of the sun; this valley, in turn, so environed with hills as to shut off a circulation of air. . . . Ground newly broken is not unapt to generate miasm. This results from the sudden exposure of long-buried vegetable matter to the influences of moisture and heat. . . . It may readily be conceived that malarious situations exist where the miasm is not sufficient in quantity to produce the effects of intermittent or bilious fever, yet where there is quite enough of it to keep a man feeling good for nothing,— he is not sick, but he is never well. I know of one country seat of this kind, where forty thousand dollars would not pay for the improvements put upon it, and where, I am free to declare, I would not think of living, even if, as an inducement, a free gift were made to me of the place. . . . Besides miasm, there are other atmospheric associations to be considered. I recall this moment a distillery, where attempt was made to get clear of the mash by throwing it into a running stream, with the anticipation of its being carried to the river, but where, on the contrary, it became a stagnant putrescent mass, impregnating the air for miles with its unendurable odor, and inducing such a typhoid tendency that half the country-side were down with fever. . . . There are, again, situations where the filth and *débris* of sewage exercise a poisoning influence on the surrounding atmosphere. This has its principal application to the neighborhood of cities and towns drained into adjoining streams. London and the Thames furnish a notable illustration. A cove, attractive as it is, may prove a receptacle for the accumulation of dead fish and other offal, which shall make untenable the charming cottage upon the bank. A deep cove has rarely healthy surroundings, the circulation of its water being too sluggish to insure freshness and vitality. Water, like blood, to be healthy, must be in a state of continuous movement.

A non-observant man, purchasing a beautiful stream, may be completely disappointed by finding that the opacity of its water depends upon a factory, of which he had never so much as heard; he may not let his children bathe in it, for he may well fear for them the fate of the fish he so plentifully finds lying dead upon the shore. A poisoned rural stream is as sad a sight as it has grown to be a common one. Always, before buying water, know what there is up stream, or what there is likely to be.

Never buy a country house without seeing to it that the foundation stands upon a higher level than some channel which may drain it, and this, by the way, is not to consider alone the dry summer day on which you go first to visit the place; you are to think of the winter and spring. Look to it that no excess of water shall be able to drown you out; some places, which in dry weather are glorious, are, in winter and spring, ankle-deep in slush and mire, and every thing about them is as wet as a soaked board. Open the front door of such a house, and a chill strikes you instantly. A fire must be kept the year round, or otherwise you live in the moisture of a vault. Places there are of this class where the question of the water from the kitchen-pump comes to absorb the attention of the whole household.

No shade is an abomination. A bilious fever fattens in the sun as does miasm in a marshy valley. Too much shade, on the contrary, and too near the house, is equally of ill import; it keeps things damp, and dampness is a breeder of pestilence. An atmosphere confined about a house by too dense foliage is like the air of an unventilated room, not fit for practical purposes. The sporadic poisons have an intimate relationship with dampness; miasm lives in it as does a snail in his shell. Besides this, it shuts out the cool breath of the summer nights, and makes restless swelterers where even a blanket might be enjoyed.—DR. JOHN DARBY, *Odd Hours of a Physician.*

2. *The House.*—So construct the dwelling from foundation to roof that no dampness can result. Give to the cellar dry walls, a cement floor, and windows enough to insure constant currents of air. Insist upon such a system of immediate and perfect sewerage as shall render contamination impossible. If "modern improvements" are afforded, see that the plumbing embraces the latest and most scientific sanitary inventions. Do not economize on this point; health, perhaps life, depends upon the perfect working of the various traps. Having employed the most skilled and intelligent plumbers, overlook their work so that you may fully understand the principle applied.

Provide for ample ventilation in every apartment, above and below. Let the sleeping-rooms be above-stairs, and furnished with appliances for moderate warmth in winter. Treat yourself and your family to as many fire-places as possible. Indulge in a spacious piazza, so placed that it will not cut off the light from the family sitting-room, and, if you can, include a balcony or two, large enough to hold a chair and a table, or a work-basket. Remember that a house is for convenience and protection *only when you can not be in the open air.*

3. *The Kitchen and the Dust-heap.—Removal of Household Refuse.*—It has to be assumed, especially where servants are not carefully overlooked, that the dust-heap of most houses will contain more or less decomposing organic matter, such as bits of meat, scales and refuse of fish, tea and coffee grounds, and the peelings of vegetables, which, though quite out of place in the ash-heap, are apt surreptitiously to be thrown upon it. Such matter soon becomes offensive and even dangerous, and a few days' retention of it in warm weather constitutes a legal nuisance. Household refuse should be carted away as often as once in two days; in extreme hot weather, daily. Where it is inexpedient to remove it frequently, it should be kept covered to the depth of two or three inches with a layer of powdered charcoal, or freshly-burnt lime, or, at least, of clear dry earth. All soil which has become foul by the soakage of decaying or vegetable matter should be similarly treated. The refuse heap should be protected from rain, and liquids should never be thrown upon it. Where obnoxious matter has been allowed to accumulate, its disturbance for removal should be conducted with special precaution, both on account of its temporary offensiveness of odor and the more serious results which may follow. It can not be too distinctly understood that cleanliness, ventilation, and dryness are the best of all deodorizers. One of the first of household regulations should be to see that no unsanitary rubbish remains in or about the dwelling. Keep the dust-heap itself at the farthest practicable remove from the house. Sow grass-seed plentifully upon the back premises, and induce tidiness in the domestics by having the kitchen door open upon a well-kept lawn.

Burning of Garbage.—The easiest, quickest, and most sanitary method of disposing of household garbage is to burn it This plan has been officially recommended by the Boards of Health in various cities. Many housekeepers have adopted it, and find it so practicable that in New York City there has become a marked decrease in the amount of household refuse collected by the scavengers. If, after every meal, the draughts of the range be opened, and all waste matter be deposited within, a few moments, or at most, a half hour, will effectually dispose of it, and prevent all the dangers that arise from its retention and accumulation. In the country, where there is plenty of ground, nearly all rubbish can be destroyed in this way and by outside fires, with the additional advantage that the ashes which are obtained are valuable as a garden fertilizer.—E. B. S.

4. *The Sewers and Drains.—How to keep out Sewer Air.*— The most perfectly flushed sewers that are made, under the latest and fullest sanitary light, must, owing to the constant entrance of greasy and other adhesive material, contain more or less of particles that "stick," and also more or less of fungi and mold; so that here, shut away from light and air, goes on the peculiar fermentation that fits it for the soil or habitat of the malarial germ. These germs, the soil once ready, take possession and multiply, whether that soil be a sewer or the blood of a person who sits calmly unconscious in a gorgeous chamber above, with a small continuation of the sewer extending untrapped up to his wash-bowl.—DR. DERBY.

Keep constant watch of your traps and drains. Cultivate the faculty of detecting sewer gas in the house. Always fear a smell; trace it to its source and provide a remedy. At the same time, bear in mind that it is not always the foul smell that is most dangerous. There is a close, sweet odor often present in bath-rooms, and about drains, that is deadly as the Upas tree. Bad air from neglected drains causes not only fevers, dysentery, and diphtheria, but asthma and other chronic disorders. Illuminating gas, escaping from pipes and prevented from exuding by frozen earth, has been known to pass sidewise for some distance into houses. Thus also the air from cess-pools and porous or broken drains finds its way, when an examination of the household entrance to the drain fails to reveal the cause of an existing effluvia. But, however bad the drain may be outside the house, there is little to fear provided the gas can escape externally. Every main drain should have a ventilating pipe carried from it directly outside the house to the top of the highest chimney. The soil-pipe inside the house should be carried up through the roof and be open at the top.

Digging for drains or other purposes should not be allowed when the mercury stands above 60°; but if, as in repairs of pipes, it becomes necessary to dig about the house in hot weather, let it be done in the middle of the day, and replace the turf as speedily as possible. If the soil be damp, or the district malarious, sprinkle quicklime upon the earth as fast as it is turned.

How to Clear Waste-pipes.— The "sewer-gas," about which so much has been written, and which is so justly dreaded, is not, as many suppose, the exclusive product of the sewer. Indeed, the foul and dangerous gases are not only found in the sewers themselves, but in the unventilated waste-pipes, and those which are in process of being clogged by the foul matter passing through them. Any obstruction in the soil or waste-pipes is therefore doubly dangerous, because it may produce an inflow of foul gas into the pipe, even though the entrance to the sewer itself has been entirely cut off.

In pipes leading from the house to the cess-pool, there is a constant accumulation of grease. This enters as a liquid, but hardens as the water cools, and is deposited on the bottom and sides of the pipes. As these accumulations increase, the water-way is gradually contracted, till the pipe is closed.

When the pipe is entirely stopped, or allows the water to fall away by drops only, proceed thus: Empty the pipe down to the trap, as far as practicable, by "mopping up" with a cloth. If the water flows very slowly, begin when the pipe has at last emptied itself. Fill the pipe up with potash, crowding it with a stick. Then allow hot water to trickle upon the potash, or pour the hot water upon it in a small stream, stopping as soon as the pipe appears to be filled. As the potash dissolves and disappears, add more water. At night a little heap of potash may be placed over the hole, and water enough poured on so that a supply of strong lye will flow into the pipe during the night.

Pipes that have been stopped for months may be cleaned out by this method, though it may call for three or four pounds of potash. The crudest kind, however, appears to act as well as the best. If the pipe is partially obstructed, a lump of crude potash should be placed where water will drip slowly upon it, and so reach the pipe. As water comes in contact with the potash, it becomes hot, thus aiding in dissolving the grease Potash, in combination with grease, forms a "soft" or liquid soap, which easily flows away. It is also destructive to all animal and most mineral matters.

Some of the most dangerous gases come from wash-basin pipes, being, perhaps, the result of the decay of the soap and the animal matter washed from the skin.

When a pipe is once fairly cleaned out, the potash should be used from time to time, in order to dissolve the greasy deposits as they form, and carry them forward to the cess-pool or sewer. —*Artisan.*

What Came from a Neighbor's Cess-pool.—Keep watch not only of your own premises, but stand on guard against those of your neighbors. Dr. Carpenter cites a case wherein "four members of a certain household were attacked with typhoid fever, one of whom narrowly escaped with her life. The circumstances left no doubt in the mind of the attending physician that the malady originated in the opening of an old cess-pool belonging to a neighboring house, then in course of demolition. The house in which the outbreak took place is large and airy, and stands by itself in a most salubrious situation. The most careful examination failed to disclose any defect either in its drainage or its water-supply; there was no typhoid in the neighborhood; and the milk-supply was unexceptional. But the neighboring house being old, and having been occupied by a school, its removal had been determined on to make way for a house of higher class; and as the offensive odor emanating from the uncovered cess-pool was at once perceived in the next garden, and the outbreak of typhoid followed at the usual interval, the case seems one which admits of no reasonable question."

5. *The Cellar.—A Typical Bad Cellar.*—Did the reader ever, when a child, see the cellar afloat at some old home in the country? You creep part way down the cellar-stairs with only the light of a single tallow-candle, and behold by its dim glimmer an expanse of dark water, boundless as the sea. On its surface, in dire confusion, float barrels and boxes, butter firkins and wash-tubs, boards, planks, hoops, and staves without number, interspersed with apples, turnips, and cabbages, while half-

drowned rats and mice, scrambling up the stairway for dear life, drive you affrighted back to the kitchen. . . . Now consider the case of one of these old farm-house cellars that has been in use fifty years or more. In it have been stored all the potatoes, turnips, cabbages, onions, and other vegetables for family food. The milk and cream, the pork and beef, and cider and vinegar, have all met with various accidents, and from time to time have had their juices, in various stages of decay, absorbed by the soil of the cellar-bottom. The cats have slept there to fight the rats and the mice, who have had their little homes behind the walls for half a century; and the sink-spouts have for the same term poured into the soil close by, their fragrant fluids. The water rushes upward and sideways into the cellar, forming, with the savory ingredients at which we have delicately hinted, a sort of broth, quite thin and watery at first, but growing thicker as the water slowly subsides and leaves its grosser parts pervading the surface of the earth, walls, and partitions. All this time the air rushes in at the openings of the cellar, and presses constantly upward, often lifting the carpets from the floors, and is breathed day and night by all who dwell in the house. Does it require learned doctors or boards of health to inform any rational person that these conditions are unfavorable to health? — MRS. PLUNKETT, *Women, Plumbers, and Doctors.*

What Came from a Crack in a Cellar Wall.—A few years ago a Boston gentleman inherited a house, situated on one of the most desirable streets of the city. Resolving to make a healthy as well as a beautiful home, he spent a large sum, and gave personal supervision to all the details of an elaborate system of plumbing. He moved in. Imagine his grief and disappointment when member after member of his family succumbed to diphtheria, and an infant and a grown daughter died. Though so deeply smitten, he did not lose his belief in the connection between cause and effect. He ordered a minute investigation of the premises by experts. A slight crack, so small as to have escaped ordinary observation, was found in the cellar wall. Investigation of the premises next door—the inmates of which were also suffering from diphtheria—showed a choked-up drain, which ought to have connected with the sewer.

but did not. The filthy ooze from this was pouring out, just where its effluvium and its disease-germs could pass without any hindrance through the crack.

Now that it is shown that gases pass through bricks and many kinds of stone, it is easy to see that the sanitary welfare of one is the sanitary welfare of all.—MRS. PLUNKETT.

6. *The Bedroom.—The Bed a Night Garment.*—There is still one of our garments to be considered, which generally is not regarded as such. I mean the bed—that piece of clothing in which we spend such a great part of our time.

The bed is not only a place of rest; it is especially our sleeping-garment, and has often to make up for privations endured during the day and the day's work, and to give us strength for to-morrow. Like our day-garments, the bed-covering must be airy and warm at the same time. We warm the bed by our body, just as we warm our clothes, and the bed warms the air which is continually flowing through it from below, upward. The regulating strata must be more powerful in their action than in our day-clothes, because during rest and sleep the metamorphosis of our tissues and the resulting heat become less; and because in a horizontal position we lose more heat by an ascending current of air than in a vertical position, where the warm ascending current is in more complete and longer contact with our upright body.

The warmth of the bed sustains the circulation in our surface to a certain degree for the benefit of our internal organs at a time when our production of heat is at its lowest ebb. Hence the importance of the bed for our heat and blood economy. Several days without rest in a bed not only make us sensible of a deficiency in the recruiting of our strength, but very often produce quite noticeable perturbations in our bodily economy, from which the bed would have protected us.—DR. MAX VON PETTENKOFFER.

Bed Ventilation.—It often happens that the desire of the energetic housekeeper to have her work done at an early hour in the morning, causes her to leave one of the most important items of neatness undone. The most effectual purifying of bed and bed-clothes can not take place, if the proper time is not allowed for the free circulation of pure air, to remove all human

21

impurities which have collected during the hours of slumber. At least two or three hours should be allowed for the complete removal of atoms of insensible perspiration which are absorbed by the bed. Every day the airing should be done; and, occasionally, bedding constantly used should be carried into the open air, and left exposed to the sun and wind for half a day.— *Home and Health.*

CIRCULATION.

The Pulse (p. 116).—The pulse which is felt by the finger does not correspond precisely with the beat of the heart, but takes place a little after it, and the interval is longer, the greater the distance of the artery from the heart. The beat of the artery on the inner side of the ankle, for example, is a little later than the beat of the artery in the temple.—HUXLEY.

The pulse is increased by exertion, and thus is more rapid in a standing than in a sitting, and in a sitting than in a lying posture. It is quickened by meals, and while varying thus from time to time during the day, is on the whole quicker in the evening than in early morning. It is said to be quicker in summer than in winter. Even independently of muscular exertion, it seems to be quickened by great altitude. Its rate is also profoundly influenced by mental conditions.—FOSTER.

Circulation of Blood in the Brain (p. 120).—Signor Mosso, who has been engaged on the subject for six years, has published some new observations on the different conditions of the circulation of the blood in the brain. He has had the privilege of observing three patients who had holes in their skulls, permitting the examination of the encephalic movements and circulation. No part of the body exhibits a pulsation so varied in its form as the brain. The pulsation may be described as tricuspid; that is, it consists of a strong beat, preceded and followed by lesser beats. It gathers strength when the brain is at work, corresponding with the more rapid flow of blood to the organ. The increase in the volume of the brain does not depend upon any change in the respiratory rhythm; for, if we take the pulse of the fore-arm simultaneously with that of the brain, we can not perceive that the cerebral labor exercises any influence upon the fore-arm, although the pulsation in the brain may be considerably modified. The emotions have a similar effect upon the circulation of the brain to that of cerebral labor. Signor Mosso has also observed and registered graphically the variations of the cerebral pulse during sleep. Generally the pulses of the wrist and the brain vary oppositely. At the moment of waking, the pulse of the wrist diminishes, while that of the brain increases. The cerebral pulsations diminish as sleep grows deeper, and at last become very weak. Outward excitations determine the same modifications during sleep as in the waking state, without waking the sleeper. A deep inspiration always produces a diminution in the volume of the brain, in consequence, probably, of the increased flow of blood into the veins of the thoracic cavity; the increase of volume in the brain, when it takes place, is, on the contrary, due to a more abundant flow of arterial blood to the encephalus.—*Popular Science Monthly, March, 1882.*

Catarrhal Colds (p. 130).—I maintain that it can be proved, with as absolute certainty as any physiological fact admits of being proved, that warm, vitiated in-door air is the cause, and cold out-door air the best cure, of catarrh. . . . Fresh cold air is a tonic that invigorates the respiratory organs when all other stimulants fail, and, combined with arm-exercise and certain dietetic alternatives, it is the best remedy for all disorders of the lungs and upper air-passages. . . . A combination of the three specifics,—exercise, abstinence, and fresh air,—will cure the most obstinate cold. . . . Frost is such a powerful disinfectant, that in very cold nights the lung-poisoning atmosphere of few houses can resist its purifying influence; in spite of padded doors, in spite of "weather-strips" and double windows, it reduces the in-door temperature enough to paralyze the floating disease-germs. The penetrative force of a polar night-frost exercises that function with such resistless vigor that it defies the preventive measures of human skill; and all Arctic travelers agree that among the natives of Iceland, Greenland, and Labrador pulmonary diseases are actually unknown. Protracted cold weather thus prevents epidemic catarrhs, but during the first thaw Nature succumbs to art: smoldering stove fires add their fumes to the effluvia of the dormitory, tight-fitting doors and windows exclude the means of salvation; superstition triumphs; the lung-poison operates, and the next morning a snuffling, coughing, and red-nosed family discuss the cause of their affliction. . . . It is a mistake to suppose that "colds" can be propagated only by direct transmission or the breathing of recently vitiated air. Catarrh-germs, floating in the atmosphere of an ill-ventilated bedroom, may preserve their vitality for weeks after the house has been abandoned; and the next renter of such a place should not move in till wide-open windows and doors and a thorough draught of several days have removed every trace of a "musty" smell.—DR. FELIX L. OSWALD, *Remedies of Nature, Popular Science Monthly, March, 1884.*

Catching Cold.—The phrase "to catch cold," so often in the mouths of physicians and patients, is a curious solecism. It implies that the term "cold" denotes something positive—a sort of demon which does not catch, but is caught by the unfortunate victims. . . . If most persons outside of the medical profession were to be asked what they consider as chiefly to be avoided in the management of sick people, the answer would probably be "catching cold." I suspect that this question would be answered in the same way by not a few physicians. Hence it is that sick-rooms are poorly ventilated, and patients are oppressed by a superabundance of garments and bed-clothes. The air which patients are made to breathe, having been already breathed and rebreathed, is loaded with pulmonary exhalations. Cutaneous emanations are allowed to remain in contact with the body, as well as to pervade the atmosphere. Patients not confined to the bed, especially those affected with pulmonary disease, are overloaded with clothing, which becomes saturated with perspiration, and is seldom changed, for fear of the dreaded "cold." . . .

A reform is greatly needed in respect to "catching cold." Few diseases are referable to the agency of cold, and even the affection commonly called a cold is generally caused by other agencies, or, perhaps, by a special agent, which may prove to be a microbe. Let the axiom, *A fever patient never catches cold,* be reiterated until it becomes a household phrase. Let the restorative influence of cool, fresh, pure atmosphere be inculcated. Let it be understood that in therapeutics, as in hygiene, the single word *comfort* embodies the principles which should regulate coverings and clothing.—AUSTIN FLINT, M.D., *in a Lecture printed in The New York Medical Journal.*

DIGESTION AND FOOD.

The Water We Drink (p. 155).—*Qualities of Pure Water.*—"A good drinking water," says Dr. Simpson (in *The Water We Drink*), "should possess the following physical characters: it should be entirely free from color, taste, or odor; it should, moreover, be cool, well aerated, soft, bright, and entirely free from all deposit. But it should be remembered that a water having all these characteristics may yet be more or less polluted by organic matter, owing to the proximity of drains and sewers. . . . Disease has frequently been traced to the use of perfectly bright and clear water, where there was no sediment, and where the animal organic matter was held in a state of solution."

In the case of diseases, such as typhoid, which attack the stomach, disease germs are removed along with the excreta; and if, as is often the case, the drainage of an infected town flows into a river, and that river is used in some after-portion of its course as a water-supply, there is great danger of such diseases being communicated. For, however well the water may be purified and filtered, we have no guarantee that it will not contain some of these disease germs, which are so small that they pass through the finest filters. It is in this way that almost all the great cholera and typhoid epidemics have spread.—*Chambers' Journal.*

Well-water Often Dangerous.—A densely crowded population soon impregnates the soil to some depth with filth, which drains into the water-course below, especially if such water is near the surface. This surface water easily penetrates a loosely walled well. Every well, therefore, should not only be widely separated from barn-yards, cess-pools, pens, sinks, and similar places, but should be made water-tight with cement, so that nothing can reach its interior except water that has been filtered through dense beds of unpolluted ground below. If these precautions are neglected, the best and deepest well may become continually contaminated by infiltration from the surrounding surface. This impure water, even when not used for family drinking, is sometimes supplied to cows, or used for washing dairy pans, or employed in diluting milk for the market, and there are many known cases in which disease has thus been disseminated. Thus, an epidemic of typhoid fever in Cambridge, Mass., was definitely traced to a dairy which supplied the victims with milk. Upon investigation it was found that a short time before there had been a typhoid patient in the farm-house, and that the well from which water was taken to wash the milk-pans had become contaminated with the specific poison brought into it from the surrounding drainage.

All suspected water should be thoroughly boiled before using it to drink. Some physicians insist that the boiling should continue for one or two hours in order entirely to destroy the bacterial germs. The heaviness and insipidity incident to boiled water may be somewhat relieved by afterward filtering it. Filtering, of itself, however, will do little toward ridding the water of microbes, which are much too minute to be arrested by the ordinary apparatus.—When journeying, where one must often take a hasty meal at a railway station, drink hot water in preference to cold. A convenient portable filter may be arranged with a bottle of powdered charcoal, and a piece of filtering paper. A traveler by briskly stirring a table-spoonful of the charcoal into a pint of water, allowing it to stand five or ten minutes, and then filtering it through the paper, may venture to relieve his thirst in almost any part of the country.

Water an Absorbent of Foul Gases.—If a pitcher of water be left uncovered in an occupied apartment for only a few hours, it will become foul from the absorption of the respired and perspired gases in the room. The colder the water, the greater the capacity to contain these gases. Water kept in a room over night is therefore unfit for drinking, and should not be used even to brush the teeth or to gargle in the throat.

Impure Ice, a Breeder of Disease.—We generally take the purity of our ice for granted, and, like the alligator in the bayou, close our mouths and swallow it. In the country, I have seen during the ice-harvesting season, wagon after wagon passing me on the road, laden with ice that had been collected from

canals, rivers, and streams receiving sewerage, and from ponds
that are in the summer-time reeking with slime, and often offensive from the quantity of decomposed vegetable and animal
matter brought in by the washing from the meadow. These
streams would be shunned as a source of water supply.

Should you interview a native regarding the slimy mud-pud-
dle before you, called Mr. So-and-so's private "ice-pond," he
would say that "in winter it is much better, and when frozen,
you know, it makes fine ice," presenting that popular though
ignorant belief that while in the act of crystallizing, water rids
itself of all its injurious qualities, however offensive it may be
in its liquid state. Unfortunately, there is enough truth in the
current idea of the elimination of noxious and foreign matter
during the process of freezing to give color to the popular
belief, but not enough to make it a safe reliance ; therefore all
means should be used to enlighten the public regarding this
subject. Experiment has shown that freezing produces little
change or effect in overcoming the poisonous influences, and ice
has often served as a vehicle to convey the germs of typhoid
and other low forms of fever. Pure ice can be procured only
from water free from impurities, and ice for domestic or surgical purposes should never be collected from ponds or streams
which contain animal or vegetable refuse, or stagnant and
muddy material.—*Journal of Reconstructives, Oct., 1887.*

The Glandular Coat of the Stomach, and How it Weeps
(p. 162).—While the food is thus being continually moved about,
it is at the same time subjected to the action of the chemical
sac. This is, as we have said, a glandular sac. It is of some
thickness, and is made of little glands bound up together with
that stringy fibrous packing material which anatomists call *connective tissue.*

If we were to imagine many gross of small India-rubber
vials all placed side by side, and bound together with hay
or straw into a great mat, and the mat rolled up into a sac,
with all the mouths of the vials turned inward, we should
have a large and coarse, but tolerably fair image of the glandular coat of the stomach. Each vial would then represent one
of the glands of this coat, one of the *gastric* or *peptic* glands,
as they are called. Each gland, however, is not always a

simple tube, but is often branched at the bottom end, and all of them are lined, except just at their mouths, with large rounded bodies, which not unfrequently almost choke up their cavity.

The rounded masses, or cells, as they are called, in the interior of each gland, form the really active part of the apparatus. Each cell is a little laboratory, which concocts out of the material brought to it or near it by the blood a certain potent, biting fluid, and is hence called a peptic or digestive cell. Each cell is born at the bottom of the tube, and in process of time travels upward toward the mouth. When it reaches the mouth, it bursts, and pours into the stomach the fluid it has elaborated, or perhaps may give it out without bursting, while it is still within its tube.

FIG. 72.

BRANCHED GASTRIC GLAND.

a. *The peptic cells.* b. *The inert cells.*

In those cases in which it has been possible to look in upon the stomach while at work (as in the famous case of Alexis St. Martin), and where the orifices of the tiny glands (for though we have compared them to bottles, they are exceedingly small) appear like little dots, tears were seen to start at the mouths of the glands, gather into drops, and finally trickle down into the lowest part of the stomach. The stomach, as it were, weeps; and indeed the weeping of tears is just such another effect of glandular activity — only ordinary tears form a mild and, chemically speaking, impotent fluid; while the fluid which the tears of the stomach weep—the *gastric juice*—is a sharp, piercing water of excessive chemical power.—HINTON.

Poisonous Milk, Cheese, and Ice-cream (p. 169).—In late years there have been many cases of poisoning by ice-cream, cheese, and milk. The poisonous principle sometimes developed in these articles of food has been made a subject of special investigation, and it has been found to be due to natural causes. Dr. Vaughan, of Michigan, after spending several months in experimenting upon samples of twelve different cheeses, which had caused three hundred cases of poisoning, finally succeeded in isolating certain poison-crystals, which he calls *Tyrotoxicon.* He says: "A few drops of an aqueous solution of these crystals placed upon the tongue produces all the symptoms observed in those who had been made sick by eating of the cheese. This was tried repeatedly upon myself, and upon some of my students who kindly offered themselves for experimentation." Dr. Vaughan afterward procured the poison-crystals from milk which had stood some months in a closed bottle, and also from a sample of ice-cream by which eighteen persons had been made ill. It was learned in the latter case that the custard, of which the ice-cream was made, had been allowed to stand in a foul atmosphere for two hours before it was frozen. By placing small bits of this poisonous cream in good milk, and allowing it to stand twenty-four hours, the whole became vitiated. This proved that the poison is due to the growth of some ferment. In the autumn of 1886, many persons in different hotels at Long Branch were poisoned by milk obtained from a certain milkman. In this case it was found that the cows were milked at noon, the warm milk being immediately placed in cans and carted eight miles during the warmest part of the day, in a very hot month. In June, 1887, nineteen persons in New York city were similarly poisoned by milk which also came from one dairy. Many of these persons had narrow escapes from death. These, and many other like instances, teach us the importance of the greatest care in every detail of milk-handling. A little dried milk formed along the seam of a tin pail, or any similar lodging-place, may be the starting-point of poison generation. A month after his first experiments with the ice-cream mentioned above, Dr. Vaughan put small pieces of the dried custard in pans of milk, and afterward made custard from this milk. This yielded tyrotoxicon as before, showing the tenacious vitality of the poison, and also explaining the fact that the precise cause of poisoning is in many cases so difficult to trace.

Fish as Food (p. 169).—It is not desirable that fish should be the sole kind of nitrogenous food eaten by any nation; and even if milk and eggs be added thereto, the vigor of such a people will not be equal to that of flesh-eating nations. At the same time, the value of fish as a part of a dietary is indicated by the larger proportion of phosphorus which it contains, and which renders it especially fitted for the use of those who perform much brain-work, or who are the victims of much anxiety and distress.—EDWARD SMITH, *in "Foods."*

For the mentally exhausted, the worried, the "nervous," and the distressed in mind, fish is not simply a food; it acts as physic. The brain is nourished by it, the "nerves"—to use the term in its popular sense—are "quieted"; the mind grows stronger, the temper less irritable, and the whole being healthier and happier when fish is substituted for butcher's meat. . . . I find persons who are greatly excited, even to the extent of seeking to do violence to themselves or to those around them, who can not sleep, and who are in an agony of irritability, become composed and contented when fed almost exclusively on fish. In such cases I have withdrawn butter, milk, eggs, and all the varieties of warm-blooded animal food; and, carefully noting the weight and strength, I find no diminution of either, while fish is supplied in such quantities as fully to satisfy the appetite.—J. MORTIMER GRANVILLE, M.D., *"Fish as Food and Physic."*

Coffee and Tea (p. 170).—Besides the alkaloid *Caffeine* which coffee contains, it also develops, in roasting, a volatile oil called Caffeone, to which is due its characteristic aroma. The main effects of coffee are due to both the caffeine and the caffeone, which are antagonistic, though not contemporaneous, in action. The volatile oil reduces arterial tension, allows a brisker flow of blood, and so increases the rapidity of the heart's action. It also acts upon the brain, and intellectual faculties in general; keeps one awake, and his mind clear. Caffeine, on the other hand, like digitalis, produces a high arterial tension, and slows the heart-beat. It exerts its chief effect upon the spinal cord, to which, like strychnia, it is an excitant. The shaking hand of the inveterate coffee-drinker is caused by caffeine. Thus a cup of coffee produces on the drinker a double effect,—of the oil and the alkaloid; the former sooner and transient, the latter later and lasting. . . . Coffee is not in itself nutritious to any marked degree; but it saves food, and also maintains life, by its exhilarating effect upon the nervous system. It is an excellent antidote to opium, producing the wakefulness that antagonizes the narcotic sleep of the drug; is now and then curative of sick headache, and is one of the standard remedies for certain forms of nausea.

To the chemist, *Tea* is much the same thing as coffee. It contains considerably more tannin, a volatile oil, and an alkaloid (theine) indistinguishable from caffeine. That the injurious effects of overdoses are due as much to the volatile oil as to the alkaloid, is shown by the fact that tea-packers are made ill by long breathing of air filled with it, and that tea-tasters in China, who avoid swallowing the infusion, can endure their trade but a few years, and leave the country with shattered nerves.

Probably every one numbers among his friends women who are actual slaves of the tea-habit, and who would find tea as hard to forsake as men find tobacco. It is not unlikely that the functional cardiac disorder, often spoken of as the "tobacco heart," due to nervous derangement, and accompanied by palpitation and pain in the cardiac region, is more often due to tea than tobacco. In fact, the disorders induced by excessive tea-drinking have been grasped as a special disease, to which has been given the name of *Theism*. This includes a train of symptoms, usually progressive, loss of appetite, pain after meals, headache, constipation, palpitation, cardiac distress, hysterical manifestations, dizziness, and paresis.—DR. MAURICE D. CLARKE, *Popular Science News.*

Tea-drinkers, as a rule, express doubts as regards the correctness of alleged poisonous properties of tea. Numerous instances of individuals of this class have been noticed who were themselves suffering from tea-poisoning. Their nerves were in a deplorably abnormal condition, the heart and brain were functionally disturbed, and the sleep less in quantity and less refreshing than it should be. . . . One's opinion of the physical disturbances which may be caused by rum, tobacco, or tea, are not worth much, when the opinion comes from a victim of the excessive use of these agents.

The tannin found in tea does not differ from that found in oak and other barks which the tanners use to convert the raw hides of animals into leather. It is a powerful astringent, which accounts for some of the peculiar physical evils to which confirmed tea-drinkers are subject.

Theine does not differ essentially from *Cocaine* (see p. 223). They both produce exaltation of the nervous system and increased powers of physical endurance. The brain is largely influenced in its functions, and long periods of wakefulness are induced. Continued use of strong infusions of either coca or tea result in great disturbance of nervous centers and functional offices, and either will produce fatal results by persistent use of inordinate quantities.

A cup of tea as served at tea-tables contains usually only a trace of the alkaloidal principle, but infinitesimal quantities are capable of exerting baneful effects upon some tea-drinkers. . . . Poisons act in a variety of ways, some slowly, and without producing pain; others act violently, and with speedy, fatal results. Inasmuch as we do not observe a very large number of clearly proved cases of acute poisoning by tea, we must conclude that it is characteristically a slow poison, and also that its influence is unlike in different individuals. . . . Four or six cups of tea, however, taken during each twenty-four hours, will in time produce tea-poisoning, and greater or less evil effects.

Tea is well enough, when its use is kept under absolute, intelligent control; but if it becomes master in any case, then it must be promptly abandoned, for danger attends the intemperate tea-drinker every hour of his life. Those advanced in life crave its stimulating effects, and it is well for them to use it in moderation; but the young should abstain from it entirely.—*Abridged from "Tea Poisoning," by* DR. NICHOLS, *in Popular Science News, December, 1887.*

Causes and Effects of Indigestion (p. 172).—When a light breakfast is eaten, a solid meal is requisite in the middle of the day. If the digestive organs are left too long unemployed, they secrete an excess of mucus, which greatly interferes with their normal functions. One meal has a direct influence on the next; and a poor breakfast leaves the stomach over-active for dinner. This is the secret of much excess in eating. The point to bear in mind is that not to eat a sufficiency at one meal makes you too hungry for the next; and that when you are too hungry, you are apt to overload the stomach, and to give the gastric juices more to do than they have the power to perform.

To eat too often, and to eat irregularly, are other sources of indigestion. People who dine at uncertain hours, and eat one meal too quickly on the last, must expect the stomach to retaliate in the long run. A very fruitful cause of dyspepsia is imperfect mastication. We remember one old gentleman who used always to warn young people on this point by saying: " Remember you have no teeth in your stomach." Nervous people nearly always eat fast, and as nearly always are the victims of nervous irritability, produced by dyspepsia. . . . To sit much in a stooping posture interferes with the stomach's action. Well-marked dyspepsia has been traced to sitting immediately after dinner in a low arm-chair, so that the body was curved forward, and the stomach compressed. . . . .

The skin, core, and kernels of fruit should be avoided. Some people are not able to digest raw apples; and dyspepsia has been sometimes greatly aggravated by eating pears. The latter fruit, in its ripest state, contains an abundance of gritty material, which, as it can not be separated in the mouth, on being swallowed irritates the mucous membrane. . . . .

Of food itself, bear in mind that hot meat is more digestible than cold; the flesh of full-grown animals than that of young ones; that land birds are more digestible than water-fowl; wild animals than domestic ones; and that in game, newly-killed birds are easier of digestion than those which have been kept a long time.—*Hints to Dyspeptics, Chambers' Journal.*

How Food Develops Energy (p. 173).—It may appear strange that the small amount of food we eat should suffice to carry our large and bulky bodies through all the varied movement of the day. But this difficulty disappears at once, when we recollect how large an amount of dormant energy can be laid by in a very small piece of matter. A lump of coal no bigger than one's fist, if judiciously employed, will suffice to keep a small toy-engine at work for a considerable time. Now, our food is matter containing large amounts of dormant energy, and our bodies are engines so constructed as to utilize all the energy to the best advantage. A single gramme of beef-fat if completely burned (that is, if every atom unites with oxygen), is capable of developing more than 9,000 heat-units; and each heat-unit, if employed to perform mechanical work, is capable of lifting a weight of one gramme to a height of 424 meters; or, what comes to the same thing, 424 grammes to a height of one meter. Accordingly, the energy contained in one gramme of beef, and the oxygen with which it unites, would be sufficient to raise the little bit of fat itself to a height of 3,816 kilometers, or almost as high as the distance from London to New York.—GRANT ALLEN *in " Why do we Eat our Dinner?"*

Danger of Too High Pressure. — A prudent fire-engineer, when his water-hose is old and weak, would not try to force as much water as he could into it. No; to prevent a rupture he would work it at a low pressure. But men seldom think of carrying out the same simple mechanical principle when there is reason to believe that the vessels of the brain are getting weak and brittle. They eat and drink just as much as they feel inclined to, and sometimes a little more. With a good digestion, nearly all they consume is converted into blood, to the yet further distention of vessels already over-distended. This high-pressure style of living produces high-pressure results. Its effects were painfully illustrated by the death of Charles Dickens. The brain-work he performed was immense; he lived generously, taking his wine as he did his meat, with a liberal hand. He disregarded the signs of structural decay, forcing his reluctant brain to do what it had once done with spontaneous ease, until all at once, under a greater tension than ordinary, a weak vessel gave way, flooding the brain with blood.—J. R. BLACK, M.D., *in "Apoplexy," Popular Science Monthly, April, 1875.*

Evils of Gluttony. — "Is it not strange," says Dr. Hunt, "how people, even the most considerate, will trifle with their stomachs? Many a person seems to prefer taking medicine to avoiding it by a proper regulation of the appetite. You may stuff the stomach to the full, year after year, but as sure as effects follow causes, so sure will you reap the accumulating penalty." A physician of extensive practice declares that he has never lived through a Christmas or Thanksgiving without frequently being consulted for ailments produced by excessive eating. He says : "It would seem as if multitudes thought they had a gluttonous license once a year, and that the most appropriate method of expressing gratitude, was by stuffing the stomach." Excessive eating produces scrofula. Surfeiting among children results in mental stupidity and unmanageable temper. . . . I am acquainted with a family, in which about the average amount of stuffing is indulged. To my expostulations, the mother has replied : "I may not be able to give my children as much education as some folks, and I may not be able to give them any property, but as long as we can get it, they shall have what they want to eat." I have spoken of their black teeth, bad breath, eruptions, and frequent sickness. "Yes," she has replied, "I know all that, but would you have me stop them before their appetites are half satisfied, and tell them, 'there, that is all you can have'? No; as long as I can get it, my children shall have enough to eat; it never shall be said that I have starved them." This indulgence of children to the full extent of their undiscriminating appetites is extreme folly and genuine unkindness. Pampered with a variety of dishes, they eat enormously, which engenders a craving for another large meal, and so on—their youthful and elastic constitutions enabling them to bear the excess without immediate serious injury. Let them be confined to one or two plain dishes at a meal, and the quantity be determined for them ; it will then be found that a growing child does not need to be stuffed, and that his appetite will soon become reasonable ; and if the food be plain, and mostly or entirely vegetable, it will soon be observed that the child's teeth are whiter, its breath sweeter, its skin clearer, its tongue cleaner, its eyes brighter, its sleep quieter, its brains sharper, and its temper more amiable. There are few changes in the management of children which would prove so beneficial as that from the present mode of cramming with a multitude of rich foods, to a plain vegetable diet, eaten in regular and moderate quantities.—Dio Lewis, *in Weak Lungs, and How to Make them Strong.*

Regular Physical Habits (p. 177).—Constipation lies at the root of a host of chronic ailments, which seem especially to beset American women. Impaired blood, nervous excitability, sick-headaches, mental depression, sleeplessness, and a long train of untold sufferings may be directly traced to this physical sin. We say *sin*, for in the large majority of instances this habit may be prevented; or, if already formed, may, by proper attention, be cured. The principal causes which lead to this deplorable state of the system are:

1. Errors in Food.
2. Errors in Exercise.
3. Inattention to Nature's laws.

Errors in Food have much to do with the evil in question. Our diet is, in general, too concentrated. We indulge ourselves with animal food two or three times a day, accompanying it with spices, condiments, greasy gravies, fine wheat bread, and a sparse amount of vegetables. We wind up our dinners with rich and heavy pastry, and our luncheons or our suppers with sugared sweetmeats and that indigestible compound often offered under the name of cake. A few cups of strong tea intensify the error. Coffee has a less astringent effect, and therefore can not be so severely arraigned for this particular consequence. When we think what delicious meals can be enjoyed from any of the cereals, well cooked, and taken with milk or cream, bread from unbolted flour, plenty of unsugared fruit, and pure rain or spring water, filtered and cooled or taken hot, with or without milk, we wonder that so many people consent day after day to use greasy pork, fried steaks, fried potatoes, hot biscuit, and in many cases poorly made coffee and tea. These are the people who make up the grand army of sallow-faced sufferers upon which the venders of patent pills and nauseous compounds thrive.

A wise mother will not allow mere culinary convenience to take precedence of the requirements of health. She will study the peculiar physical needs of each one of her children, that she may provide for each the food best suited to his or her constitution. This is not a difficult matter. "Water, not only by itself, but in some of its combinations," says Dr. Oswald, "is an effective aperient; in water-melons, and whey, for instance, but still more in conjunction with a dish of peas, or beans. No constipation can long withstand the suasion of a dose of pea-soup, or baked beans, flavored with a modicum of brown butter, and glorified with a cup of cold spring water. Moreover, the aperient effect thus produced is not followed by an astringent reaction, as in the case of drugs,—the cure, once effected, is permanent."

Errors in Exercise may lie in two directions, and over-exertion, viz., exercise carried to the point of nervous exhaustion, is as mischievous in its effect as is the other extreme. A too-long walk, for instance, may cause the very evil it is intended to cure.

As a rule, however, sedentary habits are chargeable with the greater share of influence in this unhappy state of the system. Light gymnastics within doors, a brisk walk or horseback ride without, both taken in garments suspended from the shoulders, and devoid of all constriction so that the abdominal viscera can partake in the general movement of the body, are advisable. For invalids or those incapacitated for active exercise, friction or massage treatment daily, including a vigorous kneading of the abdomen, or a relaxation of the entire muscles of the body with especial thought directed to the desired result, are often of great service.

Inattention to Physical Laws is perhaps the prime culprit. Nature always inclines to regularity, and when we do not respect her dictates, we invite the retribution which, sooner or later, she invariably inflicts. The elimination of waste from the system is an imperative necessity, and whenever it is thwarted, evil must and will follow. Aside from the avoidance of positive discomforts, suffering, and disease, there is the not unimportant consideration of bodily elasticity and a fine complexion. Let every young woman who would possess and retain a fair, delicate complexion, remember that the most important factor in its formation and retention is a clean system.

Proper diet, plenty of fruits, plenty of wholesome drink, enough exercise to send the blood pleasurably bounding through the veins, followed up and enforced by prompt recognition of the immutable laws of Health in this as well as all other organic functions, will soon work a reform that could not be so successfully effected by all the drugs in Christendom.—E. B. S.

THE NERVOUS SYSTEM.

Effect of Violent Passions upon Health (p. 202).—The man who is given to outbursts of anger is sure to experience a rapid change of the physical organs, in case he does not die in a fit of rage.

Death under such circumstances is of frequent occurrence. Sylla, Valentinian, Nerva, Wenceslas, and Isabeau of Bavaria, all died in consequence of an access of passion. The medical annals of our own time recount many instances of fatal effects following the violent brain-disturbance caused by anger. The symptoms usually are pulmonary and cerebral congestions. Still such fatal accidents as these are exceptional; as a rule, the passions of hate and anger deteriorate the constitution by slow, but sure degrees.

How, then, do we explain those morbid phenomena which have their origin in misplaced affection, in disappointed ambition, in hatred, or in anger, and which culminate either in serious chronic maladies, or in death or suicide? They all seem to start from an impairment of the cerebro-spinal centers. The continual excitation of these by ever-present emotions determines a paralysis of the central nerve-substance, and thus affects its connections with the nerves extending out to the various organs. These nerves next degenerate by degrees, and soon the great functions are compromised. The heart and the lungs cease to act with their normal rhythm, the circulation grows irregular and languishing. Appetite disappears, the amount of carbonic acid exhaled decreases, and the hair grows white, owing to the interruption of the pigmentary secretion. This general disturbance in nutrition and secretion is attended with a fall of the body's temperature and anæmia. The flesh dries up and the organism becomes less and less capable of resisting morbific influences. At the same time, in consequence of the reaction of all these disturbances on the brain, the psychic faculties become dull or perverted, and the patient falls into a decline more or less complicated and aggravated by grave symptoms. Under these conditions he dies or makes away with himself.

Two organs, the stomach and the liver, are often affected in a peculiar and characteristic way in the course of this pathological evolution. The modifications produced in the innervation, under the influence of cephalic excitement, cause a disturbance of the blood-circulation in the liver. This disturbance is of such a nature that the bile, now secreted in larger quantity, is resorbed into the blood instead of passing into the biliary vesicle. Then appears what we call jaundice. The skin becomes pale, then yellow, owing to the presence in the blood of the coloring matter of the bile. This change in the liver is usually developed slowly: sometimes, however, jaundice makes its appearance suddenly. Villeneuve mentions the case of two youths who brought a discussion to an end by grasping their swords; suddenly one of them turned yellow, and the other, alarmed at this transformation, dropped his weapon. The same author speaks of a priest who became jaundiced on seeing a mad dog jump at him. Whatever may be said of these cases, we must reckon painful affections of the soul among the efficient causes of chronic diseases of the liver.

The digestion, says the author of a work published some years ago, is completely subjected to the influence of the moral and intellectual state. When the brain is wearied by the passions, appetite and digestion are almost gone. . . . There is nowhere perfect health, save when the passions are well regulated, harmonized, and equipoised. Moral temperance is as indispensable to a calm and tranquil life as physiological temperance. . . . If it is your desire that your circulatory, respiratory, and digestive functions should be discharged properly, normally, if you want your appetite to be good, your sleep sound, your humor equable, avoid all emotions that are overstrong, all pleasures that are too intense, and meet the inevitable sorrows and the cruel agonies of life with a firm and resigned soul. Ever have some occupation to employ and divert your mind, and to make it proof against the temptations of want or of desire. Thus will you attain the term of life without overmuch disquiet and affliction.—FERNAND PAPILLON, *in the Revue des Deux Mondes.*

Brain-work, Overwork, and Worry (p. 205).—*Overstimulation of the Brain in Childhood.*—Most civilized communities have enacted laws against the employment of children in severe physical labor. This is well enough, for the muscles of young persons are tender and weak, and not, therefore, adapted to the work to which cupidity or ignorance would otherwise subject them. But no such fostering care does the State take of the *brains* of the young. There are no laws to prevent the undeveloped nervous system being overtasked and brought to disease, or even absolute destruction. Every physician sees cases of the kind, and wonders how parents of intelligence can be so blind to the welfare of their offspring as to force, or even to allow, their brains to be worked to a degree that, in many cases, results in idiocy or death. Only a few months ago I saw for the first time a boy of five years of age, with a large head, a prominent forehead, and all the other signs of mental precocity. He had read the first volume of Bryant's "History of the United States," and was preparing to tackle the other volumes! He read the magazines of the day with as much interest as did his father, and conversed with equal facility on the politics of the period. But a few weeks before I saw him he had begun to walk in his sleep, then chorea had made its appearance, and on the day before he was brought to me he had had a well-marked epileptic paroxysm. Already his mind is weakened—perhaps permanently so. Such cases are not isolated ones. They are continually occurring.

The period of early childhood—say up to seven or eight years of age—is that during which the brain and other parts of the nervous system are most actively developing, in order to fit them for the great work before them. It is safe to say that the only instruction given during this time should be that which consists in teaching children how to observe. The perceptive faculties alone should be made the subjects of systematic attempts at development. The child should be taught how to use his senses, and especially how to see, hear, and touch. In this manner, knowledge would be acquired in the way that is preeminently the natural way, and ample food would be furnished for the child's reflective powers.—DR. WM. A. HAMMOND, *Popular Science Monthly, November, 1884.*

Reserve Force.—The part which "a stock of energy" plays in brain-work can scarcely be exaggerated. Reserves are of

high moment every-where in the animal economy, and the reserve of mental force is in a practical sense more important
than any other. . . . Without this reserve, healthy brain-work
is impossible. Pain, hunger, anxiety, and a sense of mind-weari-
ness, are warning tokens of exhaustion. When the laborious
worker, overcome with fatigue, "rouses" himself with alcohol,
coffee, tea, or any other agent which may chance to suit him,
he does not add a unit of force to his stock of energy ; he simply
narcotizes the sense of weariness, and, the guard being drugged,
he appropriates the reserve. . . . Meanwhile, the effort to work
becomes daily more laborious, the task of fixing the attention
grows increasingly difficult, thoughts wander, memory fails, the
reasoning power is enfeebled; physical nerve or brain disturbance may supervene, and the crash will then come suddenly,
unexpected by on-lookers, perhaps unperceived by the sufferer
himself.

Overwork and Worry.—The miseries of "overwork," pure
and simple, are few and comparatively insignificant. . . . The
natural safeguards are so well fitted for their task that neither
body nor mind is exposed to the peril of serious exhaustion so
long as their functions are duly performed. Overwork is *impossible* so long as the effort made is natural. . . . There is then
no excuse for idleness in the pretense of possible injury. If
insane asylums were searched for the victims of "overwork,"
they would nearly all be found to have fallen a prey to "worry,"
or to the degeneracy which results from lack of purpose in life,
and of steady employment. . . . The cause or condition which
most commonly exposes the reserve of mental energy to loss
and injury is worry. When a strong and active mind breaks
down suddenly in the midst of business, it is usually worn out
by this cause rather than by the other. . . . Work in the teeth
of worry is fraught with peril. The unhappy victim is ever on the
verge of a catastrophe ; if he escape, the marvel is not at his
strength of intellect so much as at his good fortune. Worry is
disorder, however induced, and disorderly work is abhorred by
the laws of nature, which leave it wholly without remedy.

The pernicious system of *Cram* slays its thousands, because
uneducated, undeveloped, inelastic intellects are burdened and
strained with information adroitly deposited in the memory,—

as an expert valet packs a portmanteau, with the articles likely
to be first wanted on the top. *Desultory occupation*, mere
play with objects of which the true interest is not appreciated,
ruins a still larger number. But *worry*, that bane of brain-
work and mental energy, counts its victims by tens of thousands. — Dr. J. MORTIMER GRANVILLE, *in "Worry," Nineteenth
Century.*

Sleep (p. 206). — *Some Curiosities of Sleep.* — One of the
most refined and exquisite methods of torture is long continued
deprivation of sleep. The demand for unconscious rest is so im-
perious that nature will accommodate itself to the most unfavorable surrounding conditions. Thus, in forced marches, regiments
have been known to sleep while walking ; men have slept
soundly in the saddle ; and persons will sometimes sleep during
the din of battle. It is remarkable how noises to which we have
been accustomed will fail to disturb our natural rest. Those
who have been long habituated to the endless noise of a crowded
city frequently find difficulty in sleeping in the oppressive stillness of the country. Prolonged exposure to intense cold induces
excessive somnolence, and if this be induced, the sleep passes
into stupor, the power of resistance to cold becomes rapidly
diminished, and death is the inevitable result. Intense heat
often produces drowsiness, but, as is well known, is not favorable to natural sleep. . . . It is difficult to determine with
exactness the phenomena of sleep that are absolutely physiological, and to separate those that are slightly abnormal. We
can not assert, for example, that a dreamless sleep is the only
normal condition of repose of the system ; nor can we determine
what dreams are due to previous trains of thought, or to such
impressions from the external world received during sleep as
are purely physiological, and what are due to abnormal nervous
influence, disordered digestion, etc.

The most remarkable experiments upon the production of
dreams of a definite character, by subjecting a person during
sleep to peculiar influences, are those of Maury. The hallucinations produced in this way are called hypnagogic (from its deri-
vation this term is properly applied only to phenomena observed
at the instant when we fall asleep, or when we are imperfectly
awakened, and not to the period of most perfect repose), and

they occur when the subject is not in a condition favorable to sound sleep.

The experiments made by Maury upon himself are so curious and interesting that we quote the most striking of them in full.

First Observation.—I am tickled with a feather successively on the lips and inside of the nostrils. I dream that I am subjected to a horrible punishment, that a mask of pitch is applied to my face, and then roughly torn off, tearing the skin of the lip, the nose, and the face.

Second Observation.—A pair of pincers is held at a little distance from my ear, and rubbed with steel scissors. I dream that I hear the ringing of bells; this soon becomes a tocsin, and I imagine myself in the days of June, 1848. (The time of the French Revolution.)

Third Observation.—I am caused to inhale Cologne water. I dream I am in a perfumer's shop; the idea of perfumes doubtless awakens the idea of the East; I am in Cairo, in the shop of Jean Farina. . . .

Fifth Observation.—I am slightly pinched on the nape of the neck. I dream that a blister is applied, which recalls to my mind a physician who had treated me in infancy.

Seventh Observation. . . . . The words Azar, Castor, Leonore, were pronounced in my ear; on awaking I recollected that I had heard the last two words, which I attributed to one of the persons who had conversed with me in my dream.—FLINT'S *Physiology of Man.*

The transition-stage between the dream simple and the dream acted is witnessed in the spasmodic movements which a vivid dream produces in the limbs or person of the sleeper. The dreamer engages in a fierce struggle, and twitchings of his legs and arms indicate the feeble response of body to the promptings of mind removed from its wonted power over the frame. Even the dog, as he sleeps, apparently dreams of the chase, and gives vent to his sensations by the short, sharp bark, or sniffs the air, and starts in his slumber as if in response to the activity with which, in his dreaming, he is hurrying along after the object of pursuit. . . . Persons have been known to swim for a considerable time in the somnambulistic state without waking at the termination of their journey; others have safely descended the shaft of a mine, while some have ascended steep cliffs, and have returned home in safety during a prolonged sleep-vigil. (See p. 204.)—Dr. ANDREW WILSON, F.R.S.E., *What Dreams are Made of.*

Sleep and Conscience.—Edward Everett Hale says : Never go to bed in any danger of being hungry. People are kept awake by hunger quite as much as by a bad conscience. Remembering that sleep is the essential force which starts the whole system, decline tea or coffee within the last six hours before going to bed. Avoid all mathematics or intricate study of any sort in the last six hours. This is the stuff dreams are made of, and hot heads, and the nuisances of waking hours. Keep your conscience clear. Remember that because the work of life is infinite, you can not do the whole of it in any limited period of time, and that therefore you may just as well leave off in one place as another.

The Art of Rising Early.—The proper time to rise is when sleep ends. Dozing should not be allowed. True sleep is the aggregate of sleeps, or is a state consisting in the sleeping or rest of all the several parts of the organism. Sometimes one and at other times another part of the body, as a whole, may be the least fatigued, and so the first to awake ; or the most exhausted, and therefore the most difficult to arouse. The secret of good sleep is, the physiological conditions of rest being established, so to work and weary the several parts of the organism as to give them a proportionately equal need of rest at the same moment. To wake early, and feel ready to rise, a fair and equal start of the sleepers should be secured ; and the wise self-manager should not allow a drowsy feeling of unconsciousness, or weary senses, or an exhausted muscular system, to beguile him into the folly of going to sleep again when once he has been aroused. After a few days of self-discipline, the man who resolves not to doze, that is, not to allow some sleepy part of his body to keep him in bed after his brain has once awakened, will find himself, without knowing why, an early riser.

Influence of Sunlight (p. 207).—Light is an essential element in producing the grand phenomena of life, though its action is ill understood. Where there is light there is life, and any deprivation of this principle is rapidly followed by disease

of the animal frame, and the destruction of the mental faculties. We have proof of this in the squalor of those whose necessities compel them to labor in places to which the blessings
of sunshine never penetrate, as in our coal-mines, where men
having every thing necessary for health, except light, exhibit a
singularly unhealthy appearance. The state of fatuity and
wretchedness to which those individuals have been reduced, who
have been subjected for years to incarceration in dark dungeons,
may be referred to the same deprivation.—ROBERT HUNT, *Poetry
of Science.*

Effect of Dungeon Life.—"You can not imagine, Mr. Kennan," said a condemned revolutionist to me in Siberia, "the misery
of prolonged confinement in a casemate of the fortress under what
are known as dungeon conditions. My casemate was sometimes
cold, generally damp, and always gloomy. Day after day, week
after week, month after month, I lay there in solitude, hearing no
sound save that of the high-pitched, melancholy bells of the fortress cathedral, which slowly chimed the quarter-hours, and which
always seemed to say: 'Here thou liest—lie here still.' I had
absolutely nothing to do except to pace my cell from corner to
corner, and think. For a long time I used to talk to myself in
a whisper; to repeat softly every thing in the shape of literature that I could remember, and to compose speeches which,
under certain imagined conditions, I would deliver; but I finally
ceased to have energy enough to do even this, and used to sit
for hours in a sort of stupor, in which, so far as I can now
remember, I was not conscious of thinking at all. Before the
end of the first year, I grew so weak, mentally and physically,
that I began to forget words. I knew what ideas I desired to
express, but some of the words that I needed had gone from
me, and it was with the greatest difficulty that I could recover
them. It seemed sometimes as if my own language were a
strange one to me, or one which, from long disuse, I had forgotten. I greatly feared insanity, and my apprehension was
increased by the fact that two or three of my comrades in cells
on the same corridor were either insane or subject to hallucinations; and I was often roused at night and thrown into a violent chill of nervous excitement by their hysterical weeping,
their cries to the guard to come and take away somebody, or

something which they imagined they saw, or their groans and entreaties when, in cases of violent delirium, they were strapped to their beds by the *gend'armes*."—GEORGE KENNAN, *in Russian State Prisoners, The Century, March, 1888*.

The Growth and Power of Poison Habits (p. 218).—In order to distinguish a poison-stimulant from a harmless and nutritive substance, Nature has furnished us three infallible tests:

1. The first taste of every poison is either insipid or repulsive.

2. The persistent obtrusion of the noxious substance changes that aversion into a specific craving.

3. The more or less pleasurable excitement produced by a gratification of that craving is always followed by a depressing reaction. . . .

One radical fallacy identifies the stimulant habit in all its disguises: its victims mistake a process of irritation for one of invigoration. . . . Sooner or later the tonic is sure to pall while the morbid craving remains, and forces its victims either to increase the quantity of the wonted stimulant, or else to resort to a stronger poison. A boy begins with ginger-beer and ends in ginger-rum; the medical "tonic" delusion progresses from malt extract to Mumford's Elixir; and the nicotine habit once introduced, the alcohol habit often follows. The tendency of every stimulant habit is toward a stronger tonic. . . . We have found that the road to the rum-shop is paved with "mild stimulants," and that every bottle of medical bitters is apt to get the vender a permanent customer. We have found that cider and mild ale lead to strong ale, to lager-beer, and finally to rum, and the truth at last dawns upon us that the only safe, consistent, and effective plan is Total Abstinence from all Poisons.

. . . . . More than the hunger after bread, more than the frenzy of love or hatred, the poison-hunger overpowers every other instinct, even the fear of death. Dr. Isaac Jennings has illustrated this by the following example: A clergyman of his acquaintance attempted to dissuade a young man of great promise from habits of intemperance. "Hear me first a few words," said the young man, "and then you may proceed. I am sensible that an indulgence in this habit will lead to the loss of property, the loss of reputation and domestic happiness, to pre-

mature death, and to the irretrievable loss of my immortal soul ;
and now, with all this conviction resting firmly on my mind and
flashing over my conscience like lightning, if I still continue to
drink, do you suppose any thing you can say will deter me from
the practice?"

. . . . . Ignorance is a chief cause of intemperance. The
seductions of vice would not mislead so many of our young men
if they could realize the significance of their mistake. There is
still a lingering belief that, with due precaution against excess
and adulteration, a dram-drinker might "get ahead" of Nature,
and, as it were, trick her out of some extra enjoyment. There
is no hope of a radical reform till intelligent people have real-
ized the fact that this "trick" is in every instance a losing
game, entailing penalties which far outweigh the pleasures that
the novice may mistake for enjoyments. For the depression of
the vital energy increases with every repetition of the stimulating process, and in a year after the first dose all the "grateful
and exhilarating tonics" of our professional poison-venders can
not restore the vigor, the courage, and the cheerfulness which
the mere consciousness of perfect health imparts to the total
abstainer. A great plurality of all beginners underrate the difficulty of controlling the cravings of a morbid appetite. They
remember that their natural inclinations at first opposed, rather
than encouraged, the indulgence ; and they feel that at the present stage of its development they could abjure the passion
without difficulty. But they overlook the fact that the moral
power of resistance decreases with each repetition of the dose,
and that the time will come when only the practical impossibility of procuring their wonted tipple will enable them to keep
their pledge of total abstinence. It is true that, by the exercise
of a constant self-restraint, a person of great will-force may
resist the progressive tendency of the poison habit and confine
himself for years to a single cigar or a single bottle of wine per
day. . . .   But the attempt to resist that bias will overtask the
strength of most individuals. According to the allegory of the
Grecian myth, the car of Bacchus was drawn by tigers ; and it
is a significant circumstance that war, famine, and pestilence
have so often been the forerunners of veritable alcohol epidemics. . . .   The explanation is that, after the stimulant habit has

once been initiated, every unusual depression of mental or physical vigor calls for an increased application of the accustomed
method of relief. . . . Nations who are addicted to the worship
of a poison-god will use his temple as a place of refuge from
every calamity; and children whose petty ailments have been
palliated with narcotics, wine, and cordials, will afterward be
tempted to drown their greater sorrows in deeper draughts of
the same nepenthe.—FELIX L. OSWALD, M.D., *Remedies of Nature,
Popular Science Monthly, October and November, 1883.*

Dangers from the Use of Narcotics.—It may seem a
paradox, it is a truism, to say that in the value of narcotics
lies their peril. Because they have such power for good, because the suffering which they alleviate is in its lighter forms
so common, because neuralgia and sleeplessness are ailments as
familiar to the present generation as gout, rheumatism, and
catarrh were to our grandfathers, therefore the medicines which
immediately relieve sleeplessness and neuralgic pain are among
the most dangerous possessions, the most subtle temptations of
civilized life. Every one of these drugs has, besides its instant
and beneficial effect, other and injurious tendencies. The relief
which it gives is purchased at a certain price; for, at each repetition of the dose, the immediate relief is lessened or rendered
uncertain, while the mischievous influence is enhanced and aggravated; till, when the drug has become a necessity of life it
has lost the greater part, if not the whole, of its value, and
serves only to satisfy the need which itself alone has created.
. . . . We read weekly of men and women poisoned by an
overdose of some favorite sedative, burned to death or otherwise
fatally injured, while insensible from self-administered ether or
chloroform. . . . . The narcotist keeps chloroform or chloral
always at hand, forgetful or ignorant that one sure effect of the
first dose is to produce a semi-stupor more dangerous than actual
somnolence. In that semi-stupor the patient is aware, or fancies, that the dose has failed. The pain that has induced a lady
to hold a chloroformed handkerchief under her nostrils returns
while her will and her judgment are half paralyzed. She takes
the bottle from the table beside her bed, intending to pour an
additional supply upon her handkerchief. The unsteady hand
perhaps spills a quantity on the sheet, perhaps sinks with the

unstoppered bottle under her nostrils, and in a few moments she has inhaled enough utterly to stupefy, if not to kill. The sleepless brain-worker also feels that his usual dose of chloral has failed to bring sleep; he is not aware how completely it has stupefied the brain, to which it has not given rest. His judgment is gone, so is his steadiness of hand; and he pours out a second and too often a fatal dose. . . . But the cases that end in a death terrible to the family, though probably involving little or no suffering to the victim himself, are by no means the worst. A life poisoned, paralyzed, rendered worthless for all the uses of intellectual, rational, we might almost say of human existence, is worse for the sufferer himself and for all around him than a quick and painless death; and for one such death there must be twenty, if not a hundred, instances of this worst death in life. . . . The demoralization of the narcotist is not, like that of the drunkard, rapid, violent, and palpable; but gradual, insidious, perceptible at first only to close observers and intimate friends. Here and there we find a constitution upon which opium exerts few or none of its characteristic effects. Such cases are, of course, wholly exceptional; but their very existence is a danger to others, misleading them into the idea that they may dally with the tempter without falling under its yoke, or may fall under that yoke and find it a light one. I doubt, however, whether the most fortunate of its victims would encourage the latter idea; whether there be an opium-eater who would not give a limb never to have known what opium-slavery means. . . . Besides, no one can be sure, or indeed reasonably hope, that the mischief will be confined to the individual victim. That the children of drunkards are often predisposed to insanity is notorious; that the children of habitual opium-eaters inherit an unmistakable taint, whether in a diseased brain, in morbid cravings, or simply in a will too weak to resist temptation, is less notorious, but equally certain.— PERCY GREG, *Narcotics and Stimulants, Contemporary Review.*

Thus also in America scarcely a week passes but we see announced in the public prints deaths or suicides resulting from the use of narcotics. Now, it is from tobacco: A Yale College student dies from excessive smoking; another student in the same college, and as a result of the same habit, commits suicide;

a third young man is found dead in his bed in New York, from heart-disease induced by cigarettes; and so, month by month, and year by year, grows in rapid increase the list of tobacco-deaths.—Or, again, it is from opium. A Harvard student with two of his college companions in search of a new sensation, tries opium-smoking one fatal night and dies before morning; a woman in Ohio, belonging to a prominent family, dies at the age of thirty-three years, from an overdose of morphine, her body covered with hypodermic scars; another, once the respected wife of a Baptist clergyman, becomes a morphine-drunkard, drifts, step by step, into a Central New York Alms-house, and there hangs herself; a third, young, accomplished, and wealthy, falls first a victim to the morphine habit, then to opium-smoking, finally becomes the frequenter of a New York opium-joint, and so is lost forever to home, friends, and respectability.—Occasionally it is cocaine, as in the case of the Chicago physician, who, for the purposes of investigation, experiments with this new drug upon himself, his wife, and finally upon his innocent children; the entire family being found unconscious from the effects of the subtle narcotic. These are but solitary instances in an appallingly long list of similar cases, most of which have occurred within the last two years (1887-'88).

Cigarette-smoking is chargeable with a growing demoralization and mortality among boys and young men. It is no uncommon sight to see lads of ten years old and under, with the irresponsibility of ignorant childhood, puffing the dangerous cigarette, and thus undermining health and intellect at the very outset of useful existence. Even when told of the near and remote perils thus incurred, they scarcely listen, for do not they see their elders smoke and prosper? — Most of them do not understand that there is more danger to the young than to the old in the tobacco habit, more danger to some constitutions than to others, and more danger in the cigarette than even in the pipe or the cigar. Pause a moment to consider it, boys, when you are tempted to light the clean-looking, paper-covered roll and place it in your mouth. Think of the heated smoke irritating the delicate membrane in your throat, dulling your brain, and vitiating the blood which should be bounding fresh and pure through your veins. Think of the many filthy and diseased mouths from which have been cast away the tobacco refuse, picked up in streets and public places to re-appear in the "Cheap and Popular Brand" which looks to you so innocent and so attractive. It is astonishing, indeed, how an otherwise cleanly boy will consent to defile himself with these vile abominations. And yet, I have known lads who—not always with perfect politeness —would fastidiously refuse "hash" at their mother's breakfast table, but who would shortly afterward serenely place one of these unknowable compounds between their lips and walk away with the air of superior manhood!

Of *Chloral Hydrate*, Dr. Fothergill remarks: "When this was announced with a flourish of trumpets as a perfectly innocuous narcotic, the sleepless folk hailed its advent with eager acclamation. But a little experience soon demonstrated that the innocuous, harmless drug was far from the boon it was proclaimed. In fact, the impression of its harmlessness was the outcome of ignorance of its properties. Death after death, even among medical men themselves, as well as non-professional persons, have already resulted from the use, or rather misuse, of this narcotic agent."

The Bromides (of Soda or Potash), also, should be used with caution, and only on the prescription of a conscientious physician. "The bromide of potash," says Percy Greg, "is claimed not to produce sleep by stupefaction, like chloral or opium, but, at least in small doses, to allay the nervous irritability which is often the sole cause of sleeplessness. But in larger quantities and in its ultimate effects, it is scarcely less to be dreaded than chloral." Overdoses of the bromides will produce among other evil effects a peculiar eruption upon the face, which, though generally temporary, is liable to re-appear from time to time under certain conditions of the system, and especially upon a subsequent dose, however dilute.

Absinthe is a compound of absinthium (the essence of wormwood), various aromatic oils, and alcohol. Absinthium, taken in small doses, induces trembling, stupor, and insensibility; in larger doses, epilepsy. When, therefore, this dangerous essence is added to alcohol, it strengthens its influence to specific disease. Absinthe-drinking is recognized in France as such a serious vice that it has been officially prohibited in the army and navy.

Hasheesh is a syrup prepared from the leaves and flowers of Indian Hemp. Though its use in this country is comparatively small, instances are not unknown in which reckless or curious persons have fatally experimented with it. As a medicine, it is in limited use, and with results not always satisfactory. It acts in a peculiar manner upon the nervous centers, occasioning that strange condition of the nervous system called catalepsy, in which the limbs of the unconscious patient remain stationary in whatever position they may be placed. After an average dose of hasheesh, the subject becomes the helpless victim of rapidly shifting ideas, a prominent characteristic of which is an entire loss of judgment as to time and place. A larger dose produces hallucinations and delirium, with that distressing sensation of falling through endless space which is induced in some people by opium.*

* In an article entitled "An Overdose of Hasheesh" (*Popular Science Monthly*, February, 1884), Miss Mary A. Hungerford gives a vivid description of a painful experience with this drug, some portion of which is as follows:

"Being one of the grand army of sufferers from headache, I took, last summer, by order of my physician, three small daily doses of hasheesh in the hope of holding my intimate enemy in check. . . . . I grew to regard the drug as a harmless medicine, and one day, when I was assured by some familiar symptoms that my headache was about to assume an aggravated form, I took a larger quantity than had been prescribed. Twenty minutes later I was seized with a strange sinking or faintness which gave my family so much alarm that they telephoned at once for the doctor.

". . . . One terrible reality—I can hardly term it a fancy even now— that came to me again and again, was so painful that it must, I fear, always be a vividly remembered agony. . . . . I died, as I believed, although by a strange double consciousness I knew that I should again reanimate the body I had left. In leaving it I did not soar away, as one delights to think of the freed spirits soaring. . . . . I sank, an intangible, impalpable shape, through the bed, the floors, the cellar, the earth, down, down, down! Like a fragment of glass dropping through the ocean, I dropped uninterruptedly through the earth and its atmosphere, and then fell on and on forever. . . . . As time went on, and my dropping through space continued, I became filled with the most profound loneliness, and a desperate fear took hold of me that I should be thus alone forever more, and fall and fall eternally. . . . . There was, it seemed to me, a forgotten text which, if remembered, would be the spell to stop my fatal falling. I sought in my memory for it, I prayed to recall it, I fought for it madly, wrestling against the terrible fate which seemed to withhold it. Single words of it came to me in disconnected mockery, but erased themselves instantaneously. Mentally, I writhed in such hopeless agony that, in thinking of it I wonder I could have borne such excess of emotion and lived. . . . .

Concerning all these and other narcotics, it should never be forgotten that they are true poisons, sold with the mark of skull and cross-bones, useful, like strychnine and henbane, in the hands of a skillful physician, but fraught with deadly danger when otherwise employed. Their private use is never safe. The weak and nervous invalid, who can not by hygienic means build up new strength, need never hope to gain it by surreptitiously indulging in popular narcotics. Instead, he will soon discover that he has but added to his list of ills a new and fatal one.—E. B. S.

began, then, without having reached any goal, to ascend. As I rose, a great and terrible voice from a vast distance pronounced my doom: 'Fall, fall, fall, to rise again in hopeless misery, and sink again in lonely agony forever.' . . . Then ensued a wild and terrible commingling of unsyllabled sounds, so unearthly that it is not in the power of language to fitly describe them. It was something like a mighty Niagara of shrieks and groans, combined with the fearful din and crash of thousands of battles and the thunderous roar of a stormy sea. . . . . I fought my upward way in an agony which resembled nothing so much as the terrible moment when, from strangling or suffocation, all the forces of life struggle against death, and wrestle madly for another breath. In place of the woful sounds now reigned a deadly stillness, broken only at long but regular intervals by a loud report, as if a cannon, louder than any I ever heard on earth, were discharged at my side, almost shot into me, I might say, for the sound appeared to rend me from head to foot, and then to die away into the dark chaos about me in strange, shuddering reverberations. Even in the misery of my ascending I was filled with a dread expectancy of the cruel sound. It gave me a feeling of acute physical torture, with a lingering intensity that bodily suffering could not have. It was repeated an incredible number of times, and always with the same suffering and shock to me. At last the sound came oftener, but with less force, and I seemed again nearing the shores of time. Dimly in the far distance I saw the room I had left, myself lying still and death-like upon the bed, and the friends watching me. . . . . Then, silently and invisibly I floated into the room, and was one with myself again.

". . . . . 'She is conscious now,' I heard one of the doctors say, and he gently lifted the lids of my eyes and looked into them. I tried my best to throw all the intelligence I could into them, and returned his look with one of recognition. But, even with my eyes fixed on his, I felt myself going again in spite of my craving to stay. I longed to implore the doctor to save me, to keep me from the unutterable anguish of falling into the vastness and vagueness of that shadowy sea of nothingness again. I clasped my hands in wild entreaty; I was shaken by horrible convulsions—so, at least, it seemed to me at the time—but, beyond a slight quivering of the fingers, no movement was discernible by the others. . . . . For five hours I remained in the same condition—short intervals of half-consciousness and then long lapses into the agonizing experiences I have described. . . . . Coming out of the last trance, I discovered that the measured rending report like the discharge of a cannon, which attended my upward way, was the throbbing of my own heart."

23

THE SPECIAL SENSES.

An Educated Sense of Touch (p. 230). — Laura Dewey Bridgman, teacher in the Perkins Institute for the Blind, South Boston, lost her sight, hearing, and sense of smell, when she was two years of age. At the age of eight years she was taken to the institution where she yet remains. At this time, by following her mother around the house she had become familiar with home appointments, and by feeling her mother's hands and arms had also learned to sew and knit. When she first became an inmate of the Perkins Institute, she was bewildered by her strange surroundings, but after she had become used to place and people, through her one and only sense, her education was carefully begun. Through indomitable effort on the part of her preceptor, she was taught to write, read, and spell, by means of her fingers, and thus to exchange sentiments with her teachers and with others skilled in the mysterious language of the blind and the mute. She is now as proficient in the ordinary branches of learning as is the average person, possessed of all the senses. Her studies include geography, arithmetic, algebra, geometry, history, and philosophy. She makes her own clothing, can run a sewing-machine, and observes great neatness in her dress and the arrangements of her room. Her character is religious, and she has great success as a teacher. Not long since, she celebrated, on the same day, her fifty-eighth birthday and the fiftieth anniversary of her entrance to the Perkins Institute. During her earlier years, it was her practice to keep a journal, and she now has about forty manuscript books of her own making. She has also written three autobiographical sketches, several poems, and is an accomplished correspondent. When Miss Bridgman expresses pleasure, she clasps her hands and smiles. So keen and refined are her sensibilities, that it is said she can, in a small way, appreciate the beauty of music by means of the sound vibrations on the floor. — Mrs. George Archibald.

The Nose (p. 232). — *The Anatomy of the Nose.* — Probably most of us look upon the nose as a double hole in the head, by which we get, with more or less acuteness, a sense of smell, and through which we occasionally breathe. The intricate mechanism, and the skillful adaptation of means to end, which, in common with the other organs of special sense, it exhibits, naturally do not reveal themselves to any but the students of anatomy and physiology. Its fourteen bones are probably better hidden than any other fourteen bones of the body, and assist in converting what would otherwise be a mere channel of communication, into a series of cavities designed and adapted for particular purposes. The arch of four bones which forms the bridge of the nose, and which is of such strength as to enable the gymnast of the circus to perform the feat of supporting with it a man on a ladder, is pieced on with cartilage to form the nostrils, through which the nose communicates with the outer air. Similar openings behind connect it with the upper and posterior parts of the mouth. The space between these anterior and posterior openings makes a large chamber, divided by a vertical wall into halves, each of which is still further separated into three irregular cavities by three bones, called spongy, from the porosity and delicacy of their texture. The ceiling of these chambers is formed by a bone of the thinness of paper, upon which lies the front part of the brain,—a fact the Egyptians made use of in embalming their corpses, easily crushing this bone, and extracting the brain through the nostrils. This bone is called cribriform (sieve-like), because it is perforated by many minute holes, through which, from the olfactory bulbs (specialized parts of the brain in which is resident the capacity of smell) that rest on its upper surface, issue the delicate filaments of the olfactory nerves, to spread themselves over the lining membrane of the two upper spongy bones. It is in the upper chambers of the nose, therefore, that the function of smell is performed; the nerves that supply the lower spongy bone being entirely unconnected with the organs of smell. Over these latter, however, sweep in and out the currents of air when the act of respiration is properly carried out, and it is these that are especially concerned in its abnormal performance. Usually but a very little of the volume of air that traverses the lower chamber of the nose has any influence upon its upper regions; and therefore, when our attention is attracted by an odor, we sniff, in order to bring a larger quantity of air into contact with the higher parts of the nose, or olfactory cavities, where odors are perceived.

But the half has not been told of the anatomical and physiological arrangements of the nose. By minute openings its chambers have communication with many other parts of the head,—with the hollow that forms the greater part of the cheekbone; with the eye by a minute spout that carries off the lachrymal secretion, unless the tears are so abundant as to roll down the cheeks; with the front of the roof of the mouth; with the abundant cells of the bone that makes the forehead, and the congestion of whose lining membrane probably accounts for the severe headache that so often accompanies and aggravates a "cold in the head." The gateway to the inner air-passages, its abundant surfaces raise the air inspired to the temperature of the body, supply it with the moisture it lacks, and sift from it more or less of the mechanical impurities with which the atmosphere of our houses and shops is laden.— MAURICE D. CLARKE, M.D., *Popular Science News, April, 1888.*

Smell Necessary to Taste.—What we are in the habit of calling a "taste," is in most cases a compound of smell, taste, temperature, and touch—these four sensations ranking in gastronomic importance in the order in which they are here named. . . . Amusing experiments may be made, showing that without the sense of smell it is commonly quite impossible to distinguish between different articles of food and drink. Blindfold a person and make him clasp his nose tightly, then put successively into his mouth small pieces of beef, mutton, veal, and pork, and it is safe to predict that he will not be able to tell one morsel from another. The same result will be obtained with chicken, turkey, and duck; with pieces of almond, walnut, and hazelnut; with slices of apple, peach, and pear; or with different kinds of cheese, if care be taken that such kinds are chosen as do not, by their peculiar composition, betray their identity through the nerves of touch in the mouth. To hold an article of food under the nose at table would be justly considered a breach of etiquette. But there is a second way of smelling, of which most people are quite unconscious, viz., by *exhaling through the nose* while eating and drinking. . . . It is well known that only a small portion of the mucous membrane which lines the nostrils is the seat of the endings of the nerves of smell. In ordinary expiration, the air does not touch this olfactory region, but by a special effort it can be turned into that direction. . . . Instinct teaches most persons while eating to guide the air, impregnated with the fragrance of the food, to a part of the nostrils different from that used during ordinary exhalation; but, being unaccustomed to psychologic analysis of their sensations, they remain quite unconscious of this proceeding, and are, indeed, in the habit of confusing their sensations of taste, smell, touch, and temperature in a most absurd manner. . . .

In trying to ascertain by experiment how far smell, touch, and temperature enter into this compound sensation, popularly known as "taste," it is best to make use of the pungent condiments. Mustard and horse-radish, for example, have little or no taste, but reserve their pungent effect for the mucous membrane of the nose during expiration. It is an advantage to know this, for if care is taken to breathe only through the mouth, we need no longer prepare to shed tears every time we help ourselves to the mustard. The pungent quality of mustard, the fiery quality of ginger, and the cool sensation in the mouth after eating peppermint, are due to the nerves of touch and temperature, which are commonly classed as one sense, though they are quite as distinct sensations as sight and hearing, or taste and smell. . . .

There are two ways in which the effort to extract all its fragrance from a morsel of food confers a benefit.

(1.) It is necessary to keep the morsel in the mouth as long as possible. Now the habit thus formed of eating very slowly is of the utmost importance, for if farinaceous articles of food are swallowed before the saliva has had time to act on them, they are little better than so much waste material taken into the system; and if meat is not thoroughly masticated, the stomach is overloaded with work which should have been done by the teeth; the result, in either case, is dyspepsia. It has been suggested that Mr. Gladstone owes his remarkable physical vigor to certain rules for chewing food, which he adopted in 1848, and to which he has adhered ever since. "He had always," we are told, "paid great attention to the requirements of Nature, but he then laid down as a rule for his children that thirty-two bites should be given to each mouthful of meat, and a somewhat lesser number to bread, fish, etc."

(2.) Besides this indirect advantage resulting from the effort to get at the fragrant odors of food, there is a still more remarkable direct advantage. It is one of the most curious psychologic facts that odors exert a strong influence on our system, either exhilarating or depressing. While an unpleasant odor may cause a person to faint, the fumes of the smelling-bottle will restore him to consciousness. The magic and value of gastronomic odors lies in this, that they stimulate the flow of saliva and other alimentary juices, thus making sure that the food eaten will be thoroughly utilized in renovating the system.—HENRY T. FINCK, *in " The Gastronomic Value of Odors."*

Hygiene of the Ear (p. 236).—*Never Box a Child's Ear.*—Children and grown persons alike may be entirely deafened by falls or heavy blows upon the head. Boxing the ears produces a similar effect, though more slowly and in less degree, and tends to dull the sensibility of the nerve, even if it does not hurt the membrane. I knew a youth who died from a terrible disease of the ear. There had been a discharge from it since he was a child. Of course his hearing had been dull; and *his father had often boxed his ear for inattention!* Most likely that boxing on the ear, diseased as it was, had much to do with his death. And this brings me to the second point. Children should never be blamed for being inattentive, until it has been found out whether they are not a little deaf. This is easily done by placing them at a few yards' distance, and trying whether they can understand what is said to them in a rather low tone of voice. Each ear should be tried, while the other is stopped by the finger. Three things should be remembered here : 1. That slight degrees of deafness, often lasting only for a time, are very common among children, especially during or after colds. 2. That a slight deafness, which does not prevent a person from hearing when he is expecting to be spoken to, will make him very dull to what he is not expecting. 3. That there is a kind of deafness in which a person can hear pretty well while listening, but is really very hard of hearing when not listening.

Avoid Direct Draughts in the Ear.—There are some exposures especially to be guarded against. One is sitting or driving with the ear exposed to a side wind. Deafness has also been known to come from letting rain or sleet drive into the ear.

Do not Remove the Ear-wax. — It ought to be understood that the passage of the ear does not require cleaning by us. Nature undertakes that task, and, in the healthy state, fulfills it perfectly. Her means for cleansing the ear is *the wax*. Perhaps the reader has never wondered what becomes of the ear-wax. I will tell him. It dries up into thin fine scales, and these peel off, one by one, from the surface of the passage, and fall out imperceptibly, leaving behind them a perfectly clean, smooth surface. In health the passage of the ear is never dirty; but, if we attempt to clean it, we infallibly make it so. Washing the ear out frequently with soap and water keeps the wax moist when it ought to become dry and scaly, increases its quantity unduly, and makes it absorb the dust with which the air always abounds. But the most hurtful thing is introducing the corner of the towel, screwed up, and twisting it round. This does more harm to ears than all other mistakes together. It drives down the wax upon the membrane, much more than it gets it out. But this plan does much more mischief than merely pressing down the wax. It irritates the passage, and makes it cast off small flakes of skin, which dry up, and become extremely hard, and these also are pressed down upon the membrane. Often it is not only deafness which ensues, but pain and inflammation, and then matter is formed which the hard mass prevents from escaping, and the membrane becomes permanently diseased.

The Eustachian Tube. — The use of this tube is twofold. First, it supplies the drum with air, and keeps the membrane exactly balanced, and free to move, with equal air-pressure on each side; and, secondly, it carries off any fluid which may be in the drum, and prevents it from being choked by its own moisture. It is not always open, however, but is opened during the act of swallowing, by a little muscle which is attached to it just as it reaches the throat. Most persons can distinctly feel that this is the case, by gently closing the nose and swallowing, when a distinct sensation is felt in the ears. This sensation is due to a little air being drawn out of the ears through the open tube during swallowing; and it lasts for a few minutes, unless the air is again restored by swallowing with the nose unclosed, which allows for the moment a free communication between the ear and the throat. We thus see a reason for the tube being closed. If it were always open, all the sounds produced in the throat would pass directly into the drum of the ear, and totally confuse us. We should hear every breath, and live in a constant bewilderment of internal sounds. At the same time the closure, being but a light contact of the walls of the tube, easily allows a slight escape of air *from* the drum, and thus not only facilitates and regulates the oscillations of the air before the vibrating membrane, but provides a safety-valve, to a certain extent, against the injurious influence of loud sounds.

The chief use of the Eustachian tube is to allow a free interchange of air between the ear and the throat, and it is very important that its use in this respect should be understood. Persons who go down in diving-bells soon begin to feel a great pressure in the ears, and, if the depth is great, the feeling becomes extremely painful. This arises from the fact that in the diving-bell the pressure of the air is very much increased, in order to balance the weight of the water above; and thus it presses with great force upon the membrane of the drum, which, if the Eustachian tube has been kept closed, has only the ordinary uncompressed air on the inner side to sustain it. It is therefore forced inward and put upon the stretch, and might be even broken. Many cases, indeed, have occurred of injury to the ear, producing permanent deafness, from descents in diving-bells, undertaken by persons ignorant of the way in which the ear is made; though the simple precaution of frequent swallowing suffices to ward off all mischief. For, if the Eustachian tube is thus opened, again and again, as the pressure of the outside air increases, the same compressed air that exists outside passes also into the inside of the drum, and the membrane is equally pressed upon from both sides by the air, and so is free from strain. The same precaution is necessary in ascending lofty mountains.—DR. JAMES HINTON.

The Colored Curtain in the Eye (p 238).—This ring-like curtain in the eye, of gray, green, bluish-green, brown, and other colors, is one among the very many remarkable contrivances of the organic world. The eye can not bear the entrance of too much light, and the colored curtain so regulates its own movements as to serve this requirement. The dark circular aperture in the center, known as the pupil, is consequently forever altering in size; on a bright, sunshiny day, out in the open, it may be only the size of a pin's head, but at night, when there is no light stronger than starlight, it is even bigger than a pea. The eye curtain is fixed at its outer edge, leaving the inner edge to contract or expand, which it does automatically and quite independent of the will, ever preserving its circular outline. Its movements may be watched in a variety of ways, some of which we shall describe.

The common way of watching the movements of the iris is to regard it closely in a looking-glass while the amount of light entering the eyes is varied. Place yourself before a looking-glass and with your face to the window. Probably the iris will be expanded, and there will only be a very small opening or pupil in the center. Now shut one eye suddenly, while narrowly watching the other in the glass all the time. At the moment the light is cut off from one eye, the iris of the other contracts or is drawn up so as to enlarge the pupil. This shows that there is a remarkable interdependence between the curtains of the two eyes, as well as that they are affected by variations in the quantity of light falling on them.

Perhaps one of the most interesting ways of watching the movements of these sympathetic eye-curtains is one which may be followed while you are out walking on the street some dark winter night. A gas-lamp seen at a distance is, comparatively speaking, a point of light, with bars of light emanating from it in many directions. These bars, which give the peculiar spoked appearance to a star, are probably formed by optical defects of the lens within the eye, or by the tear fluid on the exterior surface of the eye, or by a combination of all these causes. Be that as it may, the lengths of the spokes of light are limited by the inner margin of the eye-curtain; if the curtain be drawn up, then the spokes are long; if the curtain be let down, or, in other words, if the pupil be very small and contracted, then one can not see any spokes at all. Hence, as I look at a distant gas-light, with its radiating golden spokes, I am looking at something which will give me a sure indication of any movements of the eye-curtains. I strike a match and allow its light to fall into the eyes; the spokes of the distant gas-lamp have retreated into the point of flame as if by magic; as I take the burning match away from before my eyes, the spokes of the gas-lamp venture forth again. The experiment may be utilized to see how much light is required to move the window-curtains of the eyes. Suppose you are walking toward two gas-lamps, A and B; B about fifty yards behind A. If you steadfastly look at B and at the golden spokes apparently issuing from it, you may make these spokes a test of how soon the light of A will move your iris. As you gradually approach A, you come at last to a position where its light is strong enough to make the spokes of B begin to shorten; a little nearer still and they vanish altogether. I have found that about a third of the light which is competent to contract the pupil very markedly will serve to commence its movement.—WILLIAM ACKROYD.

Purkinje's Figures (p. 222).—Stand in a dark room with a lighted candle in hand. Shutting the left, hold the candle very near the right eye, within three or four inches, obliquely outward and forward, so that the light shall strongly illuminate the retina. Now move the light about gently, upward, downward, back and forth, while you gaze intently on the wall opposite. Presently the field of view becomes dark from the intense impression of the light, and then, as you move the light about, there appears projected on the wall and covering its whole surface, a shadowy, ghost-like image, like a branching, leafless tree, or like a great bodiless spider with many branching legs. What is it? It is an exact but enlarged image of the *blood-vessels of the retina*. These come in at the entrance of the optic nerve, ramify in the middle layer, and therefore in the strong light cast their shadows on the bacillary layer of the retina. The impression of these shadows is projected outward into the field of view, and seen there as an enlarged shadowy image. These have been called Purkinje's Figures, from the discoverer.—PROF. JOSEPH LE CONTE, *in Sight*.

XI.

APPENDIX.

QUESTIONS FOR CLASS USE.

The questions include the Notes and the Selected Readings. The figures refer to th pages.

INTRODUCTION.

ILLUSTRATE the value of physiological knowledge. Why should physiology be studied in youth? When are our habits formed? How do habits help us? Why should children prize the lessons of experience? How does Nature punish a violation of her laws? Name some of Nature's laws. What is the penalty of their violation? Name some bad habits and their punishments. Some good habits and their rewards. How do the young ruin their health? Compare one's constitution with a deposit in the bank. Can one in youth lay up health as he can money for middle or old age? Is not the preservation of one's health a moral duty? What is suicide?

THE SKELETON.

3. How many bones are there in the body? Is the number fixed? Is the length of the different bones proportional? What is an organ? A function? Name the three uses of the bones. Why do the bones have such different shapes?

4. Why are certain bones hollow? Round? Illustrate. Compare the resisting property of bone with that of solid oak. What is the composition of bone? How does it vary? How can you remove the mineral matter? The animal matter? Why is a burned bone white and porous? What food do dogs find in bones?

5. What is the use of each of the constituents of a bone? What is "bone-black"? What is ossification? Why are not the bones of children as easily broken as those of aged persons? Why do they unite so much quicker? What are the fontanelles?

6. Describe the structure of a bone. What is the object of the filling? Why does the amount vary in different parts of a bone? What is the appearance of a bone seen through a microscope?

7. What is the periosteum? Is a bone once removed ever restored? What are the lacunæ? The Haversian canals? Why so called? *Ans.* From their discoverer, Havers. Define a bone.* What occupies the lacunæ? *Ans.* The bone-cells (osteoblasts). How do bones grow?

8. Illustrate. How does a broken bone heal? How rapidly is bone produced? Illustrate. Objects of "splints"? Describe how a joint is packed. Lubricated.

9. How are the bones tied together? What is a tissue? Illustrate. Name the three general divisions of the bones. What is the object of the skull? Which bone is movable? How is the lower jaw hinged? Describe the construction of the skull. What is a suture?

10. Tell how the peculiar form and structure of the skull adapt it for its use. Illustrate the impenetrability of the skull.

11. Describe the experiment of the balls. What does it show? What two cavities are in the trunk? Name its principal bones. Describe the spine.

12. What is the object of the processes? Of the pads? Why is a man shorter at night than in the morning? Describe the perfection of the spine.

13. Describe the articulation of the skull with the spine. Why is the atlas so called?

14. Describe the ribs. What is the natural form of the chest? Why is it made in separate pieces? How does the oblique position of the ribs aid in respiration? (See note, p. 80.)

15. How do the hip-bones give solidity? What two sets of

---

* Bone structure may be summarized as follows: A bone is a collection of *Haversian elements*, or rods. An Haversian element consists of a tube surrounded by *lamellæ*, which contain *lacunæ*, connected by *canaliculi*,—Dr. T. B. Stowell.

limbs branch from the trunk? State their mutual resemblance. Name the bones of the shoulder. Describe the collar-bone.

16. Describe the shoulder-blade. Can you describe the indirect articulation of the shoulder-blade with the trunk? Name the bones of the arm. Describe the shoulder-joint. The elbow-joint.

17. Describe the wrist. Name the bones of the hand. How many bones in the fingers? The thumb? What gives the thumb its freedom of motion?

18, 19. Name and describe the fingers. In what lies the perfection of the hand? How do the gestures of the hand enforce our ideas and feelings? Describe the hip-joint. What gives the upper limbs more freedom of motion than the lower? How does the pressure of the air aid us in walking? Illustrate.

20. Name the bones of the lower limbs. Describe the knee-joint. The patella. What is the use of the fibula? Can you show how the lower extremity of the fibula, below its juncture with the tibia, is prolonged to form a part of the ankle-joint? Name the bones of the foot. What is the use of the arch of the foot? What makes the step elastic? Describe the action of the foot as we step.

21. In graceful walking, should the toes or the heel touch the ground first? What are the causes of deformed feet? What is the natural position of the big toe? Did you ever see a big toe lying in a straight line with the foot, as shown in statuary and paintings? How should we have our boots and shoes made? What are the effects of high heels? Of narrow heels? Of narrow toes? Of tight-laced boots? Of thin soles? What are the rickets? Cause of this disease? Cure? Is there any provision for remedying defects in the body? Name one.

22, 23. What is a felon? Cure? Cause of bow-legs? How can they be prevented? Causes of spinal curvature? Cure? What is the correct position in sitting at one's desk? Is there any necessity for walking and sitting erect? Any advantage aside from health? Describe the bad effects of a stooping position. What is a sprain? Why does it need special care? What is a dislocation? How is it generally caused? How soon should it be treated?

269. What relation does man, in his general structure, bear to other vertebrates? Mention some marked physical peculiarities which distinguish him from the lower mammals.

270, 271. Describe the state of a fracture a week after its occurrence. What is this new formation called? What marks the termination of the first stage of curative progress? How do the broken ends of the bone now appear? What is the state of the fracture at the end of the second stage? What is the condition of the callus at this time? Describe the third and last series of changes. Is the process of union completed sooner in old people or in young? In the upper or lower extremities? In smaller animals or man? What length of time is required to heal a broken arm? A broken leg?

272. What gives the human hand its peculiar prehensile power? What advantage has the human thumb over that of the ape? Compare the foot of man with that of the ape. What peculiarity of the foot is particularly noticeable in man? Contrast the function of the great toe in man and in the ape.

273. Are the toes naturally flexible? How are their powers crippled? Give an instance in which the toes were trained to do the work of the fingers.

274. Why are an elastic step and a graceful carriage such rare accomplishments? What is the natural shape of the foot? Which is the longer, the great toe or the second toe? Is an even-sided symmetry necessary to the beauty of a boot?

————•••————

THE MUSCLES.

29. What relations do the skeleton and the muscles bear to each other? How is the skeleton concealed? Why is it the image of death? What are the muscles? How many are there? What peculiar property have they? Name other properties of muscles. *Ans.* Tonicity, elasticity.

30. How are they arranged? Where is the biceps? The triceps? How do the muscles move the limbs? Illustrate. What is the cause of squinting? Cure? (See p. 244.)

31. Name and define the two kinds of muscles. Illustrate each. What is the structure of a muscle? Of what is a fibril

itself composed? How does the peculiar construction of the muscle confer strength?

32. Describe the tendons. What is their use? Illustrate the advantages of this mode of attachment.

33. What two special arrangements of the tendons in the hand? Their use? How is the rotary motion of the eye obtained?

34, 35. What is a lever? Describe the three classes of levers. Illustrate each. Describe the head as a lever. What parts of the body illustrate the three kinds of levers? Give an illustration of the second class of levers. The third class. Why is the Tendon of Achilles so named? What is the advantage of the third class of levers? Why desirable in the hand? What class of lever is the lower jaw?

36. What advantages are gained by the enlargement of the bones at the joints? Illustrate. How do we stand erect? Is it an involuntary act?

37. Why can not a child walk at once, as many young animals do? Why can we not hold up the head easily when we walk on "all fours"? Why can not an animal stand erect as man does?

38. Describe the process of walking. Show that walking is a process of falling. Describe the process of running. What causes the swinging of the hand in walking? Why are we shorter when walking?* Why does a person when lost often go in a circle? In which direction does one always turn in that case?†

39. What is the muscular sense? Value of educating it? How do we gratify it?

40. What effect has exercise upon a muscle? Is there any danger in violent exercise? For what purpose should we exer-

---

* Stand a boy erect against a wall. Mark his height with a stick. Now have him step off a part of a pace, and then several whole paces. Next, let him close his eyes, and walk to the wall again. He will be perceptibly lower than the stick, until he straightens up once more from a walking position.

† Take several boys into a smooth grass lot. Set up a stick at a distance for them to walk toward. Test the boys, to find which are left-handed, or right-handed; which left-legged or right-legged. Then blindfold the boys and let them walk, as they think, toward the mark. See who varies toward the right, and who turns to the left.

24

cise? Should exercise be in the open air? What is the rule for exercise? Is a young person excusable, who leads a sedentary life, and yet takes no daily out-door exercise? What will be Nature's penalty for such a violation of her law? Will a postponement of the penalty show that we have escaped it?

41. Ought a scholar to study during the time of recess? Will a promenade in the vitiated air of the school-room furnish suitable exercise? What is the best time for taking exercise? What class of persons can safely exercise before breakfast?

42. What are the advantages of the different kinds of exercise? Should we not walk more? What is the general influence upon the body of vigorous exercise?

43. State some of the wonders of the muscles. What is the St. Vitus' dance? Cure?

44. What are convulsions? What is the locked-jaw? Causes? The gout? Cause? Cure? The rheumatism? Its two forms? Peculiarity of the acute?

45. Danger in acute rheumatism? In what does chronic rheumatism often result? What is lumbago? Give instances. What is a ganglion? Its cure? A bursa?

---

275. What is meant by the origin of a muscle? The attachment? Is a muscle always extended between two contiguous bones? Give an illustration. Can the points of origin and of attachment change offices? Illustrate. What is an important consequence of the attachment of the muscles to the bones? If, in the limb of a dead body, one end of a muscle is separated from its point of attachment, what occurs? Would the result be the same during life? To what is this phenomenon due?

276. Why are the muscles continually striving to shorten? Describe the effect when several opposing muscles are attached to one bone. When is the balanced position of the limbs best observed? Are the muscles always attached to bones? Give example. How does the flesh of man differ from that of an ox? How may the structure of muscular fibers be rudely illustrated? Describe smooth muscle-fibers. How do they differ from striated muscle-fibers?

277. In what form do smooth muscle-fibers frequently occur? In such cases, how are they usually arranged? What is the effect of their contraction? Of what especial use is this power in case of the smaller arteries? In case of the intestine?

278. In the latter instance, how does the contraction take place? Are the striated muscle-fibers voluntary or involuntary? Name an exception to this rule. Give other peculiarities of the muscle-fibers of the heart. What causes the contraction of smooth muscle-fibers? Of striated muscle-fibers? Why do little children seldom injure themselves by over-exertion? How is the danger increased in youth?

279. What class of people are in most peril from violent or excessive exercise? Why? At what age should one cease from haste of all kinds? Give instances of valuable lives lost from personal imprudence.

280. What are the effects of insufficient exercise upon the young? How does it predispose to disease? What makes the children of the laboring classes so hardy? Is a regulation step desirable in walking? Why not? Why is it more fatiguing to walk up-hill than on level ground?

281. How does the management of the breath affect this fatigue? How should a belt be worn, if used during exercise? Can other forms of exercise be successfully substituted for walking? Why not? What is the difference in movement between walking and skating? Which is the better exercise? What are the dangers from skating? What precaution should be used by those who have weak ankles?

282. Name the different action of the muscles in the forward and backward movements in rowing. What is the comparative value of rowing as an exercise? Why is it especially desirable for women? How should women dress when rowing, horseback-riding, tennis-playing, etc.? What rules should be observed by rowers? Why should the breath be allowed to escape while the oar is in the water?

283. What sanitary measures should be observed after a row? What effect has too frequent and too prolonged immersion on young swimmers? Does swimming require much muscular exertion? Why? Why does an occasional swimmer become exhausted sooner than an experienced one? On what do ease

and speed in swimming depend? Is the habit of diving desirable? Should diving ever be practiced in shallow water?

284. Why is lawn-tennis the most desirable of out-door games? *Ans.* Not only because nearly every muscle of the body is brought into exercise, but because it is one of the few field sports in which women can gracefully join. In this it shares the honor with croquet. What are the dangers attendant on lawn-tennis? From what do many of them arise? Why should tennis shoes have heels? To what class of people is horseback-riding particularly suited? What class of invalids should not indulge in bicycling and tricycling? To what class is it peculiarly beneficial?

285. What are the dangers attendant on base-ball games? Foot-ball? When may light and heavy gymnastics be profitably employed? Name a sufficient apparatus. What are the objections to gymnasium exercise? Its advantages?

THE SKIN.

49. What are the uses of the skin? Describe its adaptation to its place. What is its function as an organ? Describe the structure of the skin. The sensitiveness of the cutis. The insensitiveness of the cuticle.

50. How is the skin constantly changing? The shape and number of the cells? Value of the cuticle? How is the cuticle formed? *Ans.* By secretion from the cutis.

51. What is the complexion? Its cause? Why is a scar white? What is the cause of "tanning"? What are freckles? Albinos? Describe the action of the sun on the skin.

52. Why are the hairs and the nails spoken of under the title of the skin? Uses of the hair? Its structure? How can it be examined? What is the hair-bulb? What is it called? How does a hair grow? At what rate? When can it be restored, if destroyed? Does hair grow after death?

53. When hair has become gray, can its original color be naturally restored? What is the danger of hair-dyes? Are they of any real value? How can the hair stand on end? How do horses move their skin? Is there any feeling in a hair?

54. Illustrate the indestructibility of the hair. What are the uses of the nails? How do the nails grow? What is the mucous membrane?

55. Its composition? The connective tissue? Why so called? What uses does it subserve?

56. What is its character? How does the fat exist in the body? Its uses? State the various uses of membrane in the body. Where is there no fat? Where is there always fat?

57. Why are the teeth spoken of in connection with the mucous membrane? Name and describe the four kinds of teeth. What are the milk-teeth? Describe them. What teeth appear first?

58. Give the order and age at which they appear. When do the permanent teeth appear? Describe their growth. Which one comes first? Last?

59. Describe the structure of the teeth. How are the teeth fitted in the jaw?

60. Why do the teeth decay? What care should be taken of the teeth? What caution should be observed? What are the oil glands?

61. Use of this secretion? What are the perspiratory glands? State their number. Their total length. What are the "pores" of the skin?

62, 63. What is the perspiration? What is the constitution of the perspiration? Illustrate its value. Name the three uses of the skin. Illustrate the absorbing power of the skin. What precaution should be observed in handling a dead body? Why are cosmetics and hair-dyes injurious? What relation exists between the skin and the lungs? What lesson does this teach? When is the best time for a bath? Why?

64, 65. What is the value of friction? Why should not a bath be taken just before or after a meal? Is an excess of soap beneficial? What is the "reaction"? Explain its invigorating influence. How is it secured? General effect of a cold bath? Of a warm bath? If we feel chilly and depressed after a bath, what is the teaching? Describe the Russian vapor bath. Why is the sea-bath so stimulating?

66. How long should one remain in any bath? How does clothing keep us warm? Explain the use of linen as an article

of clothing. Cotton. Wool. Flannel. How can we best protect ourselves against the changes of our climate?

67. What colored clothing is best adapted for all seasons? Value of the nap? Furs? Thick *vs.* thin clothing? Should we wear thick clothing during the day, and in the evening put on thin clothing? Can children endure exposure better than grown persons? What is the erysipelas? How relieved?

68, 69. Eczema? What do its various forms denote? Corns? Cause? Cure? In-growing nails? Cure? Warts? Cure? Chilblain? Cause? Preventive?

---

286. Name some causes of baldness. Give Dr. Nichols' opinion. Why is frequent shampooing inadvisable? One probable reason why women are less frequently bald than men? What is the best general treatment for the hair and scalp? Upon what does the color of the hair mainly depend?

287. In cases of sudden blanching of the hair what is the effect upon the pigment? Give an illustration. How do the extra air-bubbles find their way into the hair? Does air naturally exist in the hair? What relation do the nails bear to the scarfskin?

288. What causes the horny appearance of the nails? Describe the root of the nail in its relation to the sensitive and the scarfskin. Upon what does the nail rest? What is its appearance? What is the lunula? Why is it lighter than the rest of the nail? How does the nail increase in length? In thickness? Where is the greatest thickness? How does the growth of the nail during disease, compare with its growth in health?

289. How long does it take the thumb-nail to grow from its root to its free extremity? The great toe? Give general rules for the care of the nails. How does physical cleanliness promote moral purity? What does its neglect indicate?

290. What especial care should be taken in regard to the feet? Why? Are baths a modern refinement? What can you say about the ancient Greek and Roman baths? What constitutes the value of the Turkish bath?

291. What class of people should never use this bath? To

what class of invalids is it particularly beneficial? Is sea-bathing advisable for persons of all ages? How should an inexperienced sea-bather begin? When should the sea-bath be taken?

292. How long should a delicate person remain in the water? State the danger of bathing when overheated. Under what conditions of body and of temperature should sea or river bathing be avoided? Why? Give illustration of the English soldier. How should the temperature of the water, in bathing, compare with that of the air? Of the body?

293. Describe the bathers' cramp. What are its causes? What precaution should be used by bathers in regard to the mouth and ears? Why?

294. How can a person who does not know how to swim, save himself from drowning?

295. What are the advantages of woolen clothing? Why is it particularly desirable in malarial countries? What double purpose does woolen clothing serve in semi-tropical climates?

296. Does the warmth of clothing depend on its weight? What errors are often made and with what effect? State what is said in regard to poisonous dyes in wearing apparel. Give illustration.

297. What effect has uncleanly attire on the health? Does this apply to outer as well as under garments?

RESPIRATION AND THE VOICE.

73. Name the organs of respiration and the voice. Describe the larynx. The epiglottis. The œsophagus. What is meant by food "going the wrong way"?

74. Describe the vocal cords. Their use. How is sound produced?

75. How are the higher tones of the voice produced? The lower? Upon what does loudness depend? A falsetto voice? What is the cause of the voice "changing"? What is speech? Is the tongue necessary to speech? Illustrate. (See also page 298.)

76. What is vocalization? How are talking-machines made?

77. How is *a* formed by the voice? What is *h*? Difference between a sigh and a groan? What vowel sounds are made in laughing? Does whistling depend on the voice? Tell how the various consonants are formed. What are the labials? The dentals? The linguals? What vowels does a child pronounce first?

78. Describe the wind-pipe. The bronchi. The bronchial tubes. Why is the trachea so called? Describe the structure of the lungs. What are the lungs of slaughtered animals called? Why will a piece of the lungs float on water?

79. Name the wrappings of the lungs. Describe the pleura. How is friction prevented? What are the cilia? Their use?

80. What two acts constitute respiration? In what two ways may the position of the ribs change the capacity of the chest? Describe the process of inspiration. Describe the diaphragm.

81. What is the process of expiration? How often do we breathe? What is sighing? Coughing? Sneezing? Snoring? Laughing? Crying?

82. Describe hiccough. Yawning. Its value? What is meant by the breathing capacity? How does it vary? How much, in addition, can the lungs expel forcibly? How much of the breathing capacity is available only through practice? Value of this extra supply? Can we expel all the air from our lungs? Value of this constant supply?

83. How constant is the need of air? What is the vital element of the air? Describe the action of the oxygen in our lungs. What does the blood give up? Gain? What are the constituents of the air? What are the peculiar properties and uses of each?

84. How can we test the air we exhale? What does its analysis reveal? Which is the most dangerous constituent? What occurs when we rebreathe exhaled air?

85. Describe its evil effects. What is denoted by the "Black Hole of Calcutta"? Give other illustrations of the dangers of bad air. Describe the need of ventilation. Will a single breath pollute the air?

86-95. How can we detect the floating impurities in the air? What is the influence of a fire or a light? Of a hot stove? When is the ventilation perfect? What diseases are largely owing to bad air? Should the windows and doors be tightly closed, if we have no other means of ventilation? Is not a draught of air dangerous? How can we prevent this, and yet secure fresh air? What is the general principle of ventilation? Must pure air necessarily be cold air? Are school-rooms always properly ventilated? What is the effect? Are churches? Are our bedrooms? Should children or delicate people sleep in cold rooms? Can we, at night, breathe any thing but night air? Is the night air out-of-doors ever injurious? *Ans.* In times and places of malaria, and also in very damp weather, it should be avoided, even at the risk of bad air in-doors. Describe some of the wonders of respiration.

96. How is constriction of the lungs produced? When may clothing be considered tight? What are the dangers of tight-lacing? Which would make the stronger, more vigorous, and longer-lived person, the form shown in *A* or *B*, Fig. 33? Is it safe to run any risk in this dangerous direction?

97. What is Bronchitis? Pleurisy? Pneumonia? Consumption? What is one great cause of Consumption? How may a constitutional tendency to this disease be warded off in youth? *Ans.* Besides plenty of fresh air and exercise, care should be taken in the diet. Rich pastry, unripe fruit, salted meat, and acid drinks should be avoided, and a certain quantity of fat should be eaten at each meal. — BENNETT. What is asphyxia? Describe the process for restoring such a person. (See p. 264.)

98. What is diphtheria? Its peculiarities? Danger? The croup? Its characteristics? Remedy? (See p. 260.) Causes of stammering? How cured?

---

297. How does the singing voice differ from the speaking voice? How can you prove the effect of duration of sound in speaking and singing? How do the intonations of the voice affect the meaning of words?

298. Give illustrations of speech in persons without a tongue. What is the effect of alcohol and tobacco on the throat? Do they have an influence on the voice? Does the excessive use of

tea and coffee ever affect the voice? How? To what is the hoarse tone of an inebriate due?

299, 300. What was Adelina Patti's advice with regard to stimulants and late hours? Does the respiration of woman differ from that of man? Give experiments with Indian women. What lessons do we draw from these facts? What rule should be observed in regard to the size of a bodice? What are bacteria or microbes? How is their existence revealed? What does the Germ Theory of Disease teach in regard to microbes?

301. What can you say about the microbe of putrefaction? How can you obtain it for examination? What office in Nature do bacteria seem to serve? Give the theory in regard to propagation of special disease germs. Do they always cause disease when taken into the body?*

302. State some conditions which favor the growth of disease-germs. Which prevent or retard their growth. Relate the effect of vaccination, according to the germ theory.

303, 304. If a drop of an infusion charged with bacteria be put in the extract of beef or mutton, what is the result? What would be the effect upon an open wound? Give Dr. Tyndall's personal experience. Name some efficient antidote against the bacteria of putrefaction. *Ans.* Carbolic acid solution is extensively used for this purpose. How are disease germs often disseminated? State the necessity of disinfection in regard to soiled clothing.

305. Illustrate how disease has been communicated by clothing. What is the first necessary condition to a sanitary home? What is the meaning of the word malaria? What are three active agents in the production of malaria? A fourth? De-

---

* Of the immense number and variety of micro-organisms found in Nature, only very few are disease-producing. Dr. Austin Flint says in *The Forum*, for December, 1888: "It is probable that future investigations into the physiology of digestion, will show that bacteria play an important part in this function. Pasteur has recently isolated no less than seventeen different micro-organisms in the mouth, which were not destroyed by the gastric juice. Some of these dissolved albumen, gluten, and caseine, and some transformed starch into sugar. Bacteria normally exist in great number and variety in the intestines, although the part which they take in intestinal digestion has not been accurately determined."—The number of spores introduced into the human system by respiration, when the health is perfectly sound, has been estimated at three hundred thousand a day.

scribe a typical malarious locality. How does newly-broken ground induce malaria?

306. State the different ways in which running water can be contaminated. What care should be taken in regard to the level of building site?

307. Give some of the results of a wet foundation. What rules should be observed in regard to shade? What is the effect of too dense foliage about a dwelling? In building a house, what precautions should be taken against dampness? What about the cellar? Sewerage? Plumbing? Ventilation? Fireplaces? Piazzas and balconies? Sleeping-rooms?

308. What general purpose does a house serve? What care should be taken in regard to the dust or ash heap? What is the effect if liquids or table refuse be thrown upon it? Where should it be situated? How often should refuse be carted away? If its frequent removal be inexpedient, what precaution should be used? What are the best of all deodorizers? How should the back premises be cared for? What is the best way to dispose of household garbage?

309. How can this be done? With what additional advantage? Give Dr. Derby's remarks in regard to sewers, their condition, and the results. How should traps and drains be cared for? How should bad smells be treated? Is a foul smell always the most dangerous? How do poisonous gases often find entrance to a house? What rule should be observed in regard to ventilating and soil pipes?

310. What precautions should be observed in digging about a dwelling? How do waste-pipes often become closed? How may they be cleared? What dangers arise from unventilated waste-pipes? How are wash-basin pipes contaminated? Tell what came from a neighbor's cess-pool. Can you name similar instances which have come under your own observation?

311, 312. Describe the condition and effects of a neglected cellar. Tell what came from a crack in a cellar wall.

313. What effect have brick and mortar in keeping out gases? How do bed-coverings take the place of day garments? What kind of bed-covering is desirable? Is a comfortable bed necessary to perfect health? How often and for how long time should a bed be ventilated?

THE CIRCULATION.

105. Name the organs of the circulation. Does the blood permeate all parts of the body? What is the average amount in each person? Its composition? The plasma? The red corpuscles? The white?

106. What is the size of a red cell? Are the shape and size uniform? Value of this? Illustrate. Are the disks permanent? What substances are contained in the plasma? What is fibrin?

107. In what sense is the blood "liquid flesh"? What is the use of the red disks? What is the office of the oxygen in the body? Where is the blood purified?

108. What is transfusion? Is it of value?

109. Give some illustrations. What is the cause of coagulation of the blood? Value of this property? Has the fibrin any other use?

110. What organ propels the blood? What is the location of the heart? How large is it? Put your hand over it. What is the pericardium? Describe the systole.

111. The diastole. How many chambers in the heart? What is their average size? What is meant by the right and left heart? What are the auricles? Why so called? The ventricles?

112. What is the use of the auricles? The ventricles? Which are made the stronger? Show the need of valves in the ventricles. Why are there no valves in the auricles? Draw on the board the form of the valves. Name them.

113. Describe the tricuspid valve. The bicuspid. How are these valves strengthened?

114. What peculiarity in the attachment of these cords? Describe the semi-lunar valves. What are the arteries? Why so named? What is their use? Their structure? How does their elasticity act? What is meant by a "collateral circulation"?

115. How are the arteries protected? Where are they located? Give a general description of the arterial system. What is the aorta? What is the pulse? On which arteries can we best feel it? What is the average number of beats per minute? How and why does this vary?

116. Why does a physician feel a patient's pulse? What are the veins? What blood do they carry? Describe the venous system. What vein does not lead toward the heart? Describe the valves of the veins. What valves of the heart do they resemble? What are varicose veins?

117. Where and how can we see the operation of these valves? What are the capillaries? What is the function of the capillaries?* What changes take place in this system?

118. Describe the circulation of the blood as seen in the web of a frog's foot.

119. Who discovered the circulation of the blood? How was the discovery received? What remark did Harvey make? What does that show? Name the two divisions of the circulation. Describe the route of the blood by the diagram. 1. The lesser circulation. 2. The greater circulation.

120. What is the velocity of the blood? How long does it require for all the blood to pass through the heart? How long does it take the blood to make the tour of the body? What is the average temperature of the body? How much does this vary in health? *Ans.* Not more than 2°, even in the greatest extremes of temperature.—FLINT.

121. How and where is the heat of the body generated? How is it distributed? In what diseases is the variation of temperature marked? How is the temperature of the body regulated?

122. In what way does life exist through death? Is not this as true in the moral as in the physical world? What does it teach? How rapidly do our bodies change? What are the three vital organs?

123. Name some of the wonders of the heart.

124–126. What is the lymphatic circulation? What is the thoracic duct? The lymph? The glands? What is the office of the lymphatics? What are the lacteals? Give some illustrations of the action of the lymphatics of the different organs. Should

---

* The distinctive function of the capillaries is to offer peripheral resistance to the circulation of the blood. This insures "blood pressure," a condition indispensable to the "heart-beat," and also causes leakage (transudation). This leakage brings the nutriment in contact with the tissue cells, whereby they are renewed. In the same way the air passes from the blood to the cells.

we use care in selecting wall-paper? What is meant by the sub-cutaneous insertion of morphine? How do hibernating animals live during the winter? What is a congestion? Its cause?

127. What is blushing? Why does terror cause one to grow cold and pale? How is an inflammation caused? Name its four characteristics.

128. How may severe bleeding be stopped? How can you tell whether the blood comes from an artery or a vein? Why should you know this? What is the scrofula? What are "kernels"?

129, 130. How may a scrofulous tendency of the system be counteracted? What kinds of food stimulate this disease? What is the cause of a "cold"? Why does exposure sometimes cause a cold in the head, sometimes on the lungs, and at others bring on a rheumatic attack? Why is a cold dangerous? *Ans.* It weakens the system and paves the way for other diseases. What is the theory of treating a cold? Describe the method. What is catarrh? Cause?

131, 132. How is alcohol produced? Is alcohol present in domestic wines and home-brewed ales? Are they, then, harmless drinks? What is a ferment? (See also pp. 300, 301.) What is the difference between ferments, bacteria, microbes, and fungi? *Ans.* A few investigators still look upon the micro-organisms known as bacteria and microbes as animal existences, but the larger part now concede them to be vegetable.

133. What is the effect of fermentation? What can you say concerning yeast?

134. Explain the process of making beer. Wine. What is distillation?

135, 136. Is there more than one kind of alcohol? What can you say of methyl alcohol? Amyl? Ethyl? Which is the ordinary alcohol of commerce? What is the peculiar effect of fusel oil? Is it often found in wines and spirits? Has alcohol any beneficial properties?

137, 138. Describe one of the striking effects of alcohol. What is the effect of alcohol on plant and animal life?

139, 140. What is the difference between the alcohol present in beer and cider, and that in gin and whiskey? Name another

dangerous effect of alcoholic drinks. What business consideration should deter young men from liquor-drinking?

141–143. Illustrate the general effect of alcohol upon the
circulation. Upon the heart. Is alcohol a stimulant or a narcotic? Describe how alcohol becomes the "Genius of Degeneration." Explain what is meant by "Vascular Enlargement."

144, 145. Describe the effect of alcohol upon the membranes. Upon the blood. Does it render the blood thin or
heavy? What is the difference between pure and alcoholized
blood?

145–147. Describe the effect of alcohol upon the lungs.
What form of consumption does it induce? Are liquor-drinkers
more or less liable to epidemic diseases?

---

314. How does the pulse felt by the finger correspond with
the beat of the heart? Name some agencies that influence the
pulse-beat? Which part of the body has the most varied form
of pulsation?

315. Compare the pulses of the wrist and brain in the
sleeping and the waking states. How do catarrhal colds generally arise? How are they best cured?

316. What is said of the vitality of catarrh germs? What
is a popular fallacy with regard to the care of sick-rooms?
Give Dr. Austin Flint's remarks in this connection.

DIGESTION AND FOOD.

151. Why do we need food? Why will a person starve
without food? Are the current stories of people who live without food to be relied upon? How much food is needed per day
by an adult in active exercise?

152. How much in a year? How does this amount vary?
Describe the body as a mold. As an eddy. What does food do
for us? What does food contain?

153. How is this force set free? What force is this? How

can it be turned into muscular motion, mental vigor, etc.? Do we then draw all our power from nature? What becomes of these forces when we are done with them? Do we destroy the force we use? *Ans.* No matter has been destroyed, so far as we know, since the creation, and force is equally indestructible. Compare our food to a tense spring.

154. What three kinds of food do we need? What is nitrogenous food? Name the common forms. What is the characteristic of nitrogenous food? Why called albuminous? What is carbonaceous food? Its two kinds? Constituents of sugar? Where are starch and gum ranked? Why? Use of carbonaceous food? What becomes of this heat? Composition of fat? How does fat compare with sugar in producing heat?

155. Name the other uses of carbonaceous food. From what kind of food does the body derive the greatest strength? Name the mineral matters which should be contained in our food. What can you say of the abundance and necessity of water? Ought we not to exercise great care in selecting the water we drink?* Does the character of our food influence the quantity of water we need?

156. What are the uses of the different minerals contained in food? Illustrate the importance of salt. Could a person live on one kind of food alone? Illustrate.

157. Describe the effect of living on lean meat. Show the necessity of a mixed diet. Illustrate. Show the need of digestion. Illustrate.

158. What is assimilation? Describe the general plan of digestion. What did Berzelius call digestion? Why? What amount of liquid is daily secreted by the alimentary canal? What is the alimentary canal? How is it lined? How does the amœba digest its food?

159. The hydra? Define secretion. Describe the saliva. How is it secreted? What is the amount? Its organic principle? Its use? How soon does it act? How long? What tends to check or increase the flow of saliva?

---

* Water which has passed through lead-pipes is apt to contain salts of that metal, and is therefore open to suspicion. Metallic-lined ice-pitchers, galvanized-iron reservoirs, and many soda-water fountains, are liable to the same objection. (See pp. 317, 318.)

160. Describe the process of swallowing. The stomach. Its size. Its construction. What is the peristaltic movement?

162. What is the pylorus? For what does this open? What is the gastric juice? How abundant is it? To what is its acidity due? What organic principle does it contain? How is pepsin prepared? How is the flow of gastric juice influenced?

163. What is its use? Appearance of the food as it passes through the pylorus? Why is not the stomach itself digested? What is the construction of the intestines? How are the intestines divided? What is the duodenum? Why so called? What juices are secreted here?

164. What is the bile? Describe the liver. What is its weight? Its construction? *Ans.* It consists of a mass of polyhedral cells only $\frac{1}{100}$ to $\frac{1}{2000}$ of an inch in diameter, filling a mesh of capillaries. The capillaries carry the blood to and fro, and the cells secrete the bile. What is the cyst? What does the liver secrete from the blood besides the bile? Is the bile necessary to life? Illustrate. What is its use?

165. What is the pancreatic juice? Its organic principle? Its use? Appearance of the food when it leaves the duodenum? Describe the small intestine. What is absorption? In what two ways is the food absorbed?

166. Where does the process commence? How long does it last? Describe the lacteals. Of what general system do they form a part? What do the veins absorb? Where do they carry the food? How is it modified?

167. What is glycogen? Describe the complexity of the process of digestion. What length of time is required for digestion in the stomach?

168. May not food which requires little time in the stomach need more in the other organs, and *vice versa?* Tell the story of Alexis St. Martin. What time was required to digest an ordinary meal? Apples? Eggs, raw and cooked? Roast beef? Pork? Which is the king of the meats? What is the nutritive value of mutton? Lamb? How should it be cooked? Objection to pork? What is the trichina?

169. Should ham ever be eaten raw? Value of fish? Oysters? Milk? Cheese? Eggs? Bread? Brown bread? Are warm biscuit and bread healthful? Nutritive value of corn?

170. Of the potato? Of ripe fruits? Of coffee? To what is its stimulating property due? Its influence on the system? When should it be discarded? Should children use any stimulants?

171. Effects of tea? Influence of strong tea? What is the active principle of tea? Nutritive value of chocolate? What is its active principle? Story of Linnæus? How should tea be made? What is the effect of cooking food? What precaution in boiling meat? In roasting? Object of this high temperature? What precaution in making soup? Why is frying an unhealthful mode of cooking?

172. State the five evil results of rapid eating. What disease grows out of it? If one is compelled to eat a meal rapidly, as at a railroad station, what should he take? Why? Why does a child need more food proportionately than an old person? State the relation of waste to repair in youth, in middle, and in old age. What kind and quantity of food does a sedentary occupation require? What caution should students who have been accustomed to manual labor observe? Must a student starve himself?

173. Is there not danger of overeating? Would not an occasional abstinence from a meal be beneficial? Do not most people eat more than is for their good? How should the season regulate our diet? The climate? Illustrate. What does a natural appetite indicate? How are we to judge between a natural and an artificial longing? What does the craving of childhood for sugar indicate? *

174. What is the effect upon the circulation of taking food? Should we labor or study just before or after a meal? Why not? What time should intervene between our meals? Is "lunching" a healthful practice? Eating heartily just before

---

* It does not follow from this, however, that the free use of sugar in its separate form is desirable. The ordinary articles of vegetable food contain sugar (or starch, which in the body is converted into sugar), in large proportion; and there is good reason to believe that in its naturally-combined form it is both more easily digested, and more available for the purposes of nutrition, than when crystallized. The ordinary sugar of commerce, moreover, derived from the sugar-cane, is not capable of being directly applied to physiological purposes. Cane-sugar is converted within the body into another kind of sugar, identical with that derived from the grape, before it can enter into the circuit of the vital changes.

retiring? Is it never wise to eat at this time? (See p. 337.) Why should care be banished from the table? Will a regular routine of food be beneficial?

175, 176. Describe some of the wonders of digestion. What are the principal causes of dyspepsia? How may we avoid that disease?

177. What are the mumps? What care should be taken? Is alcohol a food? Illustrate.

178-187. Compare the action of alcohol with that of water. Is the alcohol taken into the stomach eliminated unchanged? Does alcohol contain any element needed by the body? What is the effect of alcohol upon the digestion? Will pepsin act in the presence of alcohol? What is the effect of alcohol upon the liver? What is "Fatty Degeneration"? What is the effect of alcohol upon the kidneys? Does alcohol impart heat to the body? Does it confer strength? What does Dr. Kane say? Describe Richardson's experiments. Tell what peculiar influence alcohol exerts. What is alcoholism? What is heredity?

---

317. What characteristics should good drinking-water possess? Are these always proof of its purity? Will filters remove all danger of contamination? How may a river infect the entire population of a town? State how well-water may become a dangerous drink.

318. Relate how cases of fever have been caused by carelessness in dairies. How should suspected water be treated? Describe a convenient portable filter. Tell how water is affected by foul air.

319. Tell how ice may breed disease. What caution should be observed in engaging ice for our summer supply? Illustrate the structure of the glandular coat of the stomach.

320. What is the office of the cells? Describe the life-history of a cell. How does the stomach weep, and what is the character of its tears?

321. What is tyrotoxicon? Give Dr. Vaughan's experiments with cheese, milk, and ice-cream. Tell how milk may be poisoned.

322. Compare the vigor of exclusively fish-eating with flesh-eating people. What is the peculiar value of fish as a diet? To what class of people is it best suited? Name examples. Describe the principles contained in coffee. What is the effect of caffeone? Of caffeine? Give some of the specific effects of coffee. How does tea differ from coffee? Describe the injurious effects of excessive tea-drinking.

324. Compare theine and cocaine. Should children drink tea and coffee?

325. Give some causes of indigestion. Why are nervous people prone to dyspepsia? Give the comparative digestibility of various meats.

326. Describe how our food sustains our bodies. Illustrate the energy contained in one gramme of beef-fat. Why is there danger in a "high-pressure" style of living? Illustrate.

327. State the effects of gluttony. Why is it unkindness to indulge inordinate appetites in children? What should be the rule in regard to their food? What effects would follow its observance?

THE NERVOUS SYSTEM.

191. What are the organs of the nervous system? What is the general use of this system? How does it distinguish animals from plants? What are the vegetative functions? What is the gray matter? Its use? The white matter? Its use?

193. Describe the brain. What is its office? Its size? How does it vary? Illustrate. Name its two divisions.

194, 195. Describe the cerebrum. The convolutions. The membranes which bind the brain together. What can you say of the quantity of blood which goes to the brain? What does it show? What do the convolutions indicate? What is the use of the two halves of the brain? What theories have been advanced concerning it? Is every injury to the brain fatal? Illustrate. Compare the human brain with the brains of some animals.

196. What is the effect of removing the cerebrum? Describe the cerebellum. What is the arbor vitæ? What does this part

of the brain control? What are the peculiar functions of the cerebellum? Give Dr. Bastian's remarks.

197. What is the effect of an injury to the cerebellum? Describe the spinal cord. What is the medulla oblongata? Describe the nerves. Is each part of the body supplied with its own nerve? Prove it.

198. What are the motory nerves? The sensory? When will motion be lost and feeling remain, and *vice versa?* What is meant by a transfer of pain? Illustrate.

199. Name the three classes of nerves. What are the spinal nerves? Describe the origin of the spinal nerve.

199–201. What are the cranial nerves? How many pairs are there? Describe them.

201, 202. Describe the sympathetic system. What is its use? How does the brain control all the vital processes? What is meant by the crossing of the cords? What is the effect? What exception in the seventh pair of cranial nerves?

203, 204. What is reflex action? Give illustrations. Give instances of the unconscious action of the brain.* Can there be feeling or motion in the lower limbs when the spinal cord is destroyed? What does the story told by Dr. John Hunter show? Give illustrations of the independent action of the spinal cord in animals. What are the uses of reflex action?

---

* The cerebellum has its unconscious action in the processes of respiration and in the involuntary movements which are made in response to the senses, as in winking, starting back at a sound, etc. The cerebrum acts automatically in cases familiar to all. A large part of our mental activity consists of this unconscious brain-work. There are many cases in which the mind has obviously reasoned more clearly and more successfully in this automatic condition, when left entirely to itself, than when we have been cudgeling our brains, so to speak, to get the solution. Oliver Wendell Holmes has aptly expressed this fact. "We wish," he says, "to remember something in the course of conversation. No effort of the will can reach it; but we say, 'Wait a minute, and it will come to me,' and we go on talking. Some minutes later, the idea we are in search of comes all at once into the mind, delivered like a pre-paid parcel, or like a foundling in a basket, laid at the door of consciousness. How it came there, we know not. The mind must have been at work, groping and feeling for it in the dark; it can not have come of itself. Yet, all the while, our consciousness, *so far as we are conscious of our consciousness,* was busy with other thoughts."

Some interesting personal experiences upon this point are given in an article entitled "The Antechamber of Consciousness," by Francis Speir, Jr., in the *Popular Science Monthly* for March, 1888.

205. State its value in the formation of habits. How does the brain grow? What laws govern it? What must be the effect of constant light-reading? Of over-study or mental labor?

206. State the relation of sleep to repair and waste. How many hours does each person need? What kind of work requires most sleep?

206–208. What is the influence of sunlight on the body? Illustrate. Name some of the wonders of the brain.

208–213. What four stages are there in the effect of alcohol on the nervous system? Describe each. Does alcohol confer any permanent strength? What is the physiological effect of alcohol on the brain? On the mental and moral powers? What is the Delirium Tremens? Should a man be punished for a crime he commits while drunk?

214–218. What are the principal constituents of tobacco? What are its physiological effects? Who are most likely to escape injury? Is tobacco a food? What is its influence upon youth? Why are cigarettes specially injurious? What effect does tobacco have on the sensibilities? Name illustrations of the injurious effect of tobacco on young men.

219–221. How is opium obtained? What is its physiological effect? Which form of using it is most injurious? Can one give up the use of opium when he pleases? How do people sometimes take opium without knowing it?

221. What is the harmful influence of chloral hydrate? Describe its different physiological effects.

222. Compare its influence with that of alcohol. How is chloroform obtained? Does its use require great caution? Illustrate its effects.

223, 224. What is cocaine? What is its value? Its physiological effect? Its dangers?

331–333. What is the effect of extreme anger? Give the physiological explanation of this deterioration. What two organs particularly suffer? Illustrate. To what cause are many suicides referable? How can one secure a calm and tranquil life? What is the effect of forcing the brain in childhood?

334. Illustrate. How should a child be taught?

334, 335. Why should we not exhaust our energies to the last degree? What warnings does Nature give us? Do stimulants supply force? What is the effect of mental exhaustion? Which is the most common, overwork or worry? Most dangerous? What is worry? Its effect? What other causes often induce insanity?

336-338. State some curiosities of sleep. Some conditions necessary to sound and healthful slumber. How may we acquire the habit of early rising?

338, 339. Give some of the results of dungeon life.

339-347. What can you say of the growth and power of poison habits? Illustrate. How does physiological ignorance often cause intemperance? What is the usual result of a stimulant habit? In what virtue lies the peril of narcotics? Balance the good and the evil in their use. Illustrate how death often results from chloroform and chloral. What common result is worse than death? Compare the demoralization in the cases of the opium-user and the alcohol-drinker. What principle of heredity attaches to the use of opium? Give instances of deaths from tobacco, opium, etc. What can you say of cigarette-smoking? Chloral hydrate? The bromides? Absinthe? Hasheesh?

THE SPECIAL SENSES.

229, 230. What is a sense? Name the five senses. To what organ do all the senses minister? If the nerve leading to any organ of sense be cut, what would be the effect?* Sometimes persons lose feeling in a limb, but retain motion; why is this? What is the sense of touch sometimes called? Describe the organ of touch. What are the papillæ? Where are they most abundant?† What are the uses of this sense? What special

* Each organ is adapted to receive a peculiar kind of impression. Hence we can not smell with the eyes nor see with the nose. Thus, if the nerve communicating between the brain and any organ be destroyed, that means of knowledge is cut off.

† If we apply the points of a compass blunted with cork to different parts of the body, we can distinguish the two points at one twenty-fourth of an inch apart on the tongue, one sixteenth of an inch on the lips, one

knowledge do we obtain by it? Why do we always desire to handle any curious object? Can the sense of touch always be relied upon? Illustrate. What is the *tactus eruditus*? Tell how one sense can take the place of another. Give illustrations of the delicacy of touch possessed by the blind.

230–232. Describe the sense of taste. How can you see the papillæ of taste? What causes the velvety look of the tongue? Why do salt and bitter flavors induce vomiting? Why does an acid "pucker" the face? What substances are tasteless? Illustrate. Has sulphur any taste? Chalk? Sand? What is the use of this sense? Does it not also add to the pleasures of life? Why are the acts of eating, drinking, etc., thus made sources of happiness?

232, 233. Describe the organ of smell. State the intimate relation which exists between the senses of smell and taste. Name some common mistakes which occur in consequence. Must the object to be smelled touch the nose? What is the theory of smell? How do you account for the statement made in the note concerning musk and ambergris? What are the uses of this sense? Are agreeable odors healthful, and disagreeable ones unhealthful?

234–236. Describe the organ of hearing. Describe the external ear. What is the tympanum or drum of the ear? Describe the middle ear. Name the bones of the ear. Describe their structure. Describe the internal ear. By what other name is it known? What substances float in the liquid which fills the labyrinth? What is their use? Describe the fibers of Corti. What do they form? Use of this microscopic harp? Give the theory of sound. Where is the sound, in the external object or in the mind? Can there be any sound, then, where there is no mind? What advice is given concerning the care of the ear? How can insects be removed? Which sense would you rather lose, hearing or sight? Does not a blind person always excite more sympathy than a deaf one? How does the sight assist the hearing?*

twelfth of an inch on the tips of the fingers, and one half inch on the great toe; while, if they are one inch on the cheek, and two inches on the back, they will scarcely produce a separate sensation.—HUXLEY.

* In *hearing*, the attention is more or less characteristic. If we wish to

236, 237. Describe the eye. Name the three coats of which it is composed. Is it a perfect sphere? *Ans.* The cornea projects in front, and the optic nerve at the back sticks out like a handle, while the ball itself has its longest diameter from side to side. How is the interior divided? Object of the crystalline lens? How is the crystalline lens kept in place? Describe the liquids which fill the eye.

238. What is the pupil? Describe the eyelids. Why is the inner side of the eyelid so sensitive? What is the cause of a black eye? Use of the eyelashes? Where are the oil glands located? What is their use? Describe the lachrymal gland. The lachrymal lake. What causes the overflow in old age?

239. Explain the structure of the retina. Use of the rods and cones. What is the blind spot?

240. Illustrate. What is the theory of sight? Illustrate.

241, 242. State the action of the crystalline lens. Its power of adaptation. Do children ever need spectacles?

243. What is the cataract? How cured? What is color-blindness? Illustrate. What care should be taken of the eyes? Should one constantly lean forward over his book or work? What special care should near-sighted children take? By what carelessness may we impair our sight?

244. How is squinting caused? Cured? What care should be used after an illness? Should we ever read or write at twilight? Danger of reading upon the cars? What course should we take when objects get into the eye? How may they be removed?

245. Are "eye-stones" useful? Why should we never use

distinguish a distant noise, or perceive a sound, the head inclines and turns in such a manner as to present the external ear in the direction of the sound, at the same time the eyes are fixed and partially closed. The movement of the lips of his interlocutor is the usual means by which the deaf man supplies the want of hearing; the eyes and the entire head, from its position, having a peculiar and painful expression of attention. In looking at the portrait of La Condamine, it was easily recognized as that of a deaf person. Even when hearing is perfect, the eyes act sometimes as auxiliaries to it. In order to understand an orator perfectly, it seems necessary to see him—the gestures and the expression of the face seeming to add to the clearness of the words. The lesson of a teacher can not be well understood if any obstacle is interposed between him and the eyes of the listening pupil. So that if a pupil's eyes wander, we know that he is not attentive.—*Wonders of the Human Body.*

eye-washes except upon the advice of a competent physician? What rule should be observed with regard to the direction of the light when we are at work? Name some causes of near-sightedness. Remedies.

---

346. Give the account of Laura Bridgman.

347–350. Describe the anatomy of the nose. In what part of the nose is the function of smell performed? Why do we "sniff" when our attention is attracted by an odor? Give some experiments which illustrate the connection between smell, taste, and touch. Why should we retain our food in the mouth as long as possible? Of what use are gastronomic odors?

350. Why should a child's ear never be boxed? Illustrate. How can we detect inattention from deafness in a child? What should we consider in this respect?

351. Why should we avoid direct draughts in the ear? Explain the use of ear-wax. What common habit is very injurious? Why?

352, 353. What is the office of the Eustachian tube? Illustrate.

353, 354. Describe the action of the "eye-curtain." Give experiments. What are "Purkinje's Figures"? Describe experiment.

HEALTH AND DISEASE.

251–254. State some of the benefits of health. Contrast it with sickness. How were diseases formerly supposed to be caused? What remedies were used? What does modern science teach us to be the nature of disease? Give some illustrations showing how diseases may be prevented. Is it probable that the body was intended to give out in any one of its organs? What is the first step to be taken in the cure of a disease? What should be the object of medicine? What is now the chief dependence of the best physicians? What do you think concerning the common use of patent nostrums? Ought we not to use the greatest care in the selection of our physician?

GLOSSARY.

Ab dō′men (*abdo*, I conceal). The largest cavity in the body, in which are hidden the intestines, stomach, etc.

Ab sŏrb′ent (*ab*, from; *sorbeo*, I suck up).

Aç′e tab′u lum (*acetum*, vinegar). The socket for holding the head of the thigh-bone, shaped like an ancient vinegar vessel.

A çĕ′tic (*acetum*, vinegar).

Ad′i pose. Fatty.

Al bu′men (*albus*, white). A substance resembling the white of egg.

Al bu′mi nous substances contain much albumen.

Al′i ment′a ry. Pertaining to food.

Al′ka line (-lĭn) substances neutralize acids.

An′æs thet′ic. A substance that destroys the feeling of pain.

A ôr′ta. The largest artery of the body.

Ap′o plex y (-plek-se). A disease marked by loss of sensation and voluntary motion.

A′que ous (ā′-kwe-us). Watery.

A raeh′noid (*arachne*, a spider; *eidos*, form). A membrane like a spider's web covering the brain.

Ar′bôr vī′tæ means "the tree of life."

Ar′ter y (*aer*, air; *tereo*, I contain). So named because after death the arteries contain air only, and hence the ancients supposed them to be air-tubes leading through the body.

Ar tic′u late (*articulo*, I form a joint).

Ar tic′u la tion. A joint.

As phyx′ia (-fix-ē-å). Literally, no-pulse; apparent death.

As sim′i la′tion is the process of changing food into flesh, etc.

At′las. So called because, as in ancient fable the god Atlas supported the globe on his shoulders, so in the body this bone bears the head.

Au′di to ry Nerve. The nerve of hearing.

Au′ri cle (-kl) (*auris*, ear) of the heart. So named from its shape.

Bi′çeps. A muscle with two heads, or origins.

Bi eus′ pid. Tooth with two points ; also a valve of the heart.

Broŋ′chi (-kī). The two branches of the windpipe.

Broŋ′chi al Tubes. Subdivisions of bronchi.

Bur sâ (a purse). Small sac containing fluid near a joint.

Cā nīne′ (*canis*, a dog) teeth are like dog's teeth.

Cap′il la ries (*capillus*, a hair). A system of tiny blood-vessels.

Car′bon. Pure charcoal.

Car bŏn′ic Acid. A deadly gas given off by the lungs and by fires.

Ca rŏt′ids (*karos*, lethargy). Arteries of the neck, so named because the ancients supposed them to be the seat of sleep.

Car′pus. The wrist.

Car′ti lage. Gristle.

Cell. A minute sac, usually with soft walls and fluid contents.

Cel′lu lar (*cellula*, a little cell). Full of cells.

Cĕr′e bel′lum. The little brain.

Cĕr′e brum. A Latin word meaning brain.

Cer′vi cal. Relating to the neck.

Chlo′ral (klō) Hy′drate. A drug used to induce sleep.

Chŏ′roid. The second coat of the eye.

Chyle (kīle). A milky juice formed in digestion.

Chyme (kīme). From *chumos*, juice.

Cir′cu la′tion. The course of the blood through the body.

Cil′i â (the plural of *cilium*, an eyelash). Hair-like projections in the air-passages.

Clăv′i cle (klăv′-i-kl). From *clavis*, a key.

Co ağ′u la′tion. A clotting of blood.

Cŏe′çyx (a cuckoo). A bony mass below the sacrum.

Coeh′le a. A Latin word meaning snail-shell. See Ear.

Com′pound. A substance composed of two or more elements.

Con ta′ġi ous diseases are those caught by contact, the breath, etc.

Con′trac til′i ty (*con*, together; *traho*, I draw).

Con′vo lu′tion (*con*, together; *volvo*, I roll).

Côr′ne a (*cornu*, a horn). A transparent, horn-like window in the eye.

Côr′pus çle (kor′-pŭs-l). From a Latin word meaning a little body. It is applied to the disks of the blood.

Crā′ni al. Relating to the skull.

Crÿs′tal līne (*crystallum*, a crystal).

Cū ta′ne ous (*cutis*, skin). Pertaining to the skin.

Cu′ti cle (kū′-ti-kl). From a Latin word meaning little skin.

Cū′tis, the true skin.

Den′tal (*dens, dentis*, a tooth).

Di′a phragm (-frăm). The muscle dividing the abdomen from the chest.

Di ăs′to le (*diastello*, I put asunder). Dilation of the heart.

Dis′lo ca′tion. A putting out of joint.

Dôr′sal (*dorsum*, the back).

Duct. A small tube.

Du o dē′num (*duodeni*, twelve each).

Dū′ra Mā′ter (*durus*, hard; *mater*, mother). The outer membrane of the brain.

Dys pep′si å is a difficulty of digestion

E lim′i nate. To expel.

Ep′i dem′ic. A disease affecting a great number of persons at once.

Ep′i dêrm′is. The cuticle.

Ep′i glŏt′tis (*epi*, upon; *glōttis*, the tongue). The lid of the windpipe.

Ep′i the′li um. The outer surface of mucous or serous membranes.

Eu sta′chi an (yu-sta′-ki-an) Tube. So named from its discoverer, an Italian physician.

Ex crē′tion. Waste particles thrown off by the excretory organs.

Fer'men ta'tion. The process by which sugar is turned into alcohol.

Fī'brĭn (*fibra*, a fiber).

Fil'a ment (*filum*, a thread).

Func'tion. See Organ.

Gaṇ'gli on (gang'-gli-on). From *ganglion*, a knot; plu. ganglia.

Gas'tric (*gaster*, stomach).

Glands (glăndz). From *glans*, a Latin word meaning acorn. Their object is to secrete in their cells some liquid from the blood.

Glŏt'tis. The opening at the top of the larynx.

Hū'me rus. The arm-bone.

Hū'mor. A Latin word meaning moisture.

Hy'dro gen. The lightest gas known, and one of the elements of water.

Hy'ġi ene. From a Greek word meaning health.

Hўp'o glŏs'sal. Literally "under the tongue"; a nerve of the tongue.

In çi'sôr (*incido*, I cut) teeth are cutting teeth.

In'spĭ ra'tion (*in* and *spiro*, I breathe in).

In tĕs'tine (-tĭn). From *intus*, within.

Lăeh'rў mal (*lachryma*, a tear). Pertaining to tears.

Lae'te ál (*lac*, *lactis*, milk). So called from the milky look of the chyle during digestion.

La eū'nä, plu. lacunæ (*lakos*, a hole). Cavities in the bone-structure.

Lar'ynx (lăr'-ĭnx). The upper part of the windpipe.

Liğ'a ments (*ligo*, I bind) tie bones together.

Lū'brĭ cate. To oil in order to prevent friction.

Lŭm'bär (*lumbus*, a loin). Pertaining to the loins.

Lўmph (lĭmf). From *lympha*, pure water.

Lўm phat'ic (lim-fat'-ik).

Mas'ti ca'tion. The act of chewing.

Me dŭl'lä Ob lon gä'ta. The upper part of the spinal cord.

Mem′brane. A thin skin, or tissue.

Meṣ′en tĕr y. The membrane by which the intestines are fastened to the spine.

Met′a car′pal (*meta*, after; *karpos*, wrist).

Met′a tar′sal (*meta*, after; *tarsos*, the instep).

Mĭ′cro scope (*mikros*, small; *skopeo*, I see).

Mo′lar (*mola*, a mill) teeth are the grinders.

Môr′phĭne (*Morpheus*, the Greek god of sleep).

Mo′to ry. Giving motion.

Mū′cous (-kŭs) Membrane. A thin tissue, or skin, covering the open cavities of the body. See Serous.

Mū′cus. A fluid secreted by a membrane and serving to lubricate it.

Mus′cle (mŭs′-sl). A bundle of fibers covered by a membrane.

My ō′pi ȧ (*muo*, I contract; *ops*, the eye).

Nar cŏt′ic. A drug producing sleep.

Na′ṣal (na′-zal). From *nasus*, the nose.

Nĕrve (*neuron*, a cord).

Ni′tro gen Gas is the passive element of the air.

Ni troǵ′e nous. Containing nitrogen.

Nū trĭ′tion. The process by which the body is nourished.

Œ soph′a gus (ē-sŏf′-a-gŭs). The gullet; literally, a "food-carrier."

Ol fac′to ry. Pertaining to the smell.

Or′gan. An organ is a portion of the body designed for a particular use, which is called its *function;* thus the heart circulates the blood.

Os′se ous (-shēus). Bone-like.

Os′sĭ fy (*ossa*, bones; *facio*, I make).

Ox i da′tion. The process of combining with oxygen.

Ox′y ǵen. The active element of the air.

Pal′ate (*palatum*, the palate). Roof of the mouth.

Păn′cre as (*pas*, all; *kreas*, flesh). An organ of digestion.

Pa pil′la, plu. papillæ. Tiny cone-like projections.

Pa ral′y sis. A disease in which one loses sensation, or the power of motion, or both.

Pa rŏt′id (*para*, near ; *ous, otos*, ear). One of the salivary glands.

Pa tĕl′la (a little dish). The knee-pan.

Pec′to ral. Pertaining to the chest.

Pep′sĭn (*pepto*, I digest). The chief constituent of the gastric juice.

Per′i car′di um (*peri*, around ; *kardia*, the heart). The membrane wrapping the heart.

Per′i ŏs′te um (*peri*, around ; *osteon*, bone). The membrane around the bone.

Per′i stăl′tic (*peri*, round ; *stallein*, to arrange). Applied to the worm-like movement of the alimentary canal.

Phar′ynx (făr′-ĭnx). From *pharugx*, the throat.

Pī′a Mä′ter (tender mother). See Brain.

Pig′ment. A paint.

Plas′ma (plaz′-mah). The nutritious fluid of the blood.

Pleu′ra (plū′-rah). From *pleura*, a rib. The membrane that lines the chest and wraps the lungs.

Pres by o′pi a (*presbus*, old ; *ops*, the eye). A defect in the eye common to old age.

Prŏ çess. A projection. Sometimes it retains its ordinary meaning of " operation."

Pȳ lō′rus (a gate). The door-way through which the food passes from the stomach.

Pŭl′mo na ry (*pulmo*, the lungs). Pertaining to the lungs.

Ra′di us. A Latin word meaning the spoke of a wheel, a ray, etc.

Ram′i fy. To spread like the branches of a tree.

Res′pi ra′tion (*re*, again ; *spiro*, I breathe). Act of breathing.

Rĕt′i na (*rete*, a net). The expansion of the optic nerve in the eye.

Sä′crum (sacred). So named, it is said, because this bone of the pelvis was anciently offered in sacrifice.

Sa lī′va. A Latin word meaning spittle ; the fluid secreted by the salivary glands.

Scap′u lä. The shoulder-blade.

Scav′en ġer. A street-sweeper.

Sele rŏt′ic (skle-rot′-ic). The outer coat of the eye.

Se cre′tion (*secretum*, to separate).

Sed′en ta ry persons are those who sit much.

Sen′so ry Nerves. The nerves of feeling.

Se′rous Membrane. A thin tissue, or skin, covering the cavities of the body that are not open to the external air.

Se′rŭm. The thin part of the blood.

Sub cla′vi an. Located under the clavicle.

Sub lin′gual (*sub*, under; *lingua*, the tongue). The salivary gland located under the tongue.

Sub max′il la ry (*sub*, under; *maxilla*, jaw-bone). The salivary gland located under the jaw.

Sўn ō′vi a (*sun*, with; *oon*, egg). A fluid that lubricates the joints.

Sўn ō′vi al Membrane packs the joints.

Sўs′to le (*sustello*, I contract). Contraction of the heart.

Tem′po ral. An artery on the temple (*tempus*, time), so called because, as is said, the hair whitens first at that point.

Ten′dons (*tendo*, I stretch). The cords conveying motion from the muscle to the bone.

Thō′rax (a breast-plate). The cavity containing the lungs, etc.

Tib′i å. The shin-bone.

Tis′sue. A general term applied to the textures of which the different organs are composed; osseous tissue forms bones.

Trā′che a (trā′-kē-ă). Means rough, alluding to the roughened surface of the windpipe.

Tri′çeps. A muscle with three heads, or origins.

Tri cus′pid (*tres*, three; *cuspis*, point). A valve of the heart.

Tўm′pa num (a drum) of the ear.

Vas′cu lar (*vasculum*, little vessel). Full of small blood-vessels.

Ven′tri cle (-kl). A cavity of the heart.

Vĕr′te brå, plu. vertebræ (*verto*, I turn). A term applied to each one of the bones of the spine.

Vĭl′lus (*villus*, tuft of hair), plu. villi.

Vĭ′tĭ ate. To taint. To spoil.

Vĭt′re ous (*vitrum*, glass). Glassy.

Vo′mer (plowshare). A bone of the nose.

26

INDEX.

General Science.

Doerner's Treasury of Knowledge.

By CELIA DOERNER. { Part I. . . . . $0.50.
Part II. . . . . .65.

This book is designed to fill a gap in the ordinary course of instruction, and furnishes in a small compass much useful and important information. Since it combines entertainment with instruction, it will be found especially useful to parents as an addition to the child's home library.

Hooker's Child's Book of Nature. (COMPLETE.)

By WORTHINGTON HOOKER, M. D., ... $1.00.

Three parts in one: Part I. Plants; Part II. Animals; Part III. Air, Water, Heat, Light, etc. Designed to aid mothers and teachers in training children in the observation of Nature. It presents a general survey of the kingdom of Nature in a manner calculated to attract the attention of the child, and at the same time to furnish him with accurate and important scientific information.

Monteith's Easy Lessons in Popular Science.

By JAMES MONTEITH. . . . . $0.75.

This book combines the conversational, catechetical, blackboard, and object plans, with maps, illustrations, and lessons in drawing, spelling, and composition. The subjects are presented in a simple and effective style, such as would be adopted by a good teacher on an excursion with a class.

Monteith's Popular Science Reader.

By JAMES MONTEITH. . . . . $0.75.

This contains lessons and selections in Natural Philosophy, Botany, and Natural History, with blackboard, drawing, and written exercises. It is illustrated with many fine cuts, and brief notes at the foot of each page add greatly to its value.

Steele's Manual. (KEY TO FOURTEEN WEEKS' COURSE.)

By J. DORMAN STEELE, Ph. L. . . . . $1.00.

This is a manual of science for teachers, containing answers to the practical questions and problems in the author's scientific text-books. It also contains many valuable hints to teachers, minor tables, etc.

Wells's Science of Common Things.

By DAVID A. WELLS, A. M. . . . . $0.85.

This is a familiar explanation of the first principles of physical science for schools, families, and young students. Illustrated with numerous engravings. It is designed to furnish for the use of schools and young students an elementary text-book on the first principles of science.

Copies mailed, post-paid, on receipt of price. Full price-list sent on application.

AMERICAN BOOK COMPANY,

NEW YORK   ·:·   CINCINNATI   ·:·   CHICAGO.

[*70]

Astronomy.

Bowen's Astronomy by Observation.

By ELIZA A. BOWEN. . . . . $1.00.

An elementary text-book for high schools and academies, based on the most practical and interesting method of studying the subject—that of observation.

Gillet and Rolfe's First Book in Astronomy.

By JOSEPH A. GILLET and N. J. ROLFE. . . . . $1.00.

This book, while intended for junior classes, is by no means primary or elementary. It is designed as a brief course, to serve as a foundation for more extended study.

Gillet and Rolfe's Astronomy.

By JOSEPH A. GILLET and N. J. ROLFE. . . . . $1.40.

This book has been prepared by practical teachers, and contains nothing beyond the comprehension of the student of a high school or a seminary.

Kiddle's Short Course in Astronomy.

By HENRY KIDDLE, A. M. Fully illustrated. . . . $0.65.

This is a short course in Astronomy and the use of the globes. In mechanical execution it is unsurpassed.

Kiddle's New Elementary Astronomy.

By HENRY KIDDLE, A. M. . . . . $1.08.

A new manual of the elements of Astronomy, descriptive and mathematical, comprising the latest discoveries and theoretical views, with directions for the use of globes, and for studying the constellations.

Lockyer's Elementary Astronomy.

By J. N. LOCKYER, F. R. S. . . . . $1.22.

Accompanied with numerous illustrations, a colored representation of the solar, stellar, and nebular spectra, and Arago's celestial charts of the Northern and Southern Hemispheres. Especially adapted to the ants of American schools.

Ray's New Elements of Astronomy.

Revised edition. By S. H. PEABODY. . . . . . $1.20.

The elements of Astronomy with numerous engravings and star maps. The author has restricted himself to plain statements of the facts, principles, and processes of the science.

Steele's New Descriptive Astronomy.

By J. DORMAN STEELE, Ph. D. . . . . $1.00.

This book is not written for the information of scientific men, but for the inspiration of youth. The author has sought to weave the story of those far-distant worlds into a form that may attract the attention and kindle the enthusiasm of the pupil.

Copies mailed, post-paid, on receipt of price. Full price-list sent on application.

AMERICAN BOOK COMPANY,

NEW YORK ·:· CINCINNATI ·:· CHICAGO.

[*73]

Zoology and Natural History.

Cooper's Animal Life.

By SARAH COOPER. . . . . $1.25.

Animal life in the sea and on the land. A zoology for young people. Especial attention has been given to the structure of animals, and to the wonderful adaptation of this structure to their habits of life.

Holder's Elementary Zoology.

By C. F. HOLDER. . . . . $1.20.

A text-book designed to present in concise language the life-histories of the groups that constitute the animal kingdom, giving special prominence to distinctive characteristics and habits.

Hooker's Child's Book of Nature.

Part II. Animals. By WORTHINGTON HOOKER, M. D. $0.44.

While this work is well suited as a class-book for schools, its fresh and simple style can not fail to render it a great favorite for family reading.

Hooker's Natural History.

By WORTHINGTON HOOKER, M. D. . . . . $0.90.

For the use of schools and families. Illustrated by three hundred engravings. The book includes only that which every well-informed person ought to know, and excludes all which is of interest only to those who intend to be thorough zoologists.

Morse's First Book in Zoology.

By E. S. MORSE, Ph. D. . . . . $0.87.

Prepared for the use of pupils who wish to gain a general knowledge concerning the common animals of the country. The examples presented for study are such as are common and familiar to every school-boy.

Nicholson's Text-Book of Zoology.

By H. A. NICHOLSON, M. D. . . . . $1.38.

Revised edition. A work strictly elementary, designed for junior students. Illustrated with numerous engravings. It contains an Appendix, Glossary, and Index.

Steele's New Popular Zoology.

By J. DORMAN STEELE, Ph. D. . . . . $1.20.

This book proceeds, by natural development, from the lowest form of organism to man. A cut is given of every animal named, since a good picture of an object is worth more than pages of description.

Tenney's Elements of Zoology.

By SANBORN TENNEY, A. M. . . . . $1.60.

Illustrated by seven hundred and fifty wood engravings. It gives an outline of the animal kingdom, and presents the elementary facts and principles of zoology.

Tenney's Natural History of Animals.

By SANBORN TENNEY and ABBY A. TENNEY. . . . $1.20.

A brief account of the animal kingdom, for the use of parents and teachers. Illustrated by five hundred wood engravings, chiefly of North American animals.

Copies mailed, post-paid, on receipt of price. Complete price-list sent on application.

AMERICAN BOOK COMPANY,

NEW YORK .:. CINCINNATI .:. CHICAGO.

[*71]

Geology.

Andrews's Elementary Geology.

By E. B. ANDREWS, LL. D. . . . . $1.00.

This book is designed for students and readers of the Interior States, and therefore has its chief references to home geology. The scope is limited, to adapt it to beginners.

Dana's Geological Story Briefly Told.

By JAMES D. DANA, LL. D. . . . . $1.15.

With numerous illustrations. An introduction to geology for the general reader, and for beginners in the science. It contains a complete alphabetical index of subjects.

Dana's Manual of Geology.

By JAMES D. DANA, LL. D. . . . . $3.84.

This is a treatise on the principles of the science adapted to the wants of the American student, with special reference to American geological history. The illustrations are numerous, accurate, and well executed.

Dana's New Text-Book of Geology.

By JAMES D. DANA, LL. D. . . . . $2.00.

On the plan of the Manual, designed for schools and academies. The explanations are simple, and at the same time complete.

Le Conte's Compend of Geology.

By JOSEPH LE CONTE. . . . . $1.20.

A book designed to interest the pupil, and to convey real scientific knowledge. It cultivates the habit of observation by directing the attention of the pupil to scientific phenomena.

Nicholson's Text-Book of Geology.

By H. A. NICHOLSON. . . . . $1.05.

This presents the leading principles and facts of geological science within as brief a compass as is compatible with clearness and accuracy.

Steele's Fourteen Weeks in Geology.

By J. DORMAN STEELE, Ph. D. . . . . $1.00.

Designed to make science interesting by omitting those details which are valuable only to the scientific man, and by presenting only those points of general importance with which every well-informed person wishes to be acquainted.

Williams's Applied Geology.

By S. G. WILLIAMS. . . . . $1.20.

A treatise on the industrial relations of geological structure, and on the nature, occurrence, and uses of substances derived from geological sources. It gives a connected and systematic view of the applications of geology to the various uses of mankind.

Copies mailed, post-paid, on receipt of price. Full price-list sent on application.

AMERICAN BOOK COMPANY,

NEW YORK   ·:·   CINCINNATI   ·:·   CHICAGO.

[*72]

Geometry.

DAVIES'S GEOMETRIES. By CHAS. DAVIES, LL. D.

Elementary Geometry and Trigonometry. 12mo, cloth, 324 pages $1.00

Legendre's Geometry and Trigonometry. Revised by I. H. VAN AMRINGE. 8vo, sheep. 512 pages . . $1.60

THE SAME. Part I, Geometry only. 291 pages . . $1.25

Davies's Legendre's Geometry is an entirely new edition, made to conform with latest and best methods.

ECLECTIC SCHOOL GEOMETRY. (Elementary.) By E. W. EVANS, A. M. 12mo, cloth. 155 pages . . 60 cents

A revision of Evans's School Geometry by J. J. Burns, M. A., especially adapted to high schools by the addition of numerous exercises and original demonstrations.

HUNTER'S Elements of Plane Geometry. By THOMAS HUNTER, Ph. D. 12mo, cloth. 132 pages . . 60 cents

This volume is intended only for beginners—for those who are preparing for college, and for intermediate and high schools generally.

PECK'S ANALYTICAL GEOMETRY. By WM. G. PECK, Ph. D. 12mo, cloth. 212 pages $1.25

A treatise on analytical geometry, with applications to lines and surfaces of the first and second orders.

PECK'S DETERMINANTS. By WM. G. PECK, Ph. D. 12mo, cloth. 70 pages . . . . 60 cents

Designed as an introduction to a course of modern analytical geometry.

RAY'S PLANE AND SOLID GEOMETRY. 12mo cloth 276 pages . . . . 70 cents

Written for Ray's Mathematical Course by ELI T. TAPPAN, M. A.

ROBINSON'S NEW GEOMETRY AND TRIGONOM-ETRY. 8vo, calf. 453 pages $1.60

Embracing plane and solid geometry, and plane and spherical trigonometry, with numerous practical problems.

SPENCER'S INVENTIONAL GEOMETRY. (Science Primer Series.) By WM. GEO. SPENCER. 18mo, flexible cloth. 97 pages . . . . 35 cents

Introduces the beginner to geometry by putting him at work on problems which exercise his inventive and constructive faculties.

Copies of the above mailed, post-paid, to any address on receipt of price. Send for full descriptive catalogue of text-books in all departments of higher mathematics.

AMERICAN BOOK COMPANY,

NEW YORK   ·:·   CINCINNATI   ·:·   CHICAGO

GENERAL HISTORY.

THALHEIMER'S GENERAL HISTORY.

12mo, 448 pp. Half roan, illustrated . . . $1.20

Extreme brevity has here been combined with a lively and simple narrative, such as might supply the present need of young pupils while affording a symmetrical plan for the research of older ones.

SWINTON'S OUTLINES OF HISTORY.

12mo, 500 pp. Cloth $1.44

Ancient, Mediæval and Modern, with special reference to the History of Mankind. Its anatomical synopses, its maps showing the political divisions at the great epochs, its collateral information, its surveys of the great events, distinguished men, and important discoveries furnish in an entertaining style just what is valuable to the beginner of the study of history.

LORD'S POINTS OF HISTORY.

12mo, 300 pp. Cloth $1.00

The salient points in the history of the world arranged catechetically for class use or for review and examination by teacher or pupil.

GILMAN'S FIRST STEPS IN GENERAL HISTORY.

18mo, 385 pp. Cloth . . . . . . 75 cents

A suggestive outline of great compactness. Each country is treated by itself, and the United States receives special attention. Frequent maps, contemporary events in tables, references to standard works for fuller details, and a minute index constitute the "Illustrative Apparatus." The style is surprisingly vivid and at times even ornate.

FISHER'S OUTLINES OF UNIVERSAL HISTORY.

8vo, 690 pp. Cloth $2.40

This work, designed as a text-book and for private reading, is a clear and condensed narrative, brought down to the present year, comprising not only a record of political events, but also a sketch of the progress of literature, art and science from the beginning of history to the present time.

BARNES'S GENERAL HISTORY OF THE WORLD.

12mo, 600 pp. Cloth $1.60

A complete outline of the world's history. Some of the prominent features comprise: blackboard analysis; summaries to assist in review; lists of reading references; colored maps; scenes in real life; chapters on civilization; genealogical tables; foot-notes; chapters devoted to the rise of modern nations.

The pupil insensibly acquires a taste for historical reading and forgets the tediousness of the ordinary lesson in perusing the thrilling story of the past.

APPLETONS' SCHOOL HISTORY OF THE WORLD.

8vo, 491 pp. Cloth $1.22

From the earliest ages to the present time. A clear, fresh, carefully arranged and condensed work, beautifully illustrated. It treats ancient civilization in the light of the most recent discoveries. The whole history of the past condensed into a moderate-sized volume that can be readily mastered in the ordinary school year.

Copies of these or any of the publications of the American Book Company for the use of teachers or school officers, or for examination with a view to introduction, will be sent by mail, postpaid, on receipt of the list or introduction price.

AMERICAN BOOK COMPANY,

NEW YORK ∴ CINCINNATI . CHICAGO.